WORLD® AIR POWER
JOURNAL

Aerospace Publishing Ltd
AIRtime Publishing Inc.

Published quarterly by
Aerospace Publishing Ltd
179 Dalling Road
London W6 0ES
UK

ISSN 0959-7050

Aerospace ISBN   1 874023 62 X
                 (softback)
                 1 874023 63 8
                 (hardback)
Airtime ISBN   1-880588-07-2
                 (hardback)

Published under licence in USA and
Canada by AIRtime Publishing Inc.,
10 Bay Street, Westport,
CT 06880, USA

Editorial Offices:
WORLD AIR POWER JOURNAL
Aerospace Publishing Ltd
3A Brackenbury Road
London   W6 0BE   UK

Publisher: Stan Morse
Managing Editor: David Donald
Editor: Jon Lake
Associate Editor: Robert Hewson
Sub Editor: Karen Leverington
Editorial Assistant: Tim Senior

Origination and printing by
   Imago Publishing Ltd
Printed in Singapore

Europe Correspondent:
   Paul Jackson
Washington Correspondent:
   Robert F. Dorr
USA West Coast Correspondent:
   René J. Francillon
Asia Correspondent:
   Pushpindar Singh
Canada Correspondent:
   Jeff Rankin-Lowe

The editors of WORLD AIR
POWER JOURNAL welcome
photographs for possible publication,
but cannot accept any responsibility for
loss or damage to unsolicited material.

The publishers gratefully acknowledge
the assistance given by the following
people:

Gordon Bartley for his assistance with
the British Aerospace Hawk article.

Joe W. Stout of Lockheed Fort Worth,
Norris Graser, Steve Konie, Kevin
Patrick, Phil Smith and Martin Smithy
for their assistance in compiling the
Lockheed F-16 Variant Briefing.

**World Air Power Journal is a
registered trademark in the
United States of America of
AIRtime Publishing Inc.**

**World Air Power Journal is
published quarterly and is
available by subscription and
from many fine book and hobby
stores.**

**SUBSCRIPTION AND BACK
NUMBERS:**

**UK and World (except USA and
Canada) write to:
Aerospace Publishing Ltd
FREEPOST
PO Box 2822
London
W6 0BR
UK**

**(No stamp required if posted in
the UK)**

**USA and Canada, write to:
AIRtime Publishing Inc.
Subscription Dept
10 Bay Street
Westport
CT 06880, USA
(203) 266-3580
Toll-free order number in USA:
1 800 359-3003**

**Prevailing subscription rates are
as follows:
Softbound edition for 1 year:
     $58.00
Softbound edition for 2 years:
     $108.00
Softbound back numbers
(subject to availability) are
$19.00 each. All rates are for
delivery within mainland USA,
Alaska and Hawaii. Canadian
and overseas prices available
upon request. American Express,
Discover Card, MasterCard and
Visa accepted. When ordering
please include your card
number, expiration date and
signature.**

**Publisher, North America:
   Mel Williams
Subscription Director:
   Linda DeAngelis
Retail Sales Director:
   Jill Brooks
Charter Member Services
Manager:
   Janie Munroe**

WORLD AIR POWER®

AIR POWER

JOURNAL

CONTENTS

Military Aviation Review

International

UK rejoins Eurofla

In a remarkable compromise, UK Defence Secretary Malcolm Rifkind announced on 16 December that the RAF would order 25 C-130J Hercules IIs and that the UK (through BAe) will rejoin the European Future Large Aircraft (Eurofla) programme. The decision ended a hard-fought campaign, and has been seen as both a political fudge but also as a potentially clever economic and strategic move.

BAe and Shorts had maintained private venture participation in Eurofla after the UK government withdrew from the programme. Both companies have now gained the commitment to invest public money in FLA when its feasibility study is completed during 1995.

Having undertaken a fundamental redesign of the aircraft less than 12 months before the UK government's decision, Eurofla was able to present its aircraft as a firm programme during the Farnborough air show in September, having just secured the production facilities of Airbus Industrie to build the FLA.

Although the UK's need for the aircraft is urgent, current upgrading of the Transall C.160s of the Armée de l'Air and Luftwaffe will defer their replacement needs until 2010, and it may be presumed that neither country will be disposed to rush finalisation of the aircraft merely to please the UK.

One of BAe's arguments for commitment to FLA had been that lack of British support would have allowed Germany to seize design and production leadership for the wing of the next Airbus airliner – traditionally a British preserve. It was thus ironic that the UK decision in favour of FLA was the signal for a dispute to develop between Germany and the UK over the FLA's wing. Germany is offering a different design using composites instead of the UK's (aluminium) proposal and the two are due for a wind-tunnel 'fly-off' late in 1995. However, Germany is prepared to use its political position to force a decision in its favour, while the UK would consider withdrawal from FLA if it does not gain the vital wing contract.

France remains committed to FLA, although statements late in 1994 engendered further uncertainty over the type and number of engines it should have. The tactical flexibility of the turboprop was responsible for Eurofla switching from four turbofans to four propellers early in the year, although SNECMA spent the autumn promoting the concept of two large turbofans. However, the Armée de l'Air's C-in-C, General Jean-Philippe Douin, declared in favour of the four turboprops as the result of a survey of 200 actual operations and the turboprop option has also been endorsed by Defence Minister Francois Léotard. In 1995 first official funds of Fr26 million were assigned to Eurofla, which France calls the Avion de Transport Futur and to which it has accorded high priority.

Although December's compromise solution had been widely expected, there was some surprise that FLA will also replace the RAF's VC10 transports and tankers raising the UK requirement to 'between 40 and 50'.

Lockheed benefits by getting its desired 'first customer' for the C-130J as an aid to further sales. In fact, the USAF's commitment for two aircraft was confirmed first, but this does not carry the same impact as a batch of 25 for a major air force. The UK taxpayer has also gained – reaping the rewards of the financial inducements offered by Lockheed for the 'first customer'. The RAF had never wavered from its assertion that it required C-130Js immediately, rather than the promise of FLAs at some future date, although had the C-17 ever been on the menu a very different choice might have been expressed.

The first C-130J is scheduled to arrive at Boscombe Down for trials in September 1996 and deliveries to the Lyneham Transport Wing will follow six months later. It appears that all 25 will be the extended fuselage (-30) version with a cargo hold identical to the RAF's Hercules C.Mk 3.

EH101 decision for UK

On 9 March 1995 the longstanding search for a new medium-lift support helicopter for the RAF came to an end. Despite pressure from the RAF for a purchase of the Boeing CH-47D alone, Defence Secretary Malcolm Rifkind announced the service will receive a mix of 22 EH101s and 14 CH-47Ds. EH101 deliveries will commence in 1999. While the choice of the Westland/Agusta-built helicopter was largely a political one (Boeing was offering CH-47Ds at two-thirds of the price with a 200 per cent offset deal), the EH101 is undeniably a technically superior aircraft and should ultimately outlast the aging Chinook design. The contract is worth an estimated £500 million to Westland.

2ᵉ Escadrille de Chasse was France's first Mirage 2000 wing, forming in 1984. This EC 1/2 Mirage 2000C wears the squadron badges of both EC 1/2 'Cigognes' (the Stork) and EC 3/2 'Alsace', to mark the wing's 100,000th hour on type.

Western Europe

BELGIUM:

F-16 fit for combat

Early in 1995, 15 years after the first deliveries, Belgian F-16s finally received a modern threat-warning system to allow them to operate in a hostile environment. Although previously intended to participate in the defence of Western Europe in the face of who knows what in the way of threats, FAeB/BLu F-16s have not been committed to the comparatively benign skies of Bosnia because of this shortcoming. Fitting of the Dassault Carapace RWR system is now underway, 100 of which will be in place by the end of next year. Carapace will be augmented by ex-USAF AN/ALQ-131 jamming pods, 25 of which are due to be bought.

Further Falcon

Latest equipment for 21 Squadron of 15 Wing at Melsbroek is a Dassault Falcon 900B executive jet which augments two Falcon 20s. The second-hand aircraft was due to begin operations in February 1995.

FRANCE:

Defence budget for 1995

Funds have been reserved in the current year for 28 new aircraft to be purchased for the French armed forces, while 14 upgrades of existing aircraft have also been funded. Five more Dassault Rafale Ms lead the naval section, increasing the total to eight (plus two for the air force in previous years). Four more AS 565 Panthers are to be ordered for the navy, as are the first two E-2Cs and four refurbishments of Super Etendards. In the course of 1995, the Marine Nationale will take delivery of three Dassault Atlantique 2s, two Panthers and 12 modified Super Etendards, all from earlier funding.

The Armée de l'Air has a particularly thin year, its sole new funding being for three of the five extra Boeing C-135FRs it needs to boost the tanker fleet and 10 upgrades of Dassault Mirage 2000C to 2000C-5. Acceptances will comprise the last three (of 126) Mirage 2000Cs, 10 Mirage F1CT conversions from F1C, 12 Mirage 2000Ds, 11 upgraded Transall C.160Rs, three TBM700s and 30 EMBRAER Tucanos. At least two SOCATA TBM700s were delivered to ET 65 at Villacoublay in 1994 from an unannounced order, so a minimum of 11 will be in service by the end of 1995.

Army helicopters ordered are six single-engined Aérospatiale AS 550 Fennecs, three AS 555 Fennecs, four more AS 532U2 Cougars and a HORIZON battlefield surveillance system based on the Cougar. No aircraft from previous funding will be delivered this year although a surprise arrival in 1994 has been two TBM700s for 3ᵉ GHL at Rennes (joining two Reims/Cessna 406 Caravan IIs).

Franco-UK military organisation

A military development to emerge from the bilateral summit at Chartres in November 1994 was the establishment in mid-1995 of a joint Air Force Group to plan possible peacekeeping operations. This group will concentrate on logistic requirements and will comprise about 10 senior officers based at RAF Strike Command HQ, High Wycombe. An English-speaking French general will be the first commander, but leadership will alternate between the two countries. Other European nations will be invited to join later.

Rafale plans

Requirements for the Dassault Rafale were revealed late in 1994 as totalling over 400 – considerably more than the 234 called for in current planning. The last aircraft in this first series is due for delivery in 2012, the 94 single-seat and 140 two-seat aircraft providing an operational force of 60 and 120 aircraft respectively, to equip nine squadrons. It is now known that France proposes to build a further 200 Rafales between 2012 and 2022. These, and the first-generation aircraft (which will receive a mid-life update from about 2012-2015 onwards) are to remain in service until 2055. In all, 20 squadrons, each with 20 aircraft, are intended to equip with Rafales, which will become the sole front-line type in the Armée de l'Air.

In the shorter term, the air force will order 59 Rafales between 1995 and 2000 to augment the three currently on contract, plus the balance of 172 of the first batch after 2000. It expects to take delivery of only five before the end of 2000. The navy has five Rafale Ms on order, and will fund an additional 11 in 1995-2000 and 70 more thereafter, for a total of 86, of which 16 are to be delivered by 2000.

It was also disclosed that the air force plans to equip about 20 two-seat Rafales with the ASMP nuclear missile early in the next century as part of its plans to replace the Mirage IVP.

In a related announcement, it was disclosed that a retirement date of 2003 has been set for the SEPECAT Jaguar fleet. Some 94 remain operational from original deliveries of 160 Jaguar As and 40 Jaguar Bs.

Production Tucanos arrive

EMBRAER Tucano deliveries began in earnest early in 1995 against an order for 48 production aircraft to follow the two trials machines received in 1993. These, no. 438 '330-DJ' and no. 439 '330-DM', were used by CEAM at Mont-de-Marsan before the first was transferred to the Ecole de l'Air on 6 July 1994. The main batch begins with no. 456 '312-JA' and no. 457 '312-JB' which were handed over at Le Bourget by EMBRAER on 18 January.

Plans for the introduction of the Tucano to the training syllabus include the issue of five aircraft to the instructors' school (Escadron de Formation des Moniteurs) within GE315 at Cognac. The EFM has previously operated from more than one location (like the RAF's CFS) but will in future fly Epsilons, Tucanos and Alpha Jets at Cognac. The main Tucano school will be the officer training unit, the Ecole de l'Air at Salon-de-Provence, where the Division des Vols 05/312 has five component squadrons. Of these, 4 ECS (Standards Squadron) will convert from Magisters first, followed by 1 and 2 EIV (Training Squadrons). Pilot selection will soon be undertaken on the Epsilon, so 5 EIA (Grading Squadron) will relinquish its CAP10s. The other Magister squadron, 3 EIV, will disband.

Right and below: As part of the ongoing CFE treaty stipulations, Europe's last front-line 'Ginas', the G91Ys of 101° Stormo/8° Gruppo, have been withdrawn for scrapping. To mark the occasion 101° Gruppo painted up this aircraft (MM6444/8-03) with a different scheme on each side. 101° Gruppo took delivery of its first G91Y in 1970, replacing Republic F-84Fs.

Bottom: About 20 Alpha Jets survive in Luftwaffe service, following the disbandment of JBG 49 in March 1994, which this special scheme commemorated. The sole operating unit today is the Furstenfeldbrück-based FLGp (Fluglehrgruppe).

Zéphyr feels the wind of change

Aéronavale bade farewell to a long-serving aircraft type on 25 November when the final 10 Fouga CM.175 Zéphyrs were withdrawn from service with 59S at Hyères. A deck-landing version of CM.170 Magister, the Zéphyr entered service with 59S in October 1959, and 30 were built in addition to two prototypes. In total, the fleet flew 107,313 hours and accomplished 5,304 deck landings, most of its operations being land-based. In future, pilots will receive their basic training with the USN before converting to the (Super) Etendard. The final 10 Zéphyrs, all of which took part in a flypast at the retirement ceremony, were Nos 1, 5, 14, 16, 17, 21, 23, 27, 28 and 30.

Nautical numbers

At the start of 1995, the French navy disclosed that it had a strength of exactly 200 front-line aircraft comprising 55 Super Etendards (including five of the 54 scheduled for upgrading); 18 Cru-saders (including six of the 17 planned upgrades); 11 Etendard IVPs (including seven of the eight upgrades); 15 Atlantic 1s; 17 Atlantique 2s (with 11 more on order); 25 Alizés (including the first of 15 scheduled to receive a further round of modifications); 16 Super Frelons; 34 Lynxes; seven Dauphins; and the first two Panthers (from 15 on order for delivery by 1999).

Gendarmerie plans

The Gendarmerie air wing received official approval in 1994 for second-stage modernisation of its helicopter force. There will be no change in the comparatively new fleet of 29 Ecureuils, but 12 Alouette IIIs will be progressively replaced on a one-for-one basis by an as-yet unspecified type. One new helicopter will be ordered in 1996, one in 1997, two in 1998 and a fifth in 2000. A timetable for the remainder is to be determined in the next five-year defence plan. The force also revealed that it will retire its three Cessna 206 light aircraft at the end of 1995, but will not obtain replacements.

GREECE:

Alpha aspirations

Greece emerged late in 1994 as the latest air force to have designs on Germany's surplus Dassault/Dornier Alpha Jets. It is negotiating for the transfer of 60, which can probably be supplied from Luftwaffe stock without affecting the 35 aircraft remaining at Furstenfeld-brück for advanced training. The latter will, in any event, be withdrawn later in 1995 when Germany starts undertaking all advanced training on USAF T-38s at Holloman AFB.

ITALY:

Defence budget squeeze

Further cuts in the Italian 1995 defence budget seriously delayed plans for the production of the Anglo-Italian EH101 helicopter and slowed manufacture of the AMX-T and the A129 Mangusta attack helicopter. More fortunate were the Eurofighter, AV-8B Harrier and Tornado upgrade, all of which are proceeding with undiminished funds.

Money has also been found to help Piaggio, which is in financial trouble. Three P180 Avanti transports have been ordered by the army in addition to the six already bought for the AMI. Furthermore, the Capitanerie di Porto (Coast Guard) has an outstanding order for five P166-DL3 patrollers to complement 12 already in service. The DL3 has also been supplied to the AMI (six) and Guardia di Finanza (Customs) (10, plus two refurbished DL prototypes).

Yankee bows out

101° Gruppo at Cervia disbanded on 26 November, bringing the operational career of the Aeritalia G91Y ('Yankee') to a close. Its parent wing, the 8° Stormo, stood down on 10 December, along with its attached communications flight, the 608° Squadriglia Collegamenti. The only other G91Y squadron, the 13° Gruppo, was relieved of its equipment in November 1992 and now flies G91Ts in the training role alongside 201° Gruppo at Amendola (32° Stormo). The last few airworthy G91Ys have gone to the trials unit Reparto Sperimentale Volo at Pratica di Mare. Cervia will not close, as it is to receive the relocated 5° Stormo and its F-104ASAs, from Rimini.

Above: Saab JAS 39 Gripen 39-02 has been dedicated to spin trials, which are now underway. In the process it has gained this unique black finish. The full weapons load, including AIM-120, is noteworthy also.

Left: For Exercise Strong Resolve some of the Coltishall Wing Jaguars deployed to Norway, with temporary white paint obscuring the green portion of the standard camouflage.

Below: A single Operation Warden Harrier GR.Mk 7 briefly wore this substantial sharkmouth to outdo a similarly painted Armée de l'Air Mirage F1CR – and did so ably.

Two-seat AMX deliveries

Following a break of nearly two years, production of the Aeritalia/Aermacchi/EMBRAER AMX resumed late in 1994 in order to supply two-seat AMX-Ts to the air force. Four (excluding the two prototypes) had been received by the end of December, serving with 14° Gruppo of 2° Stormo at Treviso as a continuation trainers, although the main recipient of the -T model is expected to be 32 Wing, which needs to replace its G91T advanced trainers. Earlier, the AMI had received 72 production single-seat aircraft, the last on 1 February 1993. Present procurement targets are for 146 aircraft, of which 26 (including prototypes) are two-seat, but it is possible that some, or all, of the outstanding 38 AMXs will be built with two seats for operational and training roles.

International Mangusta

Agusta has modified a prototype Mangusta as the first A129 International in the hope of improving the type's export sales prospects. First flown on 9 January, the variant is recognisable by its five-bladed rotor, and is now powered by a pair of LHTEC T800s, replacing the R-R Gem/four-blade combination. The more powerful engines give the International a boost in gross weight from 4100 to 5000 kg (9040 to 11000 lb) and have raised the top speed from 136 to 150 kt (251 to 280 km/h). Also added are a M197 three-barrelled 20-mm gun in a nose turret and provision for Stinger SAMs as anti-aircraft armament. These two last-mentioned features will be retrofitted to 15 of the 30 Mangustas which the Italian army has already received from its total requirement for 60.

NETHERLANDS:

New attack helicopter

A pregnant pause followed the December announcement by the Netherlands MoD that it had selected, as expected, the AH-64 Apache as its future attack helicopter. An order for 30 or 31 was expected to be ratified by parliament on 16 December, but fell foul of opposition from the Economics Ministry, which favoured the Franco-German Tiger. Early in 1995, the air force was under pressure to make the politically correct decision and choose the Eurocopter Tiger – a foretaste of likely events if the British Army declares a preference for the Apache later in the year.

As part of the plan for acquiring new helicopters dedicated to army support, 302 Squadron was to move from Dee-

len to Gilze-Rijen on 1 June to act as a pool for the Alouette IIIs being withdrawn from 298 Squadron and, from 1996, No. 300. Disposal of the Alouettes has already begun, with the sale of two to Chad in November 1994.

SPAIN:

Ex-French Mirages

Escuadron 111 of Ala 11 at Manises received its first ex-French Mirage F1 on 14 November when two-seat F1B no. 506 was handed over at Chateaudun, reserialled C.14-87. It has been followed by four single-seat F1Cs at monthly intervals. Seven ex-Qatari Mirage F1s were received in 1994 and the remainder of the batch of 13 (two of them trainers) will come in 1997. Only at the end of that year will Ala 11 dispose of the last four Mirage F1CEs it has on loan from Ala 14 at Albacete.

UNITED KINGDOM:

UK goes into the 'black'

The British official passion for placing 'secret' classifications on the well-known or patently obvious may have, at best, backfired as a result of the unprecedented security clampdown around A&AEE Boscombe Down on the night of 26 September 1994. The official explanation that a Tornado landed while trailing a towed radar decoy which had failed to retract was probably correct, but the over-reaction of the security machine to potential display of a device already shown to all and sundry on trade stands at defence exhibitions served only to generate a media search for secret 'stealth' aircraft operating from this research establishment.

By December, both newspapers and specialist magazines were carrying allegations that the 'Northrop TR-3A Black Manta' low observables (LO) reconnaissance aircraft had been overflying Bosnia from the Wiltshire base and that one had crashed on the runway during the night in question, killing its two-man crew. TR-3A was suggested as a complement to the Lockheed F-117A and was reported overflying California in 1989-90, although no later reports have been received except for an unsubstantiated claim that the type was based in Saudi Arabia during the Gulf War.

The Boscombe link with TR-3A seems to have been a consequence of the aircraft's inward-canted rear fins. Tail surfaces of such a configuration were all that could be seen beneath the sheeting which covered the mystery aircraft as it was removed to a hangar on the aerodrome after its accident. Notwithstanding some US military air activity at Boscombe shortly after the 26 September incident (a C-5 travelling to Palmdale, a Gulfstream and a Boeing 737 with a fictitious civil registration), the supposed reasons for basing military reconnaissance aircraft at Boscombe were never convincing.

A more attractive hypothesis explaining the events of that autumn evening may now be constructed as the result of comments by US officials, recently quoted in an American journal. Sources say there is strong evidence for three Western 'stealth' aircraft programme. One of those in the former (firmer) category is a British programme, declared the same officials. The UK LO demonstrator is said by the same sources to be manned and to concentrate only on frontal area stealthiness. The source also believed that the aircraft had not yet flown.

More concrete signs of a UK 'stealth' programme are appearing at BAe's Warton plant where a special site is under construction on the south side of the airfield. Facilities include a radar cross-section testing range and a 'black' hangar in which a follow-on aircraft to Eurofighter 2000 could eventually take shape.

In such a venture, the UK could join with Germany, where a manned LO aircraft has already 'flown' as long ago as 1987. An MBB programme known as Lampyridae (Firefly), or the Medium-Range Missile Fighter, was run between 1981 and 1987, culminating in 15 'flights' of a manned, 75 per cent scale prototype in the German-Dutch wind tunnel at Emmeloord. A full-size mock-up, 40 ft (12 m) long and with a 20-ft (60-0m) wing span, was also used for radar reflectivity trials before the programme was terminated.

RAF unit moves

A study paper published on 17 November confirmed previous reports of possible moves of RAF flying units. It is proposed that the 'Red Arrows' should move to Marham and that the CFS elements at Scampton be distributed to Cranwell (Bulldog) and Linton-on-Ouse/Topcliffe (Tucano). Cranwell is also intended to profit from the closure of Finningley, with No. 6 FTS's Bulldogs and Dominies going there, while the Tucanos transfer to Linton and the Hawks to Valley. Having had second thoughts on the privatising the METS/No. 45(R) Squadron, its Jetstreams now also seem set to move to Cranwell.

It was also stated that the Joint Elementary Flying Training School at Topcliffe would move to Barkston Heath (a reserve landing ground for Cranwell) in April 1995. JEFTS is operated by a civilian contractor and flies 18 Slingsby T67M Fireflies for the benefit of RAF and FAA students.

As expected, No. 19 (R) Squadron proved to be the half of Chivenor-based No. 7 FTS to be perpetuated after the School closed on 1 October 1994 and simultaneously graduated its final course. Over the succeeding months, Chivenor's Hawks were dispersed to other units, the main recipient being No. 4 FTS at Valley, to which No. 19(R) Squadron is now attached (as the CFS Squadron), partnering Nos 74 and 208 Squadrons.

Two days after the FTS disbanded, Hawks of No. 4 FTS began using Chivenor as a base for weapon-firing detachments at Pembrey range. These detachments will eventually pass to

Above: No. 210 Sqn, part of the Kinloss-based Nimrod Wing, is celebrating both its 80th anniversary and the Nimrod's 25th birthday (in the type's 26th year) with this specially decorated Nimrod MR.Mk 2P. 1995 should be 'decision year' to upgrade or replace the 'mighty hunters'.

St Athan, but delays with building appropriate infrastructure at the Welsh base mean that Chivenor will continue to be used for at least a year. Chivenor will become a Royal Marine barracks and is being assessed as a base for the FRADU Hawks and Falcon 20s now based at Yeovilton.

Next Nimrod nominations

The Nimrod replacement programme (AST 420) was launched in January when four consortia were invited to make bids in anticipation of a contract being awarded in the late summer of 1996. As was the case with the Hercules replacement, BAe offered a proposal to refurbish the existing equipment until a maritime reconnaissance version of FLA can be produced. This Nimrod update would probably involve Boeing, which developed the Update 4 avionics for the US Navy's Orions before they were abandoned at the prototype stage. Dassault is proposing the Atlantique 2, but with its existing R-R Tyne turboprops replaced by either the Tyne Plus or Allison AE2100s (as in the C-130J). Lockheed, predictably, has the P-3C as its offering, but also using AE2100 power and Dowty propellers, plus some GEC-Marconi avionics. Finally, Loral and E-Systems are offering refurbished P-3A/B Orions with undisclosed avionics.

Jaguar developments

Jaguar GR.Mk 1B is the assigned designation of three and seven single-seaters respectively being modified by Boscombe Down and St Athan to carry the GEC Avionics TIALD laser designator pod. Another pair of trainers is also being produced, designated Jaguar T.Mk 2B. Delivery of the first aircraft to the Coltishall Wing was due early in 1995 and all will be redelivered by the end of 1995.

In a separate programme, some Jaguars are receiving a coat of permanent grey to replace the washable coat applied for operations over Bosnia. Although not quite producing a 'stealth Jaguar', the new colouring is LIR (low-infra-red) polyeurethane which complements radar-absorbent material applied to all leading edges and to the noses of fuel tanks. XZ357 arrived back from St Athan on 2 February as the first in the new scheme of Dark Sea Grey (upper sides) and Medium Sea Grey (lower, plus fin). The aircraft was delivered to No. 41 Squadron, although Nos 6 and 54 will also receive re-painted aircraft. The three units will also share the Jaguars GR.Mk 1Bs.

Tornado rebuild begins

The 16 Tornado F.Mk 3s seriously damaged by a contractor during structural refurbishment are to be rebuilt, as became clear on 24 October when the fuselage of one, plus a redundant Tornado F.Mk 2, were taken by road from the St Athan to BAe Warton to be made into one serviceable aircraft. BAe has been contracted to undertake a trial rebuild of ZE154 using the centre-section of Mk 2 ZD901, the latter being one of many withdrawn from service when the Mk 3 became available. Of 18 F.Mk 2s built, 12 are in storage, leaving three with BAe for trials, two at DRA and one test rig aircraft at RAF Coningsby.

Eastern Europe

CZECH REPUBLIC:

Upgrades and L-159 head defence modernisation plan

Although an upgrade programme for 24-36 Czech air force MiG-21MF fighters, and approval for the long-proposed purchase of 72 single-seat Aero Vodochody L-159 multi-role light combat aircraft, were key features of a CKr120 ($4.33) billion five-year armed forces modernisation plan approved in November 1994 by the national Parliament, its defence and security committee subsequently froze the CKr300 ($10.8) million upgrade funding to explore alternative options. These were mainly concerned with investigating prospects of acquiring up to 24 surplus Western fighters, and particularly ex-USAF or NATO F-16s now that their export to Eastern Europe has been cleared by the recent Presidential Directive 34.

Evaluations are also being made, however, of other Western fighters, including Belgian Mirage 5s and French Mirage F1s, as well as of later-generation air-to-air missiles, notably the MATRA Magic 2 and Rafael Python 3, to re-arm the 16 remaining Czech MiG-23ML interceptors. Two Magic 2 launches from a Czech MiG-23 have already been successfully completed at CEAM, at Mont-de-Marsan. Longer-term upgrades are also being sought for Czech Su-25 close-support aircraft and Mi-24 attack helicopters, with night-vision systems specified for the latter type.

In accordance with East European aspirations to join NATO, the Czech modernisation plan also approved the acquisition of a compatible command, control and communications centre. With the other Visegrad countries of Hungary, Poland and Slovakia, the Czechs have already agreed to US Defense Department proposals, backed by a $25 million aid package, to form unified air defence and air traffic control systems, as part of President Clinton's 1994 Regional Airspace Initiative. These systems seem likely to be mainly equipped with modern American ground radars, plus computerised control and communications equipment, although the Czech HTT Tesla Pardubice company has produced some of the most advanced ground radar equipment in Europe, including the Tamara 'stealth' system, said to be capable of tracking the Lockheed F-117.

Aero Vodochody's L-159 light attack fighter programme will take up a sizeable part of the CKr27.9 ($1.0) billion allocated to the Czech air force in the

with the rival and more conventional Tupolev Tu-330, now at an advanced stage of development. Antonov General Designer Pyotr Balabuyev, however, has said that talks have been held with Daewoo and Samsung in South Korea over their possible participation in the An-70 as a joint development project.

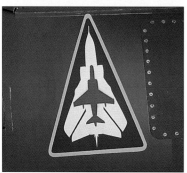

The RAF's doctrinal training establishment, the Air Warfare Centre, now controls both the SAOEU and Tornado F.Mk 3 OEU. SAOEU is moving to Waddington during 1995, and AWC markings have been applied to at least one of its Harrier GR.Mk 7s (left and right). AWC's Tornado F.Mk 3s (above) are staying put at Coningsby.

new modernisation programme, with major participation from the US industry. Apart from the L-159's AlliedSignal/ Garrett F124GA-100 turbofan, it will be equipped with Rockwell Collins avionics from a $200 million contract placed on 21 November 1994, for the integration of EFIS instrumentation, digitised multi-function displays, air data and mission computers, GPS, stores management system, FIAR pulse-Doppler radar, Flight Visions HUD, IFF, and GEC-Marconi Defence Systems RWR, plus chaff/flare dispensers. A 33-month prototype development phase will be followed by initial deliveries to the Czech air force in 1998.

POLAND:

F-16 interest intensifies

As one of several Eastern European countries (which also include Albania, Bulgaria, the Czech Republic, Estonia, Hungary, Latvia, Lithuania, Romania and Slovakia) cleared by a recent US Presidential Directive to receive conventional weapons and combat aircraft, Poland has intensified its earlier negotiations in Washington to acquire 24 or more surplus F-16s to replace its ageing MiG-21s. About 200 F-16A/Bs currently in storage at Davis-Monthan's AMARC facility have been the target of a number of cash-strapped foreign air forces looking for affordable high-performance fighters, although their refurbishing and structural inspection through Lockheed's proposed 'Falcon Up' programme would require additional funding. For Poland, this would be additional to the $230 million or so earmarked for the planned upgrade with Western avionics of its 100-strong ground-attack force of Sukhoi Su-22M4Ks and two-seat Su-22U3Ms.

An-28s delivered

Some of the 170-plus Antonov An-28 light transports built mainly for the former Soviet Union by WSK PZL-Mielec since 1980, and undelivered because of payment defaults, are being taken over by the Polish armed forces

to replace about 55 elderly An-2 biplanes still in service. The first of a required 40 (given the necessary funding) An-28TD or Bryza 1TD cargo version entered service with the 13th PLT (Transport Aviation Regiment) of the Polish air force at Krakow in October 1994, followed by initial deliveries of three An-28RMs (Bryza 1RM) equipped for SAR to the navy's 7th PLS (Special Air Regiment) at Siemirowice, near Gydnia. Six more naval An-28RMs, similarly powered by twin 960-shp (715-kW) PZL-10S turboprops, are on order, fitted with an indigenous ARS-100 360X ventral surveillance radar, plus RDS-81 weather radar, KNS-81S navigation radar, GPS and a Chelton DF-707-1 direction-finding system. Development is also continuing of the An-28B-2 Bryza 2, with an electronic warfare suite.

RUSSIA:

An-70 loss threatens programme continuation

Strenuous efforts are being made by the Antonov OKB in Kiev to complete within the next year or so a second prototype An-70 propfan military transport around a fuselage section originally built for ground static testing, following the loss of the first example in a mid-air collision with its An-72 chase aircraft on 10 February. Having made its first flight (of only 26 minutes, because of bad weather) on 16 December, and accumulated only about three hours in the air, the world's first solely propfan-powered aircraft was making its fourth test sortie, from Kiev's Gostomel factory airfield, in Ukraine, on the day of its accident. On board were the original crew of Antonov chief test pilot Sergei Maksimov as commander, and co-pilot Vladimir G. Lysenko, accompanied by a third pilot, Vladimir F. Nepochatykh, acting as navigator, plus four engineers and observers.

Original reports indicated a sudden yaw/roll divergence from straight and level flight at about 10,000 ft (3280 m) by the An-70 to be the cause of the collision with the formating An-72, raising possible suspicions concerning the new aircraft's fly-by-wire control system. However, preliminary interpretation of data from the recovered flight recorders was said to show that

'both aircraft were fully controllable' at the critical period.

Some Ukrainian sources have since claimed that the collision followed a request from the An-70 captain for Vladimir Tersky in the An-72 to change position above and to one side to observe details of the prototype's double-slotted flap operation. During this manoeuvre, the An-72 was reported to have struck the An-70's fin and rudder, while the Stupino contra-rotating propeller blades of the Zaporezhye Progress D-27 propfans destroyed an outer wing section of the An-72.

The aircraft nevertheless managed to land back at Gostomel, but the An-70 apparently entered a spin from which it was unable to recover. All seven occupants were killed, and the An-70 was totally destroyed. Already about two years behind schedule because of financial and technical problems, the development programme has been mainly funded by the Russian State Committee for Defence Branches of Industry, with smaller contributions from the Ukrainian Ministry of Machine Building to produce an An-12 replacement for the air forces of both countries.

In Kiev, the loss of the 286,520-lb (130-tonne) prototype An-70 has been put by the Deputy Prime Minister at the equivalent of $30-50 million in financial terms, but continuation of already problematical funding from Russia could be on a competitive basis

Dassault rules out joining MiG-AT group

Dassault has formally revealed its interests in the MiG-AT advanced trainer programme, which includes several other French aerospace groups as joint partners, including SNECMA and Turboméca, as suppliers of its Larzac turbofans, and Sextant Avionique, Dassault has, according to Serge Dassault, rejected plans to join the consortium. With the Yakovlev Yak-130, in which Aermacchi is involved, the MiG-AT is joint contestant in a planned fly-off evaluation for large-scale VVS purchases of a new advanced/weapons trainer to follow on from the previously-procured Aero L-39 Albatros, and for export sales.

Prototypes of both trainers had been completed earlier this year, and were due to start their flight development as a prelude to VVS evaluation in the spring. Serge Dassault said that Russia's current political instability and financial problems make it an unattractive option for industrial collaboration, although the MiG Aviation Scientific-Industrial Complex is building some Dassault Falcon components, among other Western aerospace sub-contracts.

Russia's Chechnya losses

By mid-February, when Russian operations in Chechnya climaxed with the capture of Grozny, its capital, Moscow admitted aircraft combat losses of two Mi-8s and two Mi-24 helicopters, plus a Sukhoi Su-25 ground-attack aircraft, mostly from shoulder-launched SAMs. Some 46 Mi-24 helicopters had been deployed in the Chechnya area, in two VVS eskadrilya, as well as two similar Mi-8 units, and a few Mi-26 heavy-lift helicopters.

Middle East

EGYPT:

More FMS Apaches authorised

A 33 per cent increase in Egypt's MDH AH-64A attack helicopter force is planned, according to Pentagon notifications to Congress in late 1994 of the proposed foreign military sale of another 12 Apaches, plus six spare General Electric T700 engines, four spare Hellfire ATM launchers, 34 2.75-in (70-mm) rocket launchers, and one spare TADS/PNV system, costing $318 million. A CAE-Link, six-axis motion, AH-64 mission simulator was installed last year at Abu Hammad air base.

Kaman SeaSprite order finalised

Egypt's long-planned requirement for Kaman SH-2G anti-submarine helicopters was finalised in late 1994 with a letter of agreement signed with the US government for some 10 SeaSprites, and associated equipment. These will be remanufactured to full SH-2G standards by Kaman from surplus USN SH-2F airframes stored at MASDC, with uprated General Electric T700-401 turboshaft engines and some new mission system avionics, including AlliedSignal AN/AQS-18A dipping sonar, at a cost of some $100 million.

Five of the SH-2Gs will be allocated for operation from the Egyptian navy's two ex-USN '1052'-class frigates, and with the other five operating from shore bases.

OMAN:

Pakistani trainer gift

Past liaison by Pakistan with the Omani armed forces has been continued with the recent donation to the RAFO of three Kamra-built PAC Mushshak two-seat primary trainers. Six more have also been presented to Syria.

YEMEN:

No MiG-29s expected for unified forces

Five surviving MiG-29s from 12 bought by separatist South Yemen during the mid-1994 two-month civil war, which ended in victory for the tribalist north, seem unlikely to be integrated into the unified forces now being formed from both former elements, under control of the Defence Ministry in Sana'a. As part of a Saudi-funded package of 30 combat aircraft bought from the former Soviet republic of Moldova when hostilities started in Yemen, the 12 MiG-29s (of 34 left in Moldova when the CIS disintegrated) were airlifted from Markulesti to Mukalla, in South Yemen, via Bulgaria and South Africa, in late June 1994, accompanied by five Moldovan mercenary pilots and 12 technicians. One MiG-29 was shot down during the limited operations, although its pilot ejected safely, and six others were

destroyed on the ground by the successful northern forces during the capture of Aden which led to victory on 7 July.

Thirty Iraqi air force personnel were then engaged by the new Yemeni government to transfer the remaining five MiG-29s to Sana'a, and begin training northern personnel on their maintenance and operation. It was soon obvious, however, that the MiG-29s were too few, too complex and too costly for viable Yemeni operation, and the Iraqis soon followed the Moldovan exit. Their expulsion was also designed to appease the US into releasing spares and technical support assistance for the North's remaining 11 Northrop F-5Es and two two-seat F-5Bs, which, with MiG-21s, F-7Ms, MiG-23s and Su-20/22s from both former elements, constitute the current nucleus of the Yemeni air force. Yemen's MiG-29s could therefore reappear some time soon on the international fighter market.

Above: For their 80th anniversary (which occurred in January 1995, but is celebrated in July), RAF Marham-based No. 13 Sqn has decorated this Tornado GR.Mk 1A.

Top: This Royal Navy Lynx HAS.Mk 3S (XZ237/PO) is allocated to AMG Portland, and seen here carrying a stabilised 'heli-telly' TV/electro-optical system.

Southern Asia

INDIA:

Attrition 'Fulcrums' ordered

Despite an average availability of less than 50 per cent for the survivors of its 65 MiG-29 advanced air superiority fighters and five MiG-29UB trainers bought in two batches since 1986 from the former USSR, and serious shortfalls in the 300-hour nominal TBO of their Klimov RD-33 engines, in December 1994 the IAF ordered 10 attrition replacements, including two UBs, for a reported cost of $220 million. As apparently undelivered former VVS orders, these were due for delivery in March, and India was also reported to be negotiating to buy another 30 'Fulcrums' (perhaps the first MiG-33s), plus six two-seat trainer versions, costing around $750 million.

Meanwhile, however, an IAF delegation led by Chief of Air Staff, Air Chief Marshal S. K. Kaul, began a six-month evaluation in mid-1994 of the two-seat Su-30MK long-range multi-role combat aircraft, offered for a flyaway export unit cost quoted by Sukhoi

General Designer Mikhail Simonov as only about $26 million. Reports circulating in Delhi of planned Sukhoi fighter acquisition by Pakistan were denied by Russian Prime Minister Chernomyrdin, who said that Moscow's traditional ties with India, emphasised by a five-year bilateral military co-operation agreement signed on 23 December 1994, would prevent Russian arms ever being released to the Islamabad government. Russia has offered India an initial batch of 20-30 Su-30s, plus licence-production by HAL of another 60.

ALH CTS800 turboshaft option

One of the three prototypes of HAL's 14-seat Advanced Light Helicopter, which have been undergoing flight development since 1992, is to be re-engined with CTS800 turboshaft engines following an agreement signed with AlliedSignal Aerospace and Hindustan Aeronautics early in 1995. As a commercial version of the T800 developed by the Light Helicopter Turbine

Engine Co. (LHTEC), in which AlliedSignal and Rolls-Royce/Allison have equal shares, for the US Army's RAH-66 Comanche programme, the CTS800 is rated at 1,300 shp (970 kW), and will replace the Turboméca TM333-2B engines in the existing prototypes. These were due to be joined by a fourth example in naval configuration in March, but if integration and flight trials with the CTS800 beginning later this year are successful the new engine will be installed in the production ALH, 300 of which are planned.

PAKISTAN:

New fighters sought

Having received only 40 Block 15 F-16A/Bs and having paid for 28 F-16A/B Block 15 OCUs of 111 originally contracted for through four Peace Gate FMS programmes, the Pakistan government has now given up any hopes of taking further deliveries, following the US veto on arms supplies because of Islamabad's continuing fissile material production programmes. Repayment to Pakistan of $658 million in financing credit for the undelivered F-16s has so far been refused by the US, although it has offered to help with finding a third-country buyer.

Meanwhile, Pakistan is looking elsewhere for its new fighters to counter India's continuing Russian combat aircraft procurement, and has been talking to France about the possible purchase of up to 40 Mirage 2000-5s to re-equip two PAF squadrons. Their cost, however, appears too much for the PAF budget, and more interest has been expressed in offers – apparently made in November 1994 by a visiting Russian military and industry delegation, despite contrary reassurances to India – of 30 Sukhoi Su-27 long-range air superiority fighters. These are reported to be available for almost half the price of the French aircraft, or around $1.1 billion in all.

Naval aviation reinforcements

Pakistan navy efforts to obtain alternative equipment to the three Lockheed P-3C Update 2.5 Orion maritime patrol aircraft and Kaman SH-2 ASW helicopters also vetoed by Washington appear to have been successful. France supplied three ex-French navy Breguet Atlantic Mk Is to Pakistan late in 1994 to support a similar batch delivered in 1975-76, although the new arrivals were to be stripped of their mission system avionics for use as spares. In August 1994, Britain also delivered the first two (XZ227 and XZ240) of an initial three refurbished ex-RN Westland Lynx HAS.Mk 3 ASW helicopters to the Pakistan navy, to operate from the six former Royal Navy Type 21 'Amazon'-class frigates acquired from the UK in late 1993. The third Lynx was due in Pakistan in April 1995, and the PN has options on three more to fulfil its frigate helicopter requirements.

Left: A Flight Refuelling (Cobham Group) EW-configured Falcon 20 formates with one of FRADU's newly arrived Hawks. FRADU officially retired its last Hunter in April 1995.

Below left: Armed with a pair of CBU-87 cluster bombs and AIM-9L Sidewinders this Harrier GR.Mk 7 is one of the Operation Warden detachment based at Incirlik.

Far East

CAMBODIA:

Armed forces reorganisation plans

An increase of 34 per cent in the 1995 defence budget over the previous year to Riel 220 billion ($85 million), is being used to fund the purchase of tanks, military vehicles and weapons from the Czech Republic and Poland, although about $80 million is also required to finance the planned upgrade by Israel Aircraft Industries of 15 of Cambodia's grounded combat aircraft force of 19 MiG-21s. Finance is also being sought for the similarly planned purchase of six Czech Aero L-39ZA armed jet trainers. Military aid is being sought from the ASEAN states, Australia, France, Israel, North Korea, Russia and the USA

CHINA:

US probes Israeli aid with new fighter development

Concern has been expressed in the US over reports of Israeli assistance with the reported development since 1992 by the Chengdu Aircraft Industrial Corporation at Sichuan of the new XJ-10 single-engined advanced fighter project, said to be based on IAI's Lavi multi-role aircraft programme. Jointly developed with the US, the Lavi project was cancelled in 1987 after more than $1.5 billion had been spent on R&D, but while the Israeli Defence Ministry has admitted the transfer of 'some aircraft technology' to China, it has denied that this was associated with the Lavi.

Prior to a Middle East visit, including Israel, earlier this year, US Defense Secretary William Perry said he could not confirm the accuracy of reports that China was using Lavi technology to develop a new fighter. He promised to look into the matter, however, and if it proved accurate, there would be 'difficult words' with the Israeli government. Some reports claim that the prototype canard-delta XJ-10 has been mainly built in Israel, for assembly at Sichuan, where it is expected to fly early next year.

INDONESIA:

More F-16s and Hawks planned

Additional orders for five Lockheed F-16s costing $116.5 million and 20 more BAe Hawk 100/200s worth some $676 million are planned by the Indonesian government in a $2 billion five-year armed forces' procurement programme. Indonesia has a requirement for 97 combat-capable Hawks. Other allocations include $60 million for two new air refuelling tankers, plus $425 million for 16 Sikorsky UH-60 Black Hawk utility helicopters and a similar number of training helicopters.

Above: A new addition to the Magyar Honvédseg Repülő Csapatai (Hungarian air force) is this Yakovlev Yak-52.

Below: The 306th Hikotai celebrated the JASDF's 40th anniversary, in 1994, with this specially marked F-4EJ Kai.

JAPAN:

FY95 defence procurement plans

Japanese Defence Agency funding requests in the Y47.2 trillion ($47.2 billion) FY95 defence budget – traditionally maintained at just under 1 per cent of government spending – for tri-service procurement of 74 new aircraft, have been cut to 68, of which the JGSDF will receive the most, with a total of 30. These comprise – with original requests in parentheses where changed - the following: two (four) Fuji/Bell AH-1S attack helicopters; 11 Kawasaki/MDH OH-6D utility helicopters; three (two) Mitsubishi/Sikorsky UH-60JA tactical helicopters; 13 Fuji/Bell UH-1J tactical helicopters; and two Kawasaki/Boeing CH-47J transport helicopters. The JGSDF plans to buy a total of 80 UH-60s costing $2.67 billion, to replace its 132 UH-1Js.

As the next biggest recipient, the JASDF is due to receive all but one of the 24 aircraft requested, now including five Mitsubishi/MDC F-15J fighters; one Lockheed C-130H transport; nine (10) Kawasaki T-4 intermediate trainers; one Beech 400 crew trainer; two Raytheon/BAe U-125A SAR aircraft; two Gulfstream G-4/U-4 (U-X) government transports; one Kawasaki/Boeing CH-47J heavy-lift helicopter; and two Mitsubishi/Sikorsky UH-60JA SAR helicopters. An upgraded version of the Hughes APG-65 radar or Mitsubishi Electric's FS-X radar is planned for installation in the JASDF's 223 programmed F-15Js, of which more than 200 have already been delivered.

FY95 JMSDF procurement of 15 aircraft comprises one Kawasaki/Lockheed EP-3 and one UP-3D electronic warfare/EW trainer aircraft; one Shin Meiwa US-1A SAR amphibian; two Fuji T-5 turboprop basic trainers; six (eight) Mitsubishi/Sikorsky SH-60J ASW helicopters; one UH-60J SAR helicopter; and three Kawasaki/MDH OH-6D trainer helicopters. JMSDF SH-60J procurement is now to be extended to 90 Seahawks, plus another 70 UH-60Js, in conjunction with the JASDF, for SAR, increasing overall Japanese UH/SH-60 purchases to at least 240.

FS-X requirement scaled down

Serialled 63-001, the first of four FS-X flight prototypes developed by Mitsubishi from the Lockheed/GD F-16C/D Block 40 was rolled out from MHI's Komaki Minami factory on 12 December after an eight-year R&D programme which has seen its investment budget almost double to about Y327.4 billion ($3.27 billion). At the same time, the original requirement for 130 as Mitsubishi F-1 strike-fighter replacements now seems likely to be scaled down through budget economies from 130 to between 70 and 80, and, unless production funding is included in the FY96 defence budget, the FS-X will not meet its 1999 IOC target.

With a likely production unit cost approaching $100 million, the FS-X will probably therefore be at least four times more expensive than the F-16, for service almost 20 years later, with only a relatively small increase in capability from its wider-span 25 per cent bigger co-cured composite wing, 7,000-lb (3175-kg) increase in maximum take-off weight to 49,000 lb (22226 kg), and Mitsubishi Electric Corporation (Melco) active phased-array fire-control radar. Other indigenous equipment includes fly-by-wire control software source codes, a Japan Aviation Electronics laser INS, Yokkogawa liquid-crystal multi-function cockpit displays, Shimadzu head-up display, and a Melco integrated electronic warfare system. The FS-X also has a three-piece cockpit canopy with a strengthened windscreen for bird-strike protection, and a bigger stabilator, and makes extensive use of radar reflective material on most leading-edge surfaces.

Two single-seat and two two-seat FS-X prototypes will participate in the flight development programme starting summer 1995 and ending in late 1998, while two more airframes are being built for static testing. Production FS-X aircraft will re-equip three Mitsubishi F-1 squadrons with 18 aircraft each for multi-role operations, armed with indigenous ASM-1 and ASM-2 anti-ship missiles, and Type 90 AAM-3 dogfight missiles, in addition to longer-range and radar-homing AIM-7M Sparrow AAMs.

MALAYSIA:

MiG-29 deliveries begin

The RMAF was expected to take delivery in March of the first of its 18 MiG-29s on order, including two two-seat MiG-29UB combat trainers, although some delay had been reported in training pilots and ground crews in Russia and India. Malaysia's MiG-29s were built for the Soviet air force, although undelivered, and have been modified to MiG-29SD standards with Phazotron N-019ME 'Slot Back' pulse-Doppler radar, having a single-target engagement capability. They are also being supplied with standard IR-homing Molniya R-60 (AA-8 'Aphid') and Molniya/Vympel R-73E (AA-11 'Archer') close-combat AAMs, plus Vympel R-27R/T (AA-10 'Alamo A/B') medium-range semi-active radar/IR-homing AAMs for BVR interceptions.

As originally negotiated in early 1993, the RMAF's MiG-29 package, with costs estimated at between $385 and $550 million, was also due to include two additional non-flying MiG-29UBs for use at a planned joint-

Above: This T-4, from the 306th Hikotai at Komatsu, was painted in a special scheme for the annual air show at the base, during 1994. The T-4s are operated by the F-4EJ Kai-equipped 306th Hikotai, which shares the base with the F-15Js of the 303rd Hikotai.

Right: The JASDF's 11 UH-60Js have largely been assembled from kits by Mitsubishi. They are replacing KV-107s in the SAR role and are home-based at Iruma, with detachments. This aircraft is based at Komatsu, with the Koku Kyunandan Komatsu.

venture technical service centre in Malaysia for maintenance research and technician training, plus a flight simulator from CAE Electronics in Canada. The first four of the eight two-seat night-capable MDC F/A-18D Hornets ordered by the RMAF before its MiG-29s are not due for completion before October 1995, for operation from January 1997.

CN-235/MD3-160 exchange

Although the RMAF has reduced to its original requirement for IPTN-built CN.235M twin-turboprop tactical transports from 32 to six, to begin replacing its piston-engined DHC-4 Caribou, Indonesia is apparently going ahead with its plans to acquire 20 Datwyler MD3-160 primary trainers from Malaysian production, plus 1,500 Proton vehicles in an exchange deal. The Aerospace Division of state-owned SME Technologies is also supplying a similar number of MD3-160s to replace RMAF BAe Bulldogs.

MYANMAR:

New Chinese arms package

Reports late last year of a new $400 million arms agreement with China followed an earlier $1.2 billion package acquired by Myanmar, which included 30 Chengdu F-7 fighters, six Guizhou FT-7 combat trainers, 24 NAMC A-5C ground attack aircraft (not A-5Ms as has

been frequently reported), and four Shaanxi Y-8D transports. Deliveries of these, to form Myanmar's first full combat aircraft and support element, started in May 1991 and continued until late last year, but the only aircraft so far mentioned in the new contract are 20 helicopters of unspecified type.

PHILIPPINES:

Modernisation plans

Plans dating back to 1989 for a 15-year $11 billion modernisation programme for the Philippine armed forces finally received initial approval from President Fidel Ramos at the beginning of this year. The first batch of funding, however, is only for an initial five-year period, and, at about $2 billion, is just over half the original appropriations target. It appears additional, however, to the annual defence budget, which for the current year has been set at about Ps26 billion ($1 billion), and its main priority remains the acquisition of new combat aircraft.

Apart from 24 surplus Rockwell OV-10A Bronco COIN aircraft from the US, the Philippine air force (HHP) combat element comprises only four Northrop F-5As and a single two-seat F-5B, mostly with cracked longerons, and the proposed transfer of three F-5A/Bs from South Korea has been delayed by diplomatic complications. Funding shortages have also delayed planned purchases of 18 IAI Kfir

C-7/TC-7 combat aircraft and a similar number of Aero L-39ZE armed jet trainers, and the HHP is currently exploring alternative fighter options, including ex-USAF F-16A/Bs, some of Belgium's remaining withdrawn Mirage 5s, surplus French Mirage F1s, or even Russian MiG-21s or -23s. Particular interest has also been reported in 19 surplus Kuwait air force A-4KU Skyhawks in storage at Ahmed al Jaber, and recently inspected by a PhilAF evaluation team.

SINGAPORE:

More F-16s sought

Following earlier procurement of four each Block 15(OCU) F-16A/B Fighting Falcons, and the lease until 1996 of another nine similar USAF aircraft in the US for training, the Republic of Singapore air force has been negotiating with Lockheed to increase its 9 July 1994 order for eight Pratt & Whitney F100-229-powered Block 52 F-16Cs and 10 F-16Ds by another six aircraft. These will be accompanied by additional F100 engines to those ordered for the F-16C/Ds, totalling 25, including seven spares, while the leased F-16s are to be exchanged for similar Fighting Falcons of the later series. Delivery of Singapore's 18 F-16C/Ds, together with 24-36 AIM-9S Sidewinder IR-homing and 50 AIM-7M radar-guided AAMs, plus 200,000 rounds of 20-mm ammunition, is planned by late 1998.

Northrop F-5 transfers

The RSAF's current force of some 26 Northrop F-5Es, eight RF-5Es and nine two-seat F-5Fs operating with Nos 141, 144 and 149 Sqns was supplemented last year by the purchase for $21 million of seven F-5E/Fs formerly operated by the Royal Jordanian air force. These were bought for the RSAF by Singapore Aerospace, which has a $36 million government contract to upgrade them to a similar standard to the F-5s already in service, in conjunction with Israel's Elbit Computers. Apart from the RF-5Es, RSAF F-5s are being fitted with new Mil Std 1553B digitised avionics, including the FIAR Grifo F pulse-Doppler radar, plus a Litton LN-93 ring laser gyro INS, HOTAS, Elbit mission computer, HUD and twin multi-function colour/monochrome cockpit displays, and Elisra RWR.

TAIWAN:

First front-line Ching-Kuo squadron commissioned

The first 22 production AIDC Ching-Kuo Indigenous Defensive Fighters, including seven two-seat versions, were commissioned in the RoCAF's 3rd Tactical Fighter Wing on 28

December 1994 at Ching Chuan Kang air base. They serve alongside 10 pre-production aircraft. The IDFs have replaced Lockheed F-104Gs in two of the wing's three squadrons, No. 7 squadron acting as the OTU and tactics development unit, and No. 8 being the first front-line unit. No. 28, the wing's third squadron, is currently undergoing conversion. The aircraft are tasked as multi-role fighters carrying Sky Sword 1/2 AAMs and Hsiung Feng 2 anti-ship missiles. Some 130 IDFs are now on order, reduced from the original RoCAF requirement for 250. Production rates are being scaled down in anticipation of deliveries of the 150 F-16A/B MLUs ordered in 1992.

Above: Thailand has taken delivery of two P-3Ts (formerly 152142 and 152143) and a UP-3T (152184). P-3As are already in use with 101 Sqn, Royal Thai navy, at U-Tapao AFB.

Recent Taiwanese F-16 equipment orders have included 157 AN/APG-66(V) 3 fire-control radars costing $195.8 million from Westinghouse Electric, and 80 AN/ALQ-184 ECM pods worth $100 million from Raytheon Electromagnetic Systems. Delivery was due last December of the 40 Northrop T-38 transonic trainers on three-year lease to help train the additional pilots required to man the new aircraft on order.

Australasia

AUSTRALIA:

Project Air 5367 MoU

Aermacchi has signed a Memorandum of Understanding with Hawker de Havilland Ltd and Honeywell Australia Ltd for the joint submission of the MB.339FD (Full Digital) version to meet the RAAF's Project Air 5367 requirement for a new lead-in fighter trainer to replace Australia's ageing Aermacchi MB.326Hs. Although 19 of these are being rewinged, with structural modifications to another 10, their service lives will not extend past the year 2000, and the RAAF requirement for 35-45 advanced trainers with advanced nav/attack systems is becoming increasingly urgent.

As a development of the MB.339CB, of which 18 have been operating for some time with the RNZAF, the Viper 680-43-engined MB.339FD has a new digital avionics system and EFIS-equipped 'glass' cockpits, including twin Thomson-CSF HUDs, with Sextant Avionique SMD54 three-colour liquid-crystal multi-function displays, Honeywell H-764G RLG inertial navigation platform with embedded GPS, a powerful nav/attack computer and HOTAS controls. These are representative of new-generation combat aircraft, and similar to the equipment in the 20 MB.339FDs for which Italian air force negotiations are still being finalised.

Apart from lead-in fighter training, the selected type from six short-listed finalists – also including the Aero L-59,

AMX-T, BAe Hawk 100, Dassault Alpha Jet and MDC T-45A Goshawk – must undertake army and naval support, as well as supplementary combat roles. The MB.339FD proposals include an Australian Industry Involvement (AIP) package for co-production, engineering, logistic support and technology transfer, to meet the stated requirements of the RAAF's lead-in fighter programme.

Above: A recent, but potentially short-lived, customer for the Sikorsky Black Hawk has been the Hong Kong Government Flying Service. Two S-70s are flown on numerous utility roles from police work to fire-fighting, replacing the Dauphins previously in service. Hong Kong's aircraft are S-70A-27s and may eventually join the 24 S-70Cs in use in the People's Republic of China.

NEW ZEALAND:

Wasp attrition replacement

A 'new' Westland Wasp has been put together from spares by the RNZAF to maintain the establishment of No. 3 Sqn at six available aircraft after two accidents in 1992-93. Tenders will soon be invited later this year for six Wasp replacements costing up to $NZ200 ($US90) million, for which the AS 565SA Panther and Super Lynx are among the main contenders.

Africa

NAMIBIA:

Air force expansion

A Namibian air squadron formed last year around five ex-USAF Cessna O-2 light observation aircraft has since been expanded from an Rs1.65 billion ($5 million) order from HAL for two licence-built SA 315 Cheetah (Lama) and two SA 316 Chetak (Alouette III) utility helicopters. Namibia is also interested in HAL's 14-seat Advanced Light Helicopter, while other procurement has included a Falcon 900 and a Learjet for presidential/government use.

SOUTH AFRICA:

End of the ACE?

The sole prototype all-composite Atlas ACE tandem trainer was written off in a wheels-up forced landing at Jan Smuts Airport, Johannesburg, on 14 February, almost certainly ending this promising programme. The ACE was intended as a potential new primary trainer for the SAAF, which instead selected the PC-7 Mk II Astra.

ASW helicopter requirement

Six companies, comprising Agusta, Atlas, Bell Helicopter Canada, Eurocopter, Kamov and Westland, responded by the 5 October 1994 deadline to Armscor RFPs on behalf of the South African navy for six corvette-based helicopters. These are needed for ASV and over-the-horizon targeting operations, plus possible ASW adaptation, and a purchase contract, with 100 per cent industrial offset requirements, is expected by the end of 1995.

TANZANIA:

Y-12s delivered

Chinese export sales of 58 Harbin Y-12 light turboprop transports to May 1994, have included at least two (JW 9029 and 9030) to the Tanzanian People's Defence Force Air Wing.

TUNISIA:

New light transports

A light transport capability has been acquired by the AQJJT from recent deliveries of three Let L-410UVP light twins from the Czech Republic.

ZIMBABWE:

C-130 offer

The AFZ is one of several African air forces now being offered a total of 10 ex-ANG Lockheed C-130B Hercules through US government aid programmes. Although the two C-130s being offered to Zimbabwe are on a no-cost basis, acceptance is dependent on studies proving that the AFZ could afford to man and operate them.

Central America

MEXICO:

Trainer needs and disposals

Having delivered 92 PC-7 turboprop trainers to the Fuerza Aérea Mexicana between 1978 and 1992, Pilatus was refused an export licence by the Swiss government earlier this year to fulfil an FAM order for 48 of the more powerful PC-9 versions worth some SwFr300 ($250) million. Switzerland's strict arms export controls to areas of conflict were applied in this case because of recent rebel operations in Mexico's Chiapas region, in which FAM PC-7s carrying light armament were reportedly involved, and because the FAM had specified underwing hardpoints for its PC-9s.

Twelve of 20 Mudry CAP 10B two-seat aerobatic trainers operated since 1982 by the FAM's Military Aviation School at Zapopan – and recently withdrawn – were sold in October 1994 to civil operators in the US.

While the Chilean navy has experimented with a shipboard Bell 222, more normal equipment comes in the form of the Bell 206, such as this aircraft from HU-1. This squadron is shore-based at Vina del Mar, but one of its Jetrangers is seen here aboard the 'Leander'-class frigate Minestro Zenteno.

South America

ARGENTINA:

LASCo A-4M upgrade contract signed

A $200 million upgrade contract signed with Lockheed Aircraft Services in December 1994 followed the late 1993 release by the US of 36 surplus USN A-4Ms to replace Argentina's Falklands War casualties. With spare engines, training, support equipment and 20-mm ammunition worth some $125 million, the A-4Ms are being withdrawn from storage at the USAF's AMARC facility, and the first 18 are being upgraded by LASCo in Ontario and Chino, CA. The remaining 18 will undergo similar modernisation from LASCo-supplied airframe, integrated cockpit displays and mission systems avionics kits, the latter from a $30 million AlliedSignal sub-contract, by the formerly state-owned FMA facility at Cordoba. Argentina has also been cleared to acquire a downgraded Westinghouse APG-66 radar known as the ARG-1 for the modernised Skyhawks. In an additional $200 million five-year contract, LAS has formed a new Lockheed Aircraft Argentina Services subsidiary (LAAS) to modernise and manage the privatised Cordoba factory for the agreed period from March 1995, to complete the Skyhawk upgrade, as well as to set up an international C-130 and civil aircraft maintenance centre. In FAA service, the upgraded A-4Ms will supplement the 29 A-4P Skyhawks remaining from earlier US deliveries.

Mohawk deliveries completed

A new Argentine Army Aviation (Aviación de Ejercito) unit known as Escuadron de Aviación de Exploración y Reconocimiento (Exploration and Reconnaissance Squadron) 601 has now received 43 ex-US Army Grumman OV-1D Mohawk twin-turboprop light attack and observation aircraft at Campo de Mayo. These were refurbished by Northrop Grumman's Stuart, FL, facility before deliveries started to Argentina on 19 December 1992 and are intended mainly for drug patrol and interdiction roles.

PERU:

Aircraft combat loss claims

Having operated 52 Sukhoi Su-22 ground-attack fighters of various sub-types since 1977 with zero pilot fatalities from accidents, the Fuerza Aérea Peruana was claimed by Ecuador to have lost two 'Fitters' in air combat with FAE Mirage F1JAs on 10 February, together with a Cessna A-37B shot down by a Kfir on the same date, in border clashes earlier this year in the Cordillera del Condor region. Three FAP Mil Mi-8 helicopters were also claimed destroyed by Ecuadorian Blowpipe SAMs or ground fire on 30 January and 7 February, while similar hits, with unknown results, were reported on two FAE Kfirs and an A-37B on 12 February.

Many of Peru's 48 Mi-8, Mi-17 and Mi-24 helicopters, plus Mirage 5Ps from Piura, were involved in these operations, in which Ecuadorean Pumas and other helicopters also took part. An Ilyushin Il-76 in Aeroflot markings, although possibly Ukrainian-operated, carrying Mi-8 spares and other Russian military equipment was grounded by Brazilian authorities in February when it landed at Ortaleza airport en route to Lima.

More transport deliveries

Peruvian satisfaction with the high-powered Antonov An-32 twin-turboprop tactical transport reflected in the air force acquisition from 1987 of 24, followed by more recent purchases of the first two for the navy and two more in August 1994 for the police, has resulted in the army becoming the latest customer for this type. Some 23 An-32Vs have been acquired from military and civil operators in Ukraine, and were delivered in Ejercito del Peru markings by the end of 1994. A formerly civil-operated Fokker F27-200 was also taken over by the Peruvian navy in September 1994, and the FAP is now known to have taken delivery of four Antonov An-72 'Coaler' twin-turbofan STOL freighters between April 1993 and mid-1994 for operation by Grupo 8 from Lima/Callao.

North America

CANADA:

Aircraft reductions confirmed

Further cuts to be made over the next four years in the Canadian Armed Forces as part of $C2.8 ($US1.98) billion in additional defence economies have been confirmed to include withdrawal of 12 MDC CF-18 (CF-118) Hornets and the remaining 50 or so Canadair CF-5s (CF-116s) of the Air Command. This will retain its four operational and one training Hornet squadrons, although combat unit strength will be reduced from 18 to 15, with a corresponding cut in Canada's first-line fighter strength in the planned Air Combat and Mobility Group from 72 to 60. The 12 withdrawn CF-18A/Bs will be held in reserve, alongside about 30 on overhaul or in storage, plus the 23 operating with No. 410 (OCU) Sqn at Cold Lake.

Below: Taking part in the Edwards show of October 1994 were an F-15B, F-16B, T-38A and NA-37B of the 412th Test Wing. Since October 1992 the 412th TW has been AFFTC's primary flying unit, having renumbered from the 6510th TW.

Following a Depot Level Inspection and Repair structural upgrade programme undertaken by Bristol Aerospace on 23 CF-5As and 33 two-seat CF-5Ds to extend their airframe fatigue lives from 4,000 to 6,000 hours, they have been undergoing an avionics update by the same contractors from the installation of a CF-18-type head-up display, INS, radar altimeter, throttle quadrant and other cockpit features for use as Hornet lead-in fighter trainers. Originally scheduled for 46 of the Air Command's CF-5s, this programme was later reduced to 36, and was still awaiting completion earlier this year. The first CF-5s will be offered for disposal later this year, and their role of lead-in training will be shared partly by the Air Command's remaining 119 Canadair CT-114 Tutors, also being upgraded by CAE Aviation through a $C10.4 ($US7.9) million contract, and on the CF-18 itself. Annual flying totals for CF-18 pilots are also to be reduced from about 210 to 200 hours or less, but Canada's Hornet force is to be armed with a small number of precision-guided ASMs and some are already carrying FLIR pods and LGBs.

Other aircraft retirements are planned by the turn of the century to reduce the total Air Command inventory from about 600 to 400, but replacements are still scheduled for 13 Boeing CH-113 Labrador SAR helicopters and about 23 frigate-based ASW Sikorsky CH-124A/B Sea Kings. Fifty EH101s ordered for these roles were cancelled on cost grounds in October 1993 by the incoming Liberal government, but requests for proposals for 15 off-the-shelf SAR and 35 ASW replacement helicopters will be issued later this year.

UNITED STATES:

New bomber force structure for ACC and the Reserves

The Air Force announced details during November 1994 of additional changes to the bomber force structure of Air Combat Command (ACC) and the Reserves. The changes include a consolidation of ACC's B-52 assets from four to just two units. The 2nd BW at Barksdale AFB, Louisiana activated the 11th Bomb Squadron in July 1994 to join the 20th and 96th BS, all equipped with the B-52H. The new squadron is tasked with being the formal training unit to train Stratofortress aircrew. The 5th BW at Minot AFB, North Dakota is the only other active-duty B-52 unit, also operating the H model. The latter wing had the 23rd BS as its sole flying unit for many years, although the influx of additional aircraft during the second half of 1994 necessitated the activation of the 72nd BS on 6 January 1995. The 2nd BW gained eight aircraft for an authorised strength of 40 B-52Hs, while the 5th BW was increased from 16 to 26 Stratofortresses.

Many of the additional aircraft at Barksdale and Minot had been reassigned from the 410th BW at K. I. Sawyer AFB, Michigan and the 416th BW at Griffiss AFB, New York. These two units were scheduled to inactivate in late 1994 or early 1995. K. I. Sawyer is scheduled to close on 30 September 1995, while Griffiss AFB will become a non-flying establishment housing the Rome Laboratory of Air Force Materiel Command. The last two B-52Hs to leave the 410th BW departed for Minot AFB on 21 November, while the final pair of 416th BW Stratofortresses were 60-0024 and 61-0025, which flew out to Minot AFB on 15 November 1994.

The only Reserve B-52 unit is the 93rd BS, 917th Wing at Barksdale AFB, which is an Air Force Reserve unit. The squadron completed accepting delivery of their eight aircraft during 1994. The Air Force had intended to create a B-52-equipped Bomb Squadron within the Air National Guard at Fairchild AFB, Washington, although these plans were subsequently dropped.

The foregoing details leave an imbalance, as the Air Force ordered 102 B-52Hs, of which eight had been lost to accidents, resulting in a strength of 94 in service. According to the recent announcement the 2nd BW had

Above: The US Customs Service maintains a helicopter detachment at March AFB, CA, comprising this UH-60A 'Pot Hawk' and a TV/FLIR-equipped Bell Jetranger.

Left: At William Tell 94, winners of the Top Team award were the 119th FG (ANG), the 'Happy Hooligans' from Fargo, ND. This was the 119th's fourth win and their participating F-16 ADFs were decorated with Sidewinder 'fin art' – reflecting North Dakota's association with 'Teddy' Roosevelt's Rough Riders. The Riders, who fought during the 1898 Spanish American War, were a cavalry unit largely comprised of North Dakotans. Three of the unit's F-16s still maintain the West Coast armed Zulu alert at March AFB.

40 aircraft, and the 5th BW 26, while an additional eight were with the AFRes. None had been retired from service, and only one or two were devoted to development work. Most of the remainder were on major overhaul and were therefore not available for operational duty.

At Dyess AFB, Texas the 7th Wing was assigned the 9th and 337th Bomb Squadrons, both operating the B-1B. The 337th was inactivated on 1 October 1994 when it was replaced by the 28th BS as the Lancer formal training unit. At Ellsworth AFB, South Dakota the 34th Bomb Squadron officially reformed with the B-1B on 4 April 1994. The squadron is part of the 366th Wing based at Mountain Home AFB, Idaho, with the Lancers stationed at Ellsworth AFB to avoid the unnecessary expense of establishing facilities for the bombers at Mountain Home AFB.

The 7th Wing placed two B-1Bs in what has been termed 'reconstitution reserve status' during 1994, while the 28th BW at Ellsworth AFB converted a dozen Lancers to this condition. This merely involved the aircraft being removed from active flying status and placed in storage at their home base, but in a readiness to be returned to service if needed. The reduction in the number of aircraft in service will enable a manpower cut of almost 500 people, and will permit funds to be redirected to the Lancer conventional upgrade programme.

At Grand Forks AFB, North Dakota the 319th BW was reduced to Group status during October 1993, prior to its B-1Bs being reassigned, with many of

the aircrew and aircraft joining the 34th BS at Ellsworth AFB. The 384th BW at McConnell AFB, Kansas was likewise redesignated a Bomb Group on 1 January 1994 with many of the B-1Bs joining the 184th Bomb Group, Kansas ANG further down the flight line at the same base. The 384th itself was finally inactivated in October 1994. The Air National Guard still has need to fund the conversion of the 116th FW at Dobbins AFB Georgia from the F-15A to the B-1B, with a corresponding move to Robins AFB. Despite the lack of money, the Air Force still intends to implement the re-equipment plan.

55th Wing redesignations

The 55th Wing at Offutt AFB, Nebraska redesignated a number of its flying squadrons during the summer of 1994. The 2nd Airborne Command and Control Squadron was redesignated the 7th ACCS on 19 July, as the sole operator of the EC-135C. The squadron, together with the 1st ACCS, are the last two airborne command post units in the Air Force. The 7th ACCS was previously stationed at Keesler AFB, Mississippi with the EC-130E as part of the 355th Wing, but was redesignated the 42nd ACCS when it moved to Davis-Monthan AFB, Arizona on 19 July, enabling the '7th Axe' title to reform at Offutt. The 24th Reconnaissance Squadron, which operated the RC-135S 'Cobra Ball' as well as the OC-135B Open Skies aircraft, was redesignated the 45th RS on 1 July 1994.

The wing had operated for many years without any form of fin-tip colour, although tail stripes begun to be applied at the end of 1994. The RC-135U,V and W models of the 343rd RS had adopted a green band, while the 7th ACCS EC-135Cs had a blue stripe. Cobra Ball and the Open Skies aircraft have a black stripe. During 1993 the 55th Wing operational support aircraft sported a tail band composed of two thin red stripes containing the words 'Fightin 55th'. Composed of a C-135A, C-135B and an NKC-135A, these had been retired or redistributed to other units by 1994.

The only aircraft of the 55th Wing which do not carry the 'OF' tailcode are the E-4Bs of the 1st ACCS. Their primary duty is to act as the National Airborne Command Post to co-ordinate a credible response in the event of ground command centres being destroyed during an enemy attack.

AWACS news

The 552nd Air Control Wing at Tinker AFB, Oklahoma saw its three operational squadrons and its training unit change designation on 1 July 1994. The 963rd, 964th and 965th Airborne Control Squadrons became Airborne Air Control Squadrons, while the 966th became an Airborne Air Control and Training Squadron flying a number of TC-18E airframes alongside the E-3B and C versions of the Sentry. The Pacific Air Force has two AWACS units which changed their unit titles in line with the above one month later. The 961st AACS is part of the 18th Wing at Kadena AB, Okinawa, and the 962nd AAACS at Elmendorf AFB, Alaska is assigned to the 3rd Wing. Tailcode 'OK' is displayed by aircraft of the 552nd ACW, with those deployed to Kadena and Elmendorf being repainted with 'ZZ' and 'AK' respectively.

The 552nd maintains a six-aircraft detachment at Riyadh Military City Airport, Saudi Arabia to monitor the air space above southern Iraq to prevent Saddam Hussein's aircraft from violating the United Nation's 'No-Fly Zone'. While detached to Saudi Arabia as part of Operation Southern Watch, the aircraft and personnel are temporarily assigned to the 4405th Airborne Air Control Squadron (Provisional), which enables operations to continue without the activation of a squadron manned by full-time staff.

9th Wing receives the U-2S

The Air Force accepted delivery of the first three re-engined U-2s during a ceremony at Lockheed's Advanced Developments facility at Palmdale, California on 28 October. The aircraft have been fitted with the General Electric F118-GE-101 engine in place of the Pratt & Whitney J75-P-13B, resulting in a change of designation to U-2S. The new powerplant offers an increased thrust-to-weight ratio, while providing a 16 per cent improvement in fuel consumption.

The three aircraft consisted of U-2S 80-1071 along with U-2ST two-seat trainers 80-1064 and 80-1078. The latter was formerly a single-seat U-2R which was damaged in an accident at RAF Alconbury in April 1990 and has been in store at Palmdale subsequently. Apart from the fitment of the new engine, 01078 has been rebuilt as a trainer version with raised second cockpit and dual controls.

The USAF will receive a total of 33 U-2Ss and three U-2STs, with completion due by 1998. The programme will include some of the survivors of the handful of U-2Rs which were ordered in 1968, as well as the majority of those ordered as TR-1s and U-2Rs with 1980 funding. The latter order totalled 37 airframes, including three assigned to NASA. At least three of this last order have been destroyed in accidents.

86th Wing news

The two F-16C/D squadrons of the 86th Wing at Ramstein were inactivated following the transfer of their aircraft to the 31st FW at Aviano AB, Italy. The 526th FS was inactivated on 1 July 1994 followed by the 512th FS on 1 October 1994, enabling the parent wing to be redesignated as the 86th Airlift Wing on 1 October 1994 when the C-130Es of the 37th AS were officially transferred from Rhein Main AB. The squadron will apply tailcode 'RS' to the C-130s in due course, although the other 86th AW types are unlikely to receive the two-letter identifier.

The wing is also responsible for the 75th AS with the C-9A for medevac duties throughout Europe and the Middle East, and the 7Eth AS operating the C-20A, C-21A and CT-43A. Both squadrons are responsible for aircraft assigned elsewhere in Europe, including a C-9A fitted with a V1P suite which is stationed at Chièvres, Belgium for the Commander of the Supreme Headquarters Allied Powers Europe (HQ SHAPE). This aircraft is supported by the 75th AS, while the 76th AS has administrative control of the four C-21A Learjets based at Stuttgart-Echterdingen which are used by Headquarters United States European Command (HQ USEUCOM).

C-141 retirement enhanced

The Air Force announced at the end of 1994 that it will bring forward the plan to retire the much troubled fleet of C-141B StarLifters from service, with front-line aircraft leaving the inventory by 2003 followed by those of the reserves by either 2006 or 2007. The C-141s suffered wing cracks and fatigue during high utilisation while performing thousands of sorties during the build-up to the Gulf War in 1990. A grounding order was imposed on many aircraft while the extent of the problem was assessed, with the Air Force contracting much of its routine cargo deliveries to civilian carriers while repairs were carried out. Nine

Under the wing of this VMFA (AW)-533 F/A-18D (above) is a 2,490-lb (1130-kg) AGM-62 Walleye II ER/DL glide bomb, with its AWW-7/9 datalink pod on the centreline. Walleye is a fairly recent addition to the Hornet's inventory. A more colourful change in the F/A-18 community has been this brightly painted VFA-105 aircraft (right).

C-141Bs were either too badly cracked for repairs to be carried out, or had reached their maximum airframe life of 45,000 hours, and were retired to the Aerospace Maintenance and Regeneration Center at Davis-Monthan AFB, Arizona. Surprisingly, only one other aircraft has since joined the mothballed fleet, this being NC-141A 61-2777 of the 412th Test Wing from Edwards AFB, California, which was a flying testbed for the B-2 programme until retired in 1994.

An additional four had been relegated to ground training duties with the 82nd Training Wing at Sheppard AFB, Texas. A small number of additional C-141Bs have been withdrawn at their home bases and will presumably find a new lease of life in the training role.

The StarLifters' enhanced retirement schedule will add to the problems encountered by Air Mobility Command, which simply has too many commitments and not enough fully operational aircraft to perform all their requirements. This will be welcome news for McDonnell Douglas, which anticipate rectifying the shortcomings of the C-17A, and are hoping that Congress will remove the ceiling of 40 aircraft which have been imposed, and fund additional orders.

Fourth B-2 delivered to 509th BW

The 509th Bomb Wing at Whiteman AFB, Missouri received its fourth Northrop Grumman B-2A during December 1994. The aircraft, serial 89-0332, was the 10th airframe (AV10) and was flown from the Northrop facility at Palmdale to Renton to be named 'Spirit of Washington' during a ceremony on 29 October 1994. The previous three aircraft in service with the 509th BW have also received names: 88-0328 (AV7) 'Spirit of Texas' which was delivered on 24 September 1994, 88-0329 (AV8) 'Spirit of Missouri' which initiated operational service when it was flown to

Whiteman on 17 December 1993, and 88-0330 (AV9) 'Spirit of California' which joined the 509th SW on 17 August 1994. B-2A no. 11, which is the fifth for the 509th BW, was delivered during February 1995, with a further three due to join the unit during 1995. The B-2s wear their 'WM' two-letter unit identifyer and their name on the main undercarriage doors, as the flying wing shape does not have a conventional tail or any other flat surface upon which to present these details.

Since the first example was delivered in December 1993, personnel of the 509th BW and Northrop Grumman have been working to expand the potential of the B-2 toward the common goal of the 393rd Bomb Squadron achieving its initial operational capability by 1997. ACC had initially planned to fly the first aircraft on four sorties each month, although this was soon changed when the B-2 began achieving four flights each week. A major milestone was achieved on 20 September 1994 when 88-0328 performed the first operational munitions delivery. During a seven-hour sortie from Whiteman AFB two inert Mk 82 bombs were released against a target on a range in Utah, scoring direct hits.

The test programme commenced in July 1989 when the prototype B-2A performed its maiden flight from Palmdale, California to nearby Edwards AFB. Subsequently, development of the bomber and its stealth characteristics has been ongoing at Edwards with six aircraft allocated, although two and possibly three were in temporary store outside the Northrop facility at Plant 42 at Palmdale during late 1994, including prototype 82-1066 (AV1), which will be reworked to operational standard. One of the other two airframes is believed to be a full size mock-up, while the identity of the third aircraft remains unknown.

Prior to its temporary withdrawal, the prototype was engaged on a variety of test work including the expansion of the entire flight envelope, along with day and night inflight refuelling trials. The remaining five airframes have been assigned to a variety of test programmes. 82-1067 (AV2) was delivered in a non-standard low-observable scheme and has been evaluating performance and high angle of attack capabilities, with instrumentation for dynamic loads testing; 82-1068 (AV3) has the complete avionics fit, and has been conducting tests of the Hughes APQ-181 radar and the defensive systems, as well as operational test and evaluation; 82-1069 (AV4) has been performing weapons testing, as well as investigating the effects of icing and rain on the stealth qualities. This has involved a period at Eglin AFB, Florida in the huge climatic chamber. 82-1070 (AV5) has also undertaken climatic tests, and is currently engaged on an extended programme to test the defensive avionics, as well as additional development of the detectability and survivability. Finally 82-1071 (AV6) is employed on tests of the navigation systems, radar and armament equipment. An F-4D operated by Tracor Flight Systems at Mojave, California recently commenced testing the delivery of munitions with the aid of a global positioning system.

The development programme for the B-2 is being managed by a Combined Test Force at Edwards AFB, with personnel from Northrop working alongside AFFTC representatives. The 412th Test Wing is the flying component of the AFFTC, with day-to-day operations devolved to the 412th Test Group. The latter organisation has the 420th Flight Test Squadron assigned, and is unique as all other test squadrons at Edwards AFB report directly to the parent wing.

Above: This Mi-24P 'Hind-F' was seen operating out of Nellis AFB, for a Red Flag exercise, flying on behalf of the US Army. It carries cartoon vulture nose art (to port) and is believed to be based at El Paso, alongside an Mi-8 and other foreign hardware.

Left: One of the first re-engined U-2s to be re-delivered to the USAF was this two-seat U-2ST, a U-2R rebuilt as the fourth trainer.

F-15 and F-16 fighter orders to remain terminated

A recent proposal by Lockheed Fort Worth to produce additional batches of Block 50 series F-16C/Ds at an individual price of $20 million each was rejected by the Assistant Secretary of the Air Force for Acquisition. A similar offer by McDonnell Douglas to supply additional F-15Es at $50 million per aircraft was also turned down, with the Secretary declaring that there are no plans at present to purchase any additional F-15s or F-16s. The final production F-15E was ordered during fiscal year 1992 with delivery taking place in mid-1994. The last order for F-16C/Ds for the USAF was placed in fiscal year 1994, for just 12 aircraft.

The Air Force is preparing detailed proposals to overcome the problem of its ageing fighter fleet, although it considers the number of aircraft in service to be sufficient until the next generation of fighters becomes operational. The F-22 will be the next major fighter design to enter service, with plans for sufficient examples in operational service by the year 2010 to be able to support the strategy of being able to fight and win two major regional conflicts.

In the interim, the commander of Air Combat Command (ACC) has requested USAF acquisition officials to review the overall fighter programme. This would indicate that ACC does not want the F-22 programme to suffer any budgetary cutbacks or delays to the planned entry into operational service. Even so, the fiscal year 1996 budget will have $200 million trimmed from the $2,000 million requested for the F-22's research and development funding. The Pentagon insist this reduction will delay the in-service date by no more than six months. The F-22 has assumed added importance, as a

ground attack capability is to be added to its primary role of air superiority.

The prototype development aircraft is scheduled to make its first flight in 1996, with seven F-22A single-seat and two F-22B two-seat aircraft due to join the dedicated flight test programme at Edwards AFB. Under current plans the F-22 will enter operational service in the year 2003, by which time many F-15s and F-16s currently in service will be nearing the end of their projected lives. The offer by Lockheed and McDonnell Douglas to supply their current fighter types at a fixed price has presumably been based on the premise that funding for the F-22 will be cut or delayed, resulting in a fighter gap.

Joint STARS may increase production

During October 1994 one of the two prototype E-8 Joint Surveillance and Target Attack Radar System (Joint STARS) aircraft conducted a major European sales drive. Eleven days were spent performing demonstrations of its capabilities to senior NATO personnel in the UK, Germany and Belgium. The US government together with Grumman, the prime contractor, are eager for NATO to purchase a dozen E-8s to be operated by a mixed complement of Alliance partners in a similar manner as the E-3 Sentries of the NATO Airborne Early Warning Force. These are routinely forward-deployed to bases in Norway and Italy as an ongoing commitment to oversee the security of European air space from the main Geilenkirchen, Germany. The final decision on E-8 purchase by NATO E-8s will not be made until the beginning of 1996.

Meanwhile, the US Air Force seems increasingly likely to receive more than

the 20 E-8Cs originally planned. The Deputy Defense Secretary stated recently that production may number as many as 40 E-8s for the USAF, enabling small batches of Joint STARS to be deployed to overseas locations in the western Pacific, the Middle East and Europe.

The first E-8C is due for delivery in 1996, with the 6th Reconnaissance Wing reforming at Robins AFB, Georgia as the primary Joint STARS operator under Air Combat Command. The two E-8A prototypes will be upgraded to E-8C standard once their period of development work has been completed.

Korea helicopter incident

North Korea's release of Army CW2 Bobby Hall at Panmunjom at the end of last year staved off a diplomatic crisis over a flight which began on 17 December 1994 when Hall and CW2 David Hilemon began a flight in a Bell OH-58C Kiowa observation helicopter at Camp Page, Chunchon, South Korea. Hall, a pilot with the 4/501st Aviation Brigade at Camp Page, Chunchon, took off in the OH-58C (aircraft no. 71-20796) at 10:00 a.m. using the callsign 'Razorback 19'. Although an experienced Kiowa pilot, he was new to Korea. Hilemon was less experienced.

The OH-58C Kiowa was making a familiarisation flight in a sector known as P-518 Tactical Zone, along a 'No-Fly Zone' protecting the Korean DMZ (Demilitarized Zone). Hall later said, "I didn't know I was over North Korea until I saw an air burst on my right side." The helicopter may have been hit by gunfire, although an air burst sounds consistent with a shoulder-mounted, surface-to-air missile such as an SA-7 or SA-14. The helicopter went out of control, slammed into the ground, and disintegrated, killing H."e-mon instantly.

The last time an American helicopter went down in North Korea, on 14 July 1977, the aircraft was a Vertol

CH-47 Chinook (serial no. 69-17124). Several crew members were killed and a two survived. The survivors and the remains of the deceased were returned by the North Koreans within days.

On 17 May 1963, a US Army Hiller H-23 Raven was forced down in North Korea after it strayed across the border and was hit by anti-aircraft fire. Captains Ben W. Stutts and Charleston W. Voltz were held for nine months before North Korea announced, on 17 February 1964, that it was ready to deal 'leniently' with the crew if the US apologised for the incident. The US issued an apology (stronger language than its 'regret' of 1977 and 1994) and the two men were released on 16 May 1964 after a year in captivity.

There have been other cross-border mishaps involving Cessna L-19 Bird Dogs and, in one instance, a T-6 trainer. On 17 August 1955, North Korean ground fire downed a T-6 that had crossed the DMZ. Pilot Captain Guy H. Bumpass suffered major head injuries and observer Captain Charles W. Brown was killed. Bumpass and the body of Captain Brown were released on 23 August, after just a week. North Korea also released the T-6 wreckage.

The North Koreans released CW2 Bobby Hall on 29 December, 12 days after his helicopter went down.

AH-64D Longbow Apache operational trials

The second stage of operational trials for the McDonnell Douglas AH-64D Longbow Apache was scheduled to make use of six prototypes in the US Army's IOTE (Initial Operational Test and Evaluation) exercise from 4 January through 31 March 1995 at Fort Hunter-Liggett, California. Earlier, four AH-64Ds had completed phase one of the trials, an FDTE (Force Development Test and Experimentation) exercise conducted at the same location from 1 October to 3 December 1994.

IOTE consists of two phases. The first phase at China Lake Naval Weapons Center uses four Longbow Apaches for gunnery evaluation which will compare the AH-64D to the proven AH-64A model. The second phase beginning 27 February 1995 is a 'force on force' exercise at Hunter-Liggett in a simulated combat environment.

During IOTE, Longbow Apaches are flown and maintained by Army crews without assistance from the manufacturer. Fifty-five US Army personnel including 16 pilots and 39 maintainers, primarily from the 2/299th Aviation Regiment, were involved in IOTE event. Apart from flying in realistic combat scenarios, the exercise was expected to test such goals as the ability to field-install the Longbow fire control radar in four hours.

As of 1 March 1995, the AH-64D prototype fleet had logged 3,600 flight hours. The first delivery of operational AH-64Ds is scheduled for March 1997.

Kaman mine detector

Kaman is flying an SH-2F Seasprite with an advanced developmental model of the company's Magic Lantern anti-ship mine detection device housed in an external pod. Kaman has made an unsolicited proposal to the US Navy to develop and install the system on four Sikorsky MH-53E Sea Dragons. Magic Lantern uses laser technology to detect, classify, and localise moored and floating anti-ship mines.

RAH-66 decision

As expected, the US Army has deferred procurement of the Boeing/Sikorsky RAH-66 Comanche two-seat battlefield helicopter. This will produce short-term savings of $2.1 billion over 1996-2001, but will also raise unit costs. To salvage something from the Comanche programme, two prototypes will be built for tests.

C-5 tested for airdrop role

The US Air Force has carried out tests with the Lockheed C-5 Galaxy to determine whether that aircraft will be used routinely for airdrop operations, filling gaps created by the ageing of the C-141B fleet. The tests reflect doubt whether the USAF will get its full 'buy' of 120 Douglas C-17 Globemaster IIIs to replace the C-141B. Pentagon warfighting plans require the USAF to have enough airlifters to drop a full Army brigade of 5,000 to 6,000 troops, plus their equipment. Some 126 Galaxy transports are in inventory, divided between 76 surviving C-5As (of 81 manufactured) and all 50 C-5Bs.

The tests were conducted between October 1994 and January 1995 at Dover AFB, Delaware and Fort Bragg, North Carolina where the US Army's XVIII Airborne Corps and 82nd Airborne Division are based. One hundred people and six aircraft from Dover's 436th Airlift Wing took part in the airdrop tests, which cost $3 million. Part of the tests involved dropping 10,000-lb (4536-kg) cargo pallets. Some 150 dummies weighing 320-lb (145-kg) each were dropped from the Galaxy's troop doors to simulate soldiers loaded with combat gear.

The C-5 has been capable of airdrop operations from its inception, and holds a world's record: at Pope AFB, North Carolina on 7 June 1989, a C-5B dropped four M551 Sheridan tanks and 73 troopers for a world record of 190,346 lb (86313 kg). However, the USAF has not customarily used the aircraft to deliver people and things by parachute. AMC officers wanted to know how the C-5 would perform dropping troops in formation, and whether the turbulence generated by this large aircraft interferes with troop or cargo drops. Further modifications are under consideration, including an emergency oxygen system for the Galaxy's large cargo (lower) deck. Currently, oxygen is available

Above: During February 1995 the US Navy deployed its EC-24A EW training and support aircraft to RAF Lossiemouth, Scotland, for Exercise Strong Resolve. Operating alongside it were the much-modified electronic warfare Learjets of Phoenix Aviation and the 'Smart Crow' Lears of Flight International.

Right: ASRAAM, the new short-range AAM under development for the RAF by BAe, has been test-flown aboard this Block 25 F-16C of the 39th FTS, 46th TW, at Eglin AFB. Four ASRAAMS have been carried at speeds up to Mach 1.6 and subjected to loads of +7 g and -1.5 g.

only in the 73-passenger area on the rear upper deck. Other modifications would include formation lights and SKE (station-keeping equipment).

JPATS delayed farther

The Pentagon has delayed for another six months the selection of a manufacturer and aircraft for its JPATS (Joint Primary Aircraft Training System), the intended replacement for the US Air Force Cessna T-37 and US Navy T-34C. The programme is also being stretched from 12 to 20 years, meaning that it will be completed in 2016. First deliveries to the USAF will slip a year, to 1998, while those for the Navy will be postponed for two years, to 2000.

The delay has infuriated manufacturers of the aircraft which competed in a fly-off effort in late 1994. Since the winning aircraft will not be decided until August 1995, instead of February as previously planned, the choice will be made too late for its manufacturer to compete in the Royal Australian Air Force's trainer competition, which is expected to be resolved in June.

Northrop Grumman's Pampa 2000 jet trainer was eliminated from the competition after the company test pilot was forced to help an Air Force evaluator recover from a spin. Six aircraft types remain in contention.

Carriers named

The nuclear-powered aircraft-carrier now under construction for commissioning by the US Navy in 1998 is to be named USS Harry S. Truman (CVN-75). The next carrier, construction of which is to begin in 1996 with a commissioning date in 2002, will be the USS Ronald Reagan (CVN-76). Truman will replace USS Independence (CV-62), the oldest carrier in the fleet and the only one to be home-ported overseas (in Yokosuka, Japan). Reagan will replace USS Kitty Hawk (CV-63).

X-31 loss

The no. 1 Rockwell/Daimler-Benz X-31 (BuNo. 164584) went out of control and crashed at Edwards AFB, on 19 January 1995. German test pilot Karl Lang ejected safely. The aircraft was returning from a test flight and was not employing thrust vectoring, and began a series of rapid pitching oscillations, followed by a sharp roll. Lang ejected at 18,000 ft (5573 m).

On 10 December 1994, Deputy Defense Secretary John M. Deutsch informed the German government that he was unable to secure funds to continue testing the X-31, indicating an expected premature end to the US role in the programme.

C-17 IOC

The Douglas C-17 Globemaster III achieved initial operating capability (IOC) on 17 January 1995 with the USAF's 17th Airlift Squadron, 437th Airlift Wing, at Charleston AFB, South Carolina. The occasion also marked IOC for the Air Force Reserve's 317th Airlift Squadron. A second squadron in the wing, the 14th, is now working up in the C-17.

Orion 154589 was delivered to the US Naval Research Laboratory as an EP-3B, it was modified to RP-3D standard at Jacksonville and now carries an NP-3D designation.

NATO Strikes Back

In late 1994 the war in Bosnia entered a new phase, with NATO performing its first major air strike against a Serb-held airfield, which had earlier launched an attack into Bosnia. At the same time, the threat from Serb SAMs became more intense for the United Nations aircraft.

Above: On patrol over the mountains, an F/A-18D Hornet of VMFA(AW)-224 carries a mixed load of ordnance, including AGM-65E laser-guided Maverick missiles. Two of these weapons were fired by Hornets at an SA-6 missile site during the raid on Udbina airfield.

NATO air power was drawn deeper into the Bosnian conflict after the United Nations called on the alliance to launch air strikes on Serbian airfields and missile sites during November 1994. The result was the most intense aerial combat over Europe since World War II and NATO's first major action.

As fighting escalated after the Bosnian Government Army (BiH) launched offensives throughout the war-torn country during late October and early November, United Nations Protection Force (UNPROFOR) commanders looked for ways to damp down the conflict and stop it escalating out of control. With the fate of the besieged Bosnian enclave of Bihac at stake, UNPROFOR asked NATO to strike at Serbian military positions in Bosnia and Croatia. A planned strike on Bosnian Serb artillery positions bombarding Bihac did not materialise when the guns fell silent as NATO bombers prowled above the town.

Serb air strikes

Enraged by a successful attack by the Bihac-based BiH V Corps that captured 200 sq miles (518 km²) of territory, the Bosnian Serb Army (BSA) combined with forces from the Republic of Serb Krajina (RSK) to strike back at the north-west Bosnian enclave. BSA tanks and artillery were mobilised for the counter-attack on 8 November and soon the RSK air force was called into action from its base at nearby Udbina, in Serb-occupied Croatian territory. SA-2 'Guideline' surface-to-air missiles were pressed into action in the surface-to-surface mode and 16 were fired at positions in Bihac.

Although nominally aligned to the RSK political leadership in Knin, the RSK air force maintains close links with the Bosnian Serb air force based at Banja Luka, in north-west Bosnia, and the Federal Yugoslav air force in Serbia proper. Men, material, fuel and know-how are regularly exchanged to keep the three air forces in fighting form. During November 1994 the RSK air force had a strong air unit at its main base at Udbina, including four J-22 Orao, four G-4 Super Galeb and six J-21 Jestreb/G-2 Galeb light jet strike fighters, plus one Mil Mi-8 'Hip-C' and four or five SA-341/2 Gazelle helicopters. A handful of prop-driven J-20 Kraguj COIN and other small light aircraft are also in service with the RSK air force.

Udbina was only a few minutes flying time from Bihac, and starting on 9 November the

RSK Oraos launched three hit-and-run raids against the Bihac pocket between 9 and 19 November. Hughes AGM-65 Maverick missiles, cluster bombs and napalm were all used to pound Bihac and Cazin, causing heavy damage to military targets and inflicting a large number of civilian casualties. One Orao crashed during the final attack on Cazin. NATO fighters flying Deny Flight patrols over Bosnia were vectored to intercept the RSK aircraft, but by the time they could get into position the intruders were safely back on the ground. NATO aircraft were forbidden by rules of engagement (ROE) from pursuing the aircraft into what was nominally Croatian air space.

Udbina strike

The United Nations Security Council in New York was stung into action by this flagrant breach of the UN 'No-Fly Zone' over Bosnia-Herzegovina and quickly authorised an extension of the zone into Croatian air space to allow action to be taken against Udbina. The Croatian government in Zagreb readily agreed to the extension of NATO operations in the hope that the alliance's air power would inflict damage on its Serb enemies.

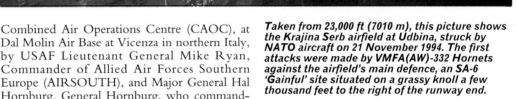

Combined Air Operations Centre (CAOC), at Dal Molin Air Base at Vicenza in northern Italy, by USAF Lieutenant General Mike Ryan, Commander of Allied Air Forces Southern Europe (AIRSOUTH), and Major General Hal Hornburg. General Hornburg, who commanded the USAF's F-15E Strike Eagle wing during the Gulf War, had only just taken over as director of the CAOC from USAF Lieutenant General James 'Bear' Chambers, who had run Operation Deny Flight since its start in April 1993.

A major strike force was assembled from Deny Flight participating forces at eight Italian air bases and the first aircraft lifted off at 1130 on 21 November. After refuelling from USAF KC-135R (319th Wing, Pisa and 100th Air Refueling Wing Det, Istres), French air force C-135FR (ERV 93, Istres) and RAF Tristar (216 Sqn, Palermo) tanker aircraft over the Adriatic, the strike force started its bomb runs at 1300. Some 45 minutes later Udbina air base was littered with wreckage, which was faithfully

Taken from 23,000 ft (7010 m), this picture shows the Krajina Serb airfield at Udbina, struck by NATO aircraft on 21 November 1994. The first attacks were made by VMFA(AW)-332 Hornets against the airfield's main defence, an SA-6 'Gainful' site situated on a grassy knoll a few thousand feet to the right of the runway end.

recorded by British, Dutch and French reconnaissance aircraft. Turkish F-16Cs were scheduled to take part in the raid but bad weather closed down their air base at Ghedi and they aborted.

Over 30 aircraft were involved in the raid, including four RAF Jaguars (Gioia del Colle Detachment), two French air force Jaguars (EC 11, Istrana) and two Mirage 2000N-K2s (EC 4, Cervia), four Royal Netherlands air force

An F-15E of the 492nd Fighter Squadron touches down at Aviano on 21 November, returning from the Udbina raid. Six F-15Es formed the backbone of the main attack force, using GBU-12 Paveway II laser-guided bombs against the runway, taxiways and defences.

At NATO bases in Italy preparations began for the strike at Udbina, after UNPROFOR's French commander, Lieutenant General Bertrand De Lapresle, requested a limited operation to put the base out of action .

The NATO strike was commanded from the 5th Allied Tactical Air Force's (5 ATAF)

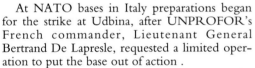

E-3 Sentries maintain a constant watch over the Bosnia-Herzegovina air space. NATO, French and RAF aircraft are involved. For the Udbina raid an NAEWF E-3A and an RAF E-3D from No. 8 Squadron provided coverage.

One Grumman/General Dynamics EF-111A Raven was dispatched to cover the Udbina attack, combining with the lethal SEAD assets (USMC Hornets) to negate the SAM threat. The Raven operated from Aviano, deployed from Cannon AFB, with the 429th Electronic Combat Squadron.

(RNLAF) F-16As (315 Sqn, Villafranca), six US Marine Corps F/A-18D Hornets (VMFA-332, Aviano), six F-15Es (492nd Fighter Squadron, Aviano), 10 F-16Cs (555th FS, Aviano) and one EF-111A (429th Electronic Combat Squadron, Aviano).

A USAF EC-130E Airborne Battlefield Command and Control Centre (42nd Airborne Command and Control Squadron, Aviano), co-ordinated the strike and provided communications links back to the CAOC. A NATO Airborne Early Warning Force E-3A Sentry AWACS (Trapani) and a RAF E-3D (8 Sqn,

Aviano) provided radar surveillance for the raid. A search and rescue force of USAF A-10As (81st FS, Aviano), MH-53J and HC-130 (USAFSOC, Brindisi), and French air force Pumas (Brindisi) was launched to pick up any downed pilots.

The first wave of the strike force aimed to take out the base's SA-6 'Gainful' surface-to-air missile (SAM) defence battery and two anti-aircraft artillery positions. First in were the 'Moonlighters' of VMFA(AW)-332 with their F/A-18Ds. Two of the aircraft launched an AGM-88 HARM each from about 13 miles (21 km) out, while the second pair launched laser-guided Mavericks from 8 miles (13 km), one each, at the SA-6 missile site, which lay to one end of the runway. The pre-emptive strike took out at least one transporter-erector-launcher

vehicle, and the Straight Flush radar van, rendering the site ineffective for the duration of the raid. The Hornets remained on station to fire more HARMs while the strike force hit the runway, but this was not needed. F-15Es hit other airfield defences.

Laser attack

Strike Eagles and French Jaguars devastated Udbina's runway and taxiways with laser-guided bombs, and they were joined by British Jaguars, Dutch F-16s and French Mirage 2000N-K2s with unguided iron bombs. USAF F-16s dropped more CBU-87s on the taxiways to complete the strike. Weapon system footage released later by NATO showed a GBU-12 500-lb Paveway II weapon from an F-15E hitting the runway dead centre.

Supporting the mission were USAF RC-135 electronic intelligence-gathering aircraft and EF-111A radar-jamming aircraft to blind any radars that tried to track the raid. A few man-portable SA-7 'Grail' heat-seeking SAMs and anti-aircraft guns tried to return fire, but the raiders were flying too high.

In early 1995 Spain made its first EF-18 Hornet detachment to Italy, allowing the 492nd FS F-15Es to return to Lakenheath for a well-earned break. The Ala 15 Hornets are equipped for anti-radar missions with AGM-88 HARM (left) and for general-purpose bombing (below).

Above: Electronic warfare support is now vital to the NATO operations over Bosnia. Replacing the 429th ECS EF-111As in early 1995 was a five-aircraft detachment of EA-6B Prowlers from VQA-130. Instead of flying from their carrier, USS Eisenhower, the Prowler force is shore-based at Aviano in Italy.

Right: A USMC F/A-18D dives on a suspected hostile position over typical Bosnian terrain. Among the weaponry is a four-round rocket pod for target-marking.

In total, 80 weapons were used against Udbina and NATO chiefs claimed every one hit its target. Television footage of the devastation caused by the raid showed huge craters in the runways and support facilities. At the request of UNPROFOR, the NATO aircraft left the RSK aircraft undamaged. The raid was only intended to deter the Serbs from using their aircraft against Bihac, and it seemed to work. Into early 1995 none tried to get airborne. However, the Serb commander of the devastated base boasted to visiting reporters that the Serbs would soon strike back at NATO and the UN.

SAM strikes

The day after the Udbina raid two Royal Navy Sea Harriers (800 NAS, HMS *Invincible*) were on a photographic reconnaissance patrol over Bihac when two SA-2 'Guideline' SAMs were fired at them from a missile site near Okota, on the edge of the Bihac pocket. The missile exploded near the British aircraft but they returned safely to their ship.

5 ATAF put up a large mission the following day to photograph the now very active Serbian SAM network around Bihac. Eight photo-reconnaissance aircraft, including British Jaguars, French Mirage F1CR (EC 30, Istrana) and Dutch F-16A(R) swept the area to locate the missile batteries. In support was a package of suppression of enemy air defences (SEAD) aircraft, comprised of four F/A-18Ds and a number of EA-6B Prowler (VMAQ-4, Sigonella) armed with HARMs, four F-15E and two French Jaguars armed with laser-guided bombs, which were ready to pounce if the Serb missile crews activated their radars to threaten the

VMFA(AW)-332 'Moonlighters' from MCB Beaufort was the USMC Hornet squadron involved in the Udbina raid. Two of their aircraft fired a HARM missile each as the opening shots of the strike. The Hornets regularly carry the intake-side FLIR and LST pods.

Above: Mirage 2000N-K2s from 4 Escadre de Chasse operated from Cervia for the airfield attack. The K2 has both conventional and nuclear capability, and over Bosnia is largely confined to the carriage of freefall bombs.

Left: Armée de l'Air Mirage 2000Cs are rarely seen with air-to-ground stores, but on Bosnia patrols the aircraft carry Mk 82 bombs in addition to the MATRA Magic 2 air-to-air missiles.

Left: Illustrating the international flavour of the operations over Bosnia, a French Boeing C-135FR refuels an RAF Tornado F.Mk 3 during a Deny Flight patrol.

NATO recce aircraft. An EF-111A was also present for jamming support. Similar refuelling, command and control, radar surveillance and rescue packages to those used on the Udbina raid were put up to support this mission.

After launching at 0920 on 23 November, once the force was over Bihac the Okota SAM site 'illuminated' a NATO aircraft with its 'Fansong' radar, so two HARMs were sent its way. Within minutes, another site across the border at Dvor in Serb-controlled Croatia also illuminated the NATO aircraft. A HARM was launched against the site, causing considerable damage. By mid-day the operation was over and NATO aircraft were safely back at their bases. Intelligence staffs were busy analysing the reconnaissance photographs of the raid. It quickly became clear that the Okota site was

not yet out of action.

After consultation with UNPROFOR commanders the recce/SEAD package was sent back into action over Bihac in the afternoon of 23 November. An F-15E destroyed two SA-2 missile launchers with laser-guided bombs and three more HARMs were fired at SA-2 and SA-6 radar sites that illuminated the NATO aircraft.

Bihac CAS

Tension throughout Bosnia was now rising fast as the BSA and RSK forces reacted angrily to the NATO strikes. Two Czech UN soldiers were taken hostage near Udbina but were soon released. Within Bosnia, UN troops around Sarajevo and in the eastern enclaves were blockaded in their positions, becoming virtually hostages. At the BSA air force's main base at Banja Luka, a team of three United Nations Military Observers (UNMOs) were turned into 'human shields' against further NATO air strikes by being tied to chairs positioned in the middle of the main runway. More Serb SAM batteries were activated near Sarajevo to threaten the UNHCR humanitarian airlift and UNPROFOR military flights into the Bosnian capital.

Around Bihac, Serb troops continued their

Above: This Etendard IVP (163) of 16F, from Foch, was hit by an SA-14 during a reconnaissance sortie, but limped into Gioia del Colle. In addition to the photo mission marks, the aircraft carries a missile and hastily-drawn cartoon.

Left: Jaguars from EC 11 at Istrana used laser-guided weapons against Udbina airfield.

Above: The French have used two variants of Mirage F1 over Bosnia, the F1CT on fighter-bomber duties and the F1CR (illustrated) for reconnaissance. This aircraft is carrying a typical load with Magic 2 missiles on the wingtips for self-defence, Phimat chaff/flare dispenser and Barax ECM pod for missile protection and a Thomson-CSF ASTAC pod on the centreline. The latter is an electronic reconnaissance system capable of detecting, locating and classifying hostile ground radars.

Below: A bombed-up Sea Harrier coasts in across Croatia. An FRS.Mk 1 was lost during December 1994 to a non-combat accident.

advance into the UN declared 'safe area' around the city limits. On the afternoon of 25 November four Serb tanks pounded the centre of the city. UNPROFOR's Bosnia commander, Lieutenant General Sir Michael Rose, faxed the BSA high command warning that unless the attacks stopped air power would be used without warning against the Serbs tanks. A 30-aircraft strike package, centred around six Hornets and six Strike Eagles, was sent over the region with orders to attack any tanks that opened fire. The Serb tanks remained silent during the night

so General Rose ordered the NATO planes not to attack. They were held in an orbit outside the Serb SAM ring and then were sent out over the Adriatic to refuel before returning to the Bihac area. With the danger passed the strike package was eventually ordered back to its bases in Italy. Three BSA SA-6 missiles were fired on the aircraft without striking home.

During the following day a pair of RAF Tornado F.Mk 3s on patrol over central Bosnia were fired upon by a SA-2 battery, but the two missiles missed their mark. It was later determined that the second missile was an SA-6. As a result, the RAF began a crash programme to equip its Tornado F.Mk 3s with extra defences. With tension still high the US Navy ordered the USS *Nassau* with the US Marine Corps 22nd Marine Expeditionary Unit to the Adriatic. Its CH-53, CH-46E, UH-1N and AH-1W helicopters were tasked to assist with CSAR support for NATO air operations.

The US Central Intelligence Agency Gnat 750 Unmanned Air Vehicle (or drone) team set up a base on the Croat island of Brac, at Bol airport, in November 1994 to observe Bosnia. Earlier in the year the team had tried to operate from Albania for a short time. To relay data from the drone to a ground station, the CIA team is using a Schweizer RG-8A ultra-quiet surveillance aircraft.

Peace talks

With the Bosnian conflict still dangerously unstable, a phalanx of international diplomats, including the UN Secretary General Boutros Boutros Ghali headed for Sarajevo during the

RAF Jaguars from Gioia del Colle have been in the thick of the action over Bosnia, including the dropping of 1,000-lb bombs on Udbina airfield. The LOROP-equipped aircraft (right) is seen just after its return from that raid, while one of the bombers (XZ367) received this mission mark (below).

last week of November. Although Sarajevo airport had been closed down by the UN because of the BSA SAM threat, special guarantees were given by Serb leaders to allow a UNPROFOR Yak-40 to fly in the diplomats. In an attempt to ease tension, UNPROFOR asked NATO to pull its aircraft out of Bosnian air space while the peace talks were progressing. AWACS surveillance continued from over the Adriatic and Hungary, while NATO combat air patrols were maintained along the southern boundary of Bosnian air space, ready to intervene if necessary.

By 4 December the Serbs had released all the UN convoys they had been detaining and NATO aircraft resumed their patrols over Bosnia. UN commanders denied a request by the commander of the Bangladeshi battalion in Bihac for CAS on 13 December in retaliation for an RSK missile attack on a UN APC which killed a crew member and wounded others. The RSK refused permission for a UN helicopter to fly a CASEVAC mission to take out the casualties. The day before the BSA fired two more SA-2s at Bihac town.

Throughout the Bihac crisis the Croatian air force had regularly been flying helicopter resupply missions to the BiH V Corps, with six Mi-8/17, Gazelle and Bell 206 helicopters a day flying into the pocket from Lucko air base, near Zagreb. One helicopter was lost on 4 December when it blew-up at the base. Other Croatian aircraft were spotted making resupply flights to the Bosnian government's newly built airstrip at Kakanj in central Bosnia.

A Royal Navy Sea King helicopter flying over Mount Igman to collect General Rose from Sarajevo was shot at by BiH troops and badly damaged on 15 December. The helicopter was hit in the fuel tank and rotor blades but made an emergency landing at the UN helicopter landing site (HLS) at Kiseljak. A Royal Navy Sea Harrier FRS.Mk 1 was lost on 15 December in a flying accident over the Adriatic and the pilot was rescued by a helicopter from

Left: An F-16C of the 555th FS launches from Aviano for the Udbina raid. As well as AIM-9s and AIM-120s, the aircraft is armed with CBU-87s for attacking the airfield taxiways.

the Spanish carrier *Principe de Asturias*. Two days later a French navy Etendard from the *Foch* was hit by an SA-14 SAM over central Bosnia and had to divert to Gioia del Colle.

After the arrival of former US President Jimmy Carter on a UNPROFOR Yak-40 on 18 December for a peace mission, the UN felt confident enough to re-open Sarajevo airport on the day before, allowing UNPROFOR An-32s carrying UN military personnel to land. Fourteen flights landed on 20 December and some 30 flights were planned for the following day. General Rose was able to fly to Bihac from Split by Sea King on 29 December in an attempt to broker a ceasefire in the pocket.

The airlift gathered pace until 1 January 1995 when a Bel Air-chartered Il-76 overshot the runway and ploughed into a UN check point. No crew were injured but the airport was shut down for three days as the wreckage was removed. Once back in operation the UNHCR managed to push some 20 flights into Sarajevo, along with 10 UNPROFOR flights.

The airlift was temporarily suspended on 7 January after two UNPROFOR aircraft were hit by gunfire, but it resumed on the following day with 17 flights planned. British, Canadian, French, German and USAF military aircraft, along with aircraft chartered by four NGOs and the ICRC continued to bear the brunt of the effort. By 15 January 1995 some 11,502 UNHCR flights had landed at Sarajevo carrying 141,762 tonnes of aid.

During the summer of 1994 several Air National Guard and Air Force Reserve units deployed aircraft to Aviano to relieve the hard-pressed USAFE units. An ANG A-10 detachment included aircraft from the 118th FS/Connecticut ANG at Bradley IAP (left) and the 172nd FS/Michigan ANG at Battle Creek (below).

*Above: Illustrating a true mixed load, this **USMC F/A-18D** carries two **AIM-9Ms**, one **AIM-7 Sparrow**, one **AGM-65E Maverick**, a **FLIR** pod and two **Mk 82** bombs.*

*Right: This Russian-operated **Yak-40** flies on **UNPROFOR** duties. The Yaks are widely used on in-theatre staff transport.*

On 24 January Lieutenant General Sir Michael Rose flew out of Sarajevo on an UNPROFOR Yak-40 to complete his year's posting as commander of the UN's Bosnia-Herzegovina Command. His successor Lieutenant General Rupert Smith flew into Sarajevo on a Yak-40 two days later. With no sign of peace, NATO air power continued on patrol over the former Yugoslavia. **Tim Ripley**

BRIEFING

Lockheed SR-71
Return of the Blackbird

The Lockheed SR-71 Blackbird will soon be back in service, but not without another round of controversy similar to that which attended the aircraft's grounding five years ago. In October 1994 a reluctant US Air Force was directed by Congress to revive three aircraft for limited operations by mid-1995.

When the Pentagon withdrew the high-profile Mach 3 spyplane, it said publicly that the heavy cost of maintenance and operations could no longer be justified, now that reconnaissance satellites were so sophisticated. But in top-secret briefings to senior Congressmen, a further reason was apparently cited. A successor for the Blackbird was being developed at a highly-classified level. The briefings addressed the serious concern expressed by legislators, that the 'fighter/bomber Mafia' running the US Air Force was throwing away a valuable national capability.

According to many published accounts, that successor was a manned, hypersonic vehicle code named Aurora, possibly using exotic propulsion techniques, possibly launched into the edge of space via a piggyback ride from a mothership. Lockheed's 'Skunk Works' was the main contractor, and the vehicle was in flight test (if not already operational) out of the large secret air base at Groom Lake, Nevada.

These Aurora theories were consistently denied by the Pentagon, Congressional sources, and

NASA 832 (64-17971) arrives at Palmdale after its short delivery hop from Edwards on 12 January 1995. The aircraft was crewed by NASA's Steve Ishmael (pilot) and Marta Bohn-Meyer (flight engineer).

even by Lockheed itself. Indeed, in an autobiography published in October 1994, just weeks before his death, former 'Skunk Works' boss Ben Rich repeated the denial, adding that the Aurora codename (which was inadvertently revealed as a classified budget line item in 1985) actually referred to B-2 funding.

Whatever the truth (and the weight of evidence supports the existence of at least some experimental hypersonic vehicles, though not necessarily manned), the Air Force's critics in Congress were not mollified. The Senate Armed Services Committee attempted unsuccessfully to revive the Blackbird following the Iraqi invasion of Kuwait in 1990. The discontent rumbled on, and when concern mounted earlier in 1994 over nuclear weapons development by North Korea, Senator Robert Byrd made his move. This powerful veteran who chairs the Senate Appropriations Committee asked Lockheed what it would take to get the Blackbirds flying again. Equipped with the answer, Byrd inserted $100 million for that purpose in the Fiscal Year 1995 budget.

The move was opposed by some legislators, especially in the House of Representatives, where the chairman of the committee which oversees US intelligence activities described it as "an incredible waste of taxpayer money." Byrd said that the Pentagon had repeatedly lied to him about the status of classified programmes. The so-called successor to the Blackbird was nowhere near ready. Byrd and the Senate prevailed, and a contract was issued to Lockheed in late 1994.

(Recent reports suggest that the 'black' programme in question was

actually a large but subsonic unmanned aerial vehicle (UAV), using advanced stealth and endurance technology to operate undetected at high altitude for long periods over 'denied' territory. The 150-ft (45-m) wingspan UAV was being developed by Lockheed and Boeing but consumed several hundred million dollars before being cancelled in 1994. The two contractors are now working together on a less technically ambitious UAV for high-altitude reconnaissance, which at the time of writing was due for roll out in public at the 'Skunk Works' in June 1995.)

Most of the 20 remaining Blackbirds were dispersed to museums soon after the programme was terminated, but three were kept in storage at Palmdale by Lockheed, and another three were loaned to NASA at Edwards AFB for supersonic flight research, including one SR-71B pilot trainer. NASA did not attract as much 'business' for the Blackbirds as it had hoped; they flew only occasionally, and one of the two SR-71s was kept in flyable storage.

This aircraft (s/n 17971/NASA 832) kicked off the revived US Air Force programme on 12 January 1995, when it made the five-minute hop from Edwards to the

'Skunk Works' overhaul facility at Palmdale. Meanwhile, Lockheed chose s/ns 17967 and 17968 as the best two of the three Palmdale-stored Blackbirds to resume flying. All three are now under cover and being refurbished. 17971 will be delivered to the Air Force in early May, and put into operation by late June.

Former Blackbird pilot Jay Murphy is the newly-appointed SR-71 programme manager for Lockheed. He says there should be few problems restoring the sleek black 'sleds' to prime condition. "They've been well taped and sealed, and with a 90 per cent titanium structure, there is no rust." Similarly, the unique high-temperature hydraulic system using steel O-rings instead of rubber has not deteriorated, although tank seals could be a problem. Consumables such as hydraulic fluid, the tetraethyl borane (TEB) for engine start, and the special low-volatility JP-7 fuel are all available, with fuel storage tanks at some potential operating locations and the ability to deploy using fuel bladders elsewhere. According to Murphy, there are $750 million worth of spare parts available in store, a legacy from 1987 when SR-71 programme funding reached a peak.

Still, the critics insist that the Blackbird cannot be operated again for only $100 million per annum. "There's no way to justify $500,000 - 600,000 per flight," remarked a Republican Congressman from California in late January, adding that he wanted the SR-71 funding for Fiscal Year 1996 cancelled in favour of reconnaissance UAVs.

Murphy admits that the vital

A 1994 overview of Lockheed's Site 2 at Palmdale shows the three SR-71As (17962, 17967, 17968) kept in storage for the Air Force. Two are on the main ramp while the third is behind Building 602, parked next to a spraylat-covered A-12 (06937). In addition to these aircraft, SR-71A 17973 and A-12 06924 are on display at Palmdale in the Blackbird Air Park, while two-seat A-12B 06927 awaits eventual museum display (in Los Angeles) within the main Skunk Works complex. Site 2 is the main U-2 overhaul depot, hence the presence of three 'Dragon Ladies'.

refuelling tanker support is not factored into the cost, but the ace up his sleeve is to use contractor maintenance and operation, rather than have the Air Force do it. Lockheed has based its costing on its own successful support of an eight-year SR-71 detachment at Mildenhall in the UK, where 18 'Skunk Works' people replaced 80 blue-suiters. Initially, at least, the revived operation will be based at Edwards, where the flight simulator and Pratt & Whitney's technical support for the J58 powerplants can be shared with NASA. Only two or three flight crews will be qualified, drawn from the five former SR-71 pilots and slightly more RSOs who are still in the US Air Force. The contract calls for deployments to forward operating locations (Osan, Mildenhall, or Taif, perhaps) for up to 30 days, to fly missions every other day.

Back in 1989, Air Force bean-counters were anti-Blackbird because they were footing the entire bill for operations while much of the intelligence 'take' went to other government entities, such as the US Navy or the CIA. That concern has been met this time by drawing the funds from the Defence Airborne Reconnaissance Organization (DARO), a tri-service agency that now runs all the Pentagon's non-satellite reconnaissance programmes. The revived SR-71 operation will be controlled, as before, by the Air

Force's 9th Reconnaissance Wing at Beale AFB, California, where two U-2 squadrons are also based.

The U-2's ability to loiter and return reconnaissance data to ground stations in real time via datalink gave it a significant advantage over the SR-71 in tactical reconnaissance scenarios. That weakness is being addressed this time, according to Murphy, who notes that SR-71 datalink development was started in the 1980s but not funded further. All the sensors needed to equip three aircraft have been located; the SR-71 previously carried a Loral ASARS-1 reconnaissance radar, long-focal length and optical-bar cameras, and an Elint system.

As word of the SR-71's revival spread, Murphy took calls from far and wide as former pilots, mechanics and operations people made their bids to rejoin the programme. "It's an emotional thing: we all love this airplane," he says. Thanks to the senior senator from West Virginia, they now have an opportunity to resume that interrupted love affair. Maybe they should rename it the BlackByrd!

Chris Pocock

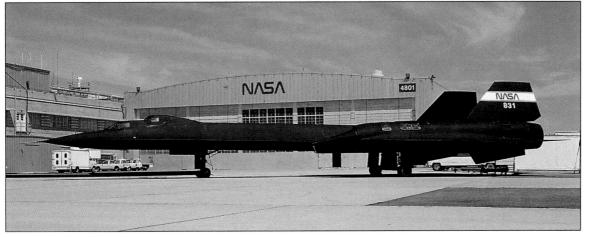

NASA's SR-71B trainer (64-17956/ 844) is to be used to requalify two or three crews for the Air Force.

Saab AJS 37 Viggen

The Flygvapen's new 'Thunderbolt'

To prepare its future pilots for its next-generation fighter – the JAS 39 Gripen – the Swedish air force (Flygvapen) has embarked on a comprehensive overhaul of its attack and reconnaissance Viggens. The ongoing AJS programme, through a substantial avionics and weapons upgrade, will provide a true multi-role capability and enable Sweden's pilots to train effectively for Gripen operations.

Between 1971 and 1980, Saab delivered 180 'first-generation' Viggens, comprising 108 AJ 37 'attack' Viggens, 28 of the chisel-nosed photo-reconnaissance SF 37s, 27 radar-equipped maritime recce SH 37s and some 17 two-seat Sk 37 trainers. From the outset the Viggen was intended as a mission-specific aircraft. Cadres of pilots trained for precise roles, with little cross-over between communities (certainly not between AJ and JA 37 'fighter' Viggen pilots). The advent of the JAS 39 Gripen, intended as a multi-role replacement for all 329 of the Swedish Viggens, brought with it a reappraisal of the Viggen's future.

Future Gripen pilots would be required to be competent in a variety of air-to-air and air-to-ground missions, with a range of new weapons. As a result, by the early 1990s, a wide-ranging upgrade programme had been proposed for the 'first-generation' Viggens to prepare the pilots to become future Gripen 'drivers' and the aircraft as JAS 39 lead-in trainers. This is not to infer that the upgraded aircraft are in anyway relegated to a second-line role. The AJS 37 programme, as first announced (in the late 1980s), was to equip AJ, SF, SH and Sk 37 Viggens with improved avionics and the full range of weapons planned for the JAS 39 (in addition to all those currently in the Flygvapen inventory). Furthermore, the AJ 37 would be tasked with a reconnaissance role and it seemed, from early press releases at least, that the SF, SH and JA 37 would become virtually identical.

The AJS (*Attack Jakt Spaning* – Attack, Fighter, Reconnaissance) concept was initially driven by the appearance of the Saab Rb 15F air-to-surface missile, intended for the JAS 39. Development of this ASM, a key Gripen weapon, progressed well in advance of the JAS 39. Instead of storing it, the Flygvapen looked for ways of fitting Rb 15F to the AJ 37, which would remain in front-line use, Gripen or no Gripen, for years to come. Viggen on-board systems have been constantly updated since the type's introduction and it was found that a newly-developed Ericsson multi-processor unit, matched with a MIL-STD 1553B databus, would make the AJ 37/Rb 15F combination a straightforward one. Furthermore, the same databus could also be fitted to the reconnaissance Viggens, and the AJS 37 was born.

The heart of the AJS upgrade lies with these extensive software additions, coupled with the databus, routed to all the Viggen's weapons

Above left: Hidden in the trees around F7's Såtenäs home, and also along the main roads between it and the surrounding towns, are several roadstrips and aircraft dispersals. The wing's Viggens regularly practise wartime dispersed operations from these locations, under the protection of air force Ranger units. This AJS 37 has rearmed (in only 15 minutes) and is taxiing fast for departure.

Left: A former F13 AJS 37 (in the company of an AJSF 37) sports the Rb 15F ASM. This powerful weapon greatly expands the Viggen's maritime attack reach.

pylons (in the case of the AJ 37). The MIL-STD 1553 digital databus was introduced by the USAF in the mid-1980s (as the 1553A) and is now the *de facto* standard military spec, high-speed wiring fit for the rapid transmission of data between avionics sub-systems. A databus is a system capable of handling and transmitting/receiving inputs (such as targeting or EW information) from a number of remote sources or terminals (such as weapons pylons). It relies on a shielded, twisted, cable pair (in this case not more than 100 m/328 ft in length to avoid signal degradation) transmitting coded pulses at 1 Mhz, in the form of 16-bit words. The 1553B databus has been improved over its original form by the addition of improved redundancy features (in the event of failure) and more efficient data transmission.

The AJS 37 programme, as it exists today, adds significant new capabilities to Sweden's Viggens while not being as radical an overhaul as some believed. Financial restrictions have limited the extent of the SF 37 upgrade and the two-seat Sk 37s are not included in the current programme. In total, 98 aircraft (not 115 as stated by Saab) are included in the upgrade, which by mid-1995 was 75 per cent complete. This comprises 48 AJ 37s, 25 SH 37s and 25 SF 37s. The latter aircraft are now being referred to as AJSH and AJSF 37s, respectively.

The AJS 37 is essentially a software upgrade, with no exterior changes to distinguish aircraft. Even in the cockpit the changes are evident only on the expanded weapons panel at the lower right-hand side of the instrument panel. Actual radar displays will change considerably, but the Flygvapen is publicity-shy on the subject of Viggen radar in general, and, invariably, even inactive displays are covered in public.

The upgraded AJ 37 is compatible with the Rb 15F ASM and DWS 39 stand-off munitions dispenser of the JAS 39. At the moment, not all the AJ 37 fleet is Rb 75 (AGM-65) Maverick capable, but the complete introduction of this weapon has not been included as an AJS37 goal. Air-to-air armament has been improved from two Rb 24 (AIM-9J) Sidewinders to a maximum of six Rb 74s (AIM-9Ls). Cannon pods (using 30-mm ADEN guns once carried by Swedish Hunter Mk 50s) can also be used in the air-to-air role. AJS-standard AJ 37s will not carry any podded recce system, such as is planned for the Gripen. They will use their existing radar ('tweaked') for surveillance missions – in the same style as the

Above: This Viggen is the AJS 37 seen opposite, arriving on its roadway strip. It exchanged its air-to-ground payload for an air-to-air fit of Sidewinders within minutes.

Right: This was the first AJS 37 conversion to be delivered, to now-disbanded F6 wing. It carries a pair of Rb 05 ASMs, which are now being superseded.

long-range PS-371/A unit of the SH 37 – but will not carry the latter's podded night camera or LOROP system. Flygvapen sources state the AJS 37 will have a limited Elint capability, but will not elaborate.

The SH 37 will receive the full range of improved weapons options – six Sidewinders will be carried, fully utilising the underwing stations, instead of just the two 'shoulder' pylons previously available. Fitting the 1553B databus will allow the SF 37 to carry six Sidewinders also, but no guns, rockets or bombs. At present, AJSF 37s are intended to operate in the recce/fighter roles only. They will retain their camera noses with no further modifications, and will not be fitted with the SH 37 radar, as once believed.

One item that will be carried by all AJS aircraft is the Flygvapen's specially developed PLA (Planer-ingsAnlägging) computerised mission planning/debriefing system. Using a removable cartridge, computer-generated target maps can be carried by each aircraft, these including all available threat information. After a sortie the cartridge, containing all the relevant mission data, can be removed and replayed on the squadron's own PLA computer. This system is an essential component of the Flygvapen's ACM programme. Combining the data from a number of aircraft, tactical scenarios on the scale of a Red Flag exercise can be played out, having used fully instrumented aircraft instead of a vast instrumented range. It is a cost-effective and very accurate method that can fulfil the needs of an air force unable to afford a full-scale ACMI facility.

Redeliveries of the AJS 37 have been underway for over two years. Aircraft have been replaced on a one-for-one basis among all the six squadrons that will now fly the type. Units are intended to be re-equipped 'in parallel' and ultimately all will operate a mix of AJS, AJSH and AJSF aircraft. The dedicated recce squadrons will disappear as a result, and their pilots will be reassigned. Angelhölm-based F10 formed the first AJS 37 unit on 1 July 1993 by declaring a newly-established third squadron which flies alongside the two surviving J 35J Draken squadrons of F10.

The AJS programme is due for completion on 1 July 1996, by which time the AJS 37 will be on strength with F10 (one squadron), F7 (two squadrons), F15 (two squadrons) and F21 (one squadron). This is part of a substantial ongoing reduction in A/S 37 Viggen numbers. While the eight air-defence JA 37 squadrons will remain untouched, the eight and a half (including the OCU) A/S 37 squadrons extant in 1992 will be whittled down to four AJS 37 squadrons in 1997, with the arrival of the JAS 39.

F7 (long the Flygvapen's 'AJ 37 OCU') will be the first JAS 39 unit, and is hoped to begin conversion to the Gripen in October 1996. In anticipation of this, the wing is already operating AJS 37s as a 'multi-role lead-in trainer' for

its first batch of 15-20 JAS 39 pilots. In the same way that an operational procedure and tactics team (TU 39) has been set up to prepare for the Gripen, a similar team (TU AJS) has been established at F15 to prepare pilots and units to get the best from the AJS 37s. One squadron of Hälsinge-based F15 has long operated a mix of AJ and Sk 37s as a Viggen OCU, although it now has two full-strength AJ 37 squadrons thanks to the 1994 disbandment of F6. F15 will continue to operate a squadron of Sk 37s and the option remains to upgrade these in 2002, if funds allow.

An outline upgrade plan for the JA 37 has been drawn up for (notional) implementation in 2012. This may include the addition of Rb 15F and DWS 39 capability, though not Rb 75, bombs or rockets. Quite apart from this, the JA 37 is also scheduled to receive AIM-120 AMRAAMs, replacing its existing Rb 71 Sky Flash missiles.

While the Flygvapen has invested heavily in the Gripen it will be a long time before it ceases to rely on the Viggen. The first Gripen squadron is expected to become operational in 1997, and initial deliveries are aimed at replacing the 'attack' Viggens. Despite this, AJ 37s will survive well into the next century (along with their JA 37 siblings), and as AJS 37s they will remain an effective fighting force.

BRIEFING

Sukhoi Su-24MP 'Fencer-F'

New electronic warrior

Flight tested in 1979 as the T-6MP, the prototype Su-24MP marked an attempt to replace the ageing Yak-28PP 'Brewer-E' then operating as the standard tactical EW jamming platform in Frontal Aviation service. The Yak-28PP was then becoming embarrassingly long in the tooth, and the age of the airframes was making the type increasingly difficult to support, although its relatively good performance characteristics allowed it to remain fairly viable.

The Yak-28PP EW suite was based on the Sirena RWR which detects, classifies, identifies and roughly locates hostile emissions. This is linked to the semi-automatic Buket *Samolotnaya Pomekovaya Statsiya* (SPS) jamming unit. Buket is available in three versions, SPS-22-28, SPS-44-28 and SPS-55-28, but exactly which is fitted to the Yak-28PP remains unknown. The Buket equipment is bulky, filling

This (unidentified) centreline pod is seen most often on Su-24MPs. Remarkably free of protuberances, it carries obvious dielectric panels fore and aft. 'Hockey stick' antennas on the intakes probably serve the Fasol jamming system.

the former bomb bay, and the system's antennas are located inside a canoe fairing mounted on the underside of the fuselage. Buket is also carried by the Tupolev Tu-16PP 'Badger-J'.

On the Yak-28PP, Buket is augmented by SPS-5-28 Fasol, which is designed specifically to jam search radars. 'Hockey stick' swept blade antennas are located under the engine intakes. Similar antennas are fitted to the Tu-22P and Tu-22PD 'Blinder-E' which are also fitted with Fasol. Unidentified receiver antennas are clustered around the root of the Yak-28PP's nose probe, and elsewhere. A pair of ASO-21 chaff/flare dispensers are scabbed onto the engine nacelles, and a pair of UV-16-57UM rocket pods are usually carried under the outer wings. These contain 16 S-5P 57-mm chaff rockets, and are used for laying chaff ahead of the aircraft.

The Su-24MP was designed from the outset with a more modern integrated and automated EW suite, although the option of simply repackaging equipment from the Yak-28PP into redundant Su-24 bomber airframes was reportedly

The cockpit of the Su-24MP – full dual flight controls are fitted, and the EWO in the right-hand seat also has duplicated main flight instruments. Compared to the Su-24MR and Su-24M, the EWO has no radar display, but instead has a simple switch panel, which seems to be for the directional jamming antennas.

considered. An interim EW Su-24 SEAD/EW variant may even have been actually produced, based on the 'Fencer-C'. The photos taken at Pushkin, near Leningrad, and published in *World Air Power Journal* Volume 6 may illustrate this version. Thus the new variant has a Landish EW system, with Los, Mimoza and Fasol jammers and a new SPO-15 Bereza RWR. This promised to offer a considerable improvement over the Yak-28PP equipment, but development problems delayed production until 1983. The Su-24MP airframe is closely based on that of the Su-24M 'Fencer-D' bomber. It lacks the bomber's Kaira electro-optical system, but retains the twin underfuselage fairings usually associated with the bomber's internal cannon (starboard) and ammunition stowage (port). The port fairing has also been described as containing a recording camera, but this seems to be erroneous.

The Su-24MP also lacks the bomber version's Orion-A attack radar but, like the Su-24MR, probably retains Relief TFR in a shortened dielectric nosecone. The

entire nose is painted white, to simulate the appearance of the bomber, with its bigger radar. Behind the new, smaller nose cone, and mainly on the portion of the forward fuselage that is painted white, is a row of four 'hockey stick' antennas for the Fasol jammer. The outer pair is carried on the lower part of the intakes.

The Su-24MP can reportedly carry two different types of centreline pod, but only one of these has been photographed. It does not resemble the Shpil-2M laser recon-

An Su-24MP of the 11th ORAP landing at its Welzow base. The Welzow-based Su-24MPs were extremely camera shy, and departed for Chortkov soon after the Berlin wall came down. They formed the third eskadrilya of the regiment.

Beneath the tarpaulins the nearest Su-24MP in this line-up of four 'Fencers' appears to be carrying some kind of pod or fairing on the lower corner of the intake, although this would be in the same position as the starboard 'hockey stick' antenna for the Fasol jamming system. The access panels on the sides of the nose are immediately apparent.

naissance pod, or the slab-sided Tangazh Elint pod seen on Su-24MRs. Underwing pylons are inevitably carried, but stores have not been noted on these.

Production of the Su-24MP was sporadic, and was interspersed with batches of Su-24M and export Su-24MK bombers, and with batches of Su-24MR reconnaissance aircraft. Total production has been estimated at eight or 12, but the true figure may be slightly higher. At least eight served with the 11th ORAP at Welzow in East Germany until June 1991, when they were withdrawn to join the Yak-28PPs of the 118th ORAP at Chortkov in the Ukraine. These subsequently joined the newly independent Ukrainian air force. Four more aircraft (perhaps earlier withdrawals from East Germany, Poland or Hungary) were redeployed to a base in Russia itself. This makes the Su-24MP one of the rarest aircraft in current front-line service.

Development and production of the Su-24MR has now reportedly been abandoned due to shortcomings in the equipment fit, and a version of the Su-34 (formerly known as the Su-27IB) will be produced to fulfill the tactical EW role. In the meantime, the Yak-28PP (once reported as having been retired) will soldier on. These elderly aircraft serve with the 118th ORAP at Chortkov, with the 151st ORAP at Shchuchin,

The Su-24MP's most obvious external 'recognition feature' is a prominent dielectric fairing below the nose. Its purpose is unknown. This aircraft has an adaptor on the outboard pylon to allow the carriage of a defensive AAM, probably an IR-homing short-range R-60 (AA-8 'Aphid').

Byelorussia, and with a number of Russian air force regiments, including one (perhaps a trials or tactics development unit) at Pushkin. **Jon Lake**

Panavia Tornado GR.Mk 1B

A female pilot for the new Tornado ship-killer

Re-equipment of Nos 12 and 617 Squadrons with the Tornado GR.Mk 1B, which will be featured in greater detail in a forthcoming issue of *World Air Power Journal*, is now complete. The units are operational in the dual overland and anti-shipping roles, with a range of weapons which includes the BAe Sea Eagle ASM. The Lossiemouth wing recently hit the headlines when a press facility was arranged to celebrate one of its pilots becoming 'combat ready' in December 1994. A milestone in any pilot's career, the event was newsworthy because the pilot in question was Flight Lieutenantt Jo Salter, the RAF's first female fast jet pilot.

The 24 Tornados converted to GR.Mk 1B standards are believed to be ZA374 (AJ-D), ZA375 (AJ-W), ZA399 (AJ-C), ZA407 (AJ-G), ZA409 (FQ), ZA411 (AJ-S), ZA447 (FA), ZA450 (FB), ZA452 (FC), ZA453 (FD), ZA455 (FE), ZA456 (AJ-Q), ZA457 (AJ-J), ZA459 (AJ-B), ZA456 (AJ-Q), ZA460 (AJ-A), ZA461 (AJ-M), ZA465 (AJ-F), ZA469 (AJ-O), ZA471 (AJ-K), ZA473 (FG), ZA474 (FF), ZA490 (FJ), and ZA491 (FK). The aircraft with FA-FZ codes belong to No. 12

Squadron, and the World War II-style AJ- series 'Dambuster' codes are applied to the aircraft of No. 617 Squadron.

Reports that aircraft have been delivered to an interim standard, wired for only two Sea Eagles, cannot be confirmed, nor is it clear whether the theoretical maximum load will be four or five missiles. Sea Eagle is a sea-skimming anti-ship missile with a range of about 68 miles (110 km). After launch it cruises at low level, regulating height with a radar altimeter and relying on inertial guidance. As it nears the target it switches to its active J-band radar for acquisition and for guidance to the target. A 507-lb (230-kg) warhead is fitted.

An overall dark grey colour scheme continues to undergo evaluation on the Tornado (for both the GR.Mk 1 and the GR.Mk 1B). Plans to allow the aircraft to carry

Surprisingly, on the Jo Salter/GR.Mk 1B press facility, the RAF did not fly an aircraft carrying the Sea Eagle missile. The Tornado GR.Mk 1B's payload/range characteristics are allegedly less impressive than the Buccaneer's, although the GR.Mk 1B's advanced avionics fit and all-weather capability makes it a more capable aircraft in this specialist attack role.

Flight Lieutenant J. M. Salter, the RAF's first female fast-jet pilot, is now combat ready with No. 617 Squadron. She is one of a growing band of female RAF aircrew.

buddy refuelling pods are also believed to be under consideration. During the Gulf War, the RAF reportedly acquired 15 Sargent Fletcher 28-300 inflight-refuelling pods from Germany, these having previously been used by the Marineflieger's own Tornados. At least nine aircraft (ZA365, ZA367, ZA410, ZA411, ZD712, ZD714, ZD741, ZD743 and ZD812) were 'plumbed' to carry these tanks

before the programme was abandoned. There are now plans to fit some GR.Mk 1Bs with Flight Refuelling Mk 20B refuelling pods rendered surplus by the retirement of the Victor K.Mk 2. **Jon Lake**

Left: A pair of Shenyang J-8 II 'Finback-Bs' patrols over the Xisha Islands. The type's similarity in shape to the MiG-21 (from which its aerodynamic design was derived) is readily apparent in this view. The solid nose is believed to house a radar broadly comparable to the MiG-23's 'High Lark'. An estimated 35 J-8 IIs have been built, in small batches, and production continues sporadically. The aircraft serves with both the air force and the navy. A version with inflight refuelling and upgraded weapons systems is reportedly under development for the air arm of the People's Liberation Navy.

The People's Air Power

Snapshots from behind the 'Bamboo Curtain'

Further to the Air Power Analysis of Far East Air Arms in Volume 7 of *World Air Power Journal*, we present a hitherto unseen selection of newly unearthed photos illustrating aircraft of the People's Liberation Army Air Force in action. Despite the recent delivery of Sukhoi Su-27s, the backbone of Chinese air power is still provided by indigenously-built derivatives of much older Soviet aircraft types, which continue to be aggressively marketed by the nationalised aviation industry. The aircraft may be old fashioned and may have limited lives, but they are rugged and cheap.

Above left: Red and blue fuselage stripes betray this aircraft as being one of the J-8 II development aircraft operated by the Shenyang Aircraft Corporation. It is seen here launching a salvo of indigenous rockets. The J-8 II is compatible with the Qingan HF-16B rocket pod, containing 12 57-mm air-to-air rockets, or with a 90-mm air-to-surface rocket usually carried in fours.

Left: For long-range combat air patrols, the J-8 II can carry up to three external fuel tanks on the centreline and outboard underwing pylons, leaving inboard hardpoints clear for the carriage of weapons. The centreline Type 23-3 23-mm cannon pod is permanently fitted.

Right: A gaggle of J-8 'Finback-As' is seen in flight. The original version of the J-8 had a single-piece forward-hinging canopy.

Below: This F-7M demonstrator wears the camouflage which may have been applied to aircraft exported to Iran and Zimbabwe. The underwing missiles are IR-homing PL-5s.

Left: F-7 IIs line up prior to delivery to an undisclosed customer. The pale blue and sand-yellow camouflage scheme is extremely unusual. The aircraft being towed along in front of the line-up are F-7Ms and wear Bangladesh-style camouflage with Chinese national insignia, perhaps applied temporarily.

Above: This evocative night photograph includes two aircraft labelled as F-7PG and F-7MG, hitherto unknown variant designations. The other aircraft in the photo are marked simply as F-7Ms. All wear CAC demonstrator serials and externally appear similar to the latest F-7M/F-7P configuration.

Right: The J-7 III has been rarely photographed, and this illustration is perhaps the most revealing. It clearly shows that this Chinese 'Fishbed' is broadly equivalent to the MiG-21MF 'Fishbed-J' whose external appearance it matches very closely. It has blown flaps, an underfuselage 23-mm gun pod, AI radar in an enlarged inlet centrebody, a broad-chord tailfin, bulged spine and anti-blast fences above the auxiliary intakes. The aircraft is powered by the Wopen WP-13, a development of the WP-7 which powers other J-7 variants.

Above: Despite the introduction of improved versions, the original Chinese copies of the MiG-21, the Chengdu J-7 I and J-7 II remain in front-line service with the People's Liberation Army air force. These aircraft are J-7 IIs, identifiable by their undernose pitots and separate windscreens. The J-7 I also featured an undernose pitot, but had a one-piece canopy.

Below: China is probably alone among operators of the Nanchang Q-5 in not camouflaging its examples of this low-level ground attack aircraft. These aircraft have formation flying marks painted on the wing fences and fuselage sides so that all a wingman needs to do is to line up the two half circles to know he is in perfect echelon formation. It may not be very tactical, but it is pretty.

Above: An F-7M in Bangladeshi camouflage, but with prominent Chinese national markings, displays the array of weapons that it can carry. Underwing, the aircraft carries a pair of PL-7 IR-homing AAMs, while in front of it are an array of 250- and 500-kg bombs. In the next row are pairs of PL-5s and AIM-9P Sidewinders, together with the Norinco Type 30-1 cannon and ammunition. In front of these are an array of rocket pods, a centreline fuel tank and packs of unpodded rockets.

Above and left: Chinese weapons have proved particularly popular among some of the nations hindered by Western arms embargoes and restrictions. Some might unkindly say that a list of CATIC's customers might read like a list of the World's pariah nations, but this is unfair. Nevertheless, Iran, Iraq, North Korea, Pakistan, Sri Lanka and Tanzania (all of whom have problems with Western arms suppliers) are among the nations that depend heavily on China for their combat aircraft, as does Myanmar (formerly Burma), whose Nanchang A-5s are seen in these two photographs.

Right: The prototype A-5M is seen in typical export camouflage. This is an upgrade of the basic A-5C designed by Alenia and CATIC using a new nav-attack system based on that fitted to the AMX. The aircraft embodies a host of improvements including an NVG-compatible cockpit, a laser rangefinder, provision for an inflight-refuelling probe, and uprated engines.

Below: Xian H-6A 'Badgers' drop conventional high-explosive bombs during an exercise. They wear the current two-tone grey colour scheme now applied to most surviving Chinese Tu-16 versions. The H-6A remains China's only medium bomber, and shoulders the responsibility for the manned bomber element of China's nuclear triad.

Above: These PLA Air Force H-6As wear low-visibility colours, with serials and national insignia applied in light grey. The H-6A is mainly an unlicensed copy of the basic Tu-16 'Badger'.

Right: A head-on view of an H-6 IV, the dedicated anti-shipping version of the basic Chinese 'Badger'. The drum-like radome houses a new search and targeting radar compatible with the C-601 Silkworm ASM.

Dassault/SABCA
Mirage 5BA MirSIP/Elkan

Above: By the time BA-60 made its maiden flight as the MirSIP prototype, on 28 December 1992, Belgian defence minister M. Leo Delcroix had already decided that all Belgian Mirages would be retired by the end of 1993, and that the upgraded aircraft would not be taken into service. Seen here in bare metal finish, with composite canard foreplanes in dark green, BA-60 was later painted up in an attractive overall air defence grey, with black red and gold MirSIP logos and cheatline for display at the 1993 Paris Air Salon. The aircraft was eventually brought up to full Elkan standards as the penultimate single-seater sold to Chile, with the serial 719.

Conceived and funded as a means of keeping the Mirage 5 viable into the 21st century to augment the Belgian air force F-16 fleet, the Mirage Safety Improvement Programme was effectively killed when post-Cold War defence cuts reduced the number of fighters required by the Belgian Air Force. The programme was by then almost fully-funded, however, and enormous cancellation penalties made it cheaper to complete the upgrade programme than to scrap it, while by selling the upgraded aircraft there would be a chance of recovering the programme costs.

By the late 1980s it was becoming clear that if the Belgian air force was going to maintain its fighter strength into the 21st century, it would be necessary to acquire more F-16s, buy other new aircraft, or refurbish some of its elderly Mirage 5BAs, which were nearing the end of their useful lives. Accordingly, during 1986, it was decided to renovate and update sufficient aircraft to allow two squadrons to retain the Mirage for between 12 and 18 years further service. The project was originally known as AMELIE (Advanced Mirage by Enhancement and Life Extension), and reportedly included the installation of a new powerplant. The programme was briefly (by 1987) known simply as the Mirage Update Programme, still covering the upgrade of sufficient aircraft to equip two squadrons, and including the recce-tasked Mirage 5BRs of No. 42 Squadron. Defence cuts in 1989 imposed a funding limit of BFr3.5 billion ($87

Left: The Mirage 5 was finally retired from Belgian air force service in December 1993, BD-12 making a ceremonial last flight in a specially applied silver colour scheme, and bearing the unit markings of all four Mirage 5 operators. Some Mirage 5BAs and 5BDs were reworked and sold to Chile, but only four unmodified Mirage 5BRs were exported, leaving the remaining 14 survivors in storage.

million) on the programme, this later being increased to BFr4.2 billion ($112.75 million) divided into BFr2.7 billion ($66 million) for new equipment and BFr1.5 billion ($36.75 million). The refurbishing and upgrade programme was reduced in scope slightly, to cover only 15 Mirage 5BAs and five Mirage 5BDs to equip a single squadron (No. 8) and was renamed MirSIP (Mirage Safety Improvement Programme), a deliberately modest title intended to convey the impression that the upgrade would be a minimalist affair intended only to keep the selected aircraft safely airworthy, thereby improving its chances of being accepted by the Belgian Parliament.

Avionics update

In fact, the programme was considerably more ambitious, and was aimed at improving the core operational capability of the basic Mirage 5. The dropping of plans to upgrade the Mirage 5BRs was compensated for by the incorporation of plans to make the upgraded Mirage 5BAs compatible with what was coyly described as a 'range of reconnaissance sensors'. Thus, SABCA was contracted to rewire and refurbish Mirage 5BAs and Mirage 5BDs, but would also install fixed canard foreplanes and a new nav/attack suite in the aircraft. This consisted of a new SAGEM UTR-90 nav/attack computer, a SAGEM ULISS 92 INS, a Thomson-CSF TMV630 laser rangefinder (on single-seat aircraft only), and a Ferranti wide-angle HUD. The aircraft would also receive single-point pressure refuelling, a liquid oxygen breathing system and strobe anticollision lights. The replacement of the original Martin-Baker Mk 4 ejection seats (capable of operation at ground level only at speeds in excess of 90 kt; 167 km/h) by new zero-zero Martin-Baker Mk 12 rocket seats was contracted for separately.

Integration

SABCA worked closely with SAGEM to integrate the new avionics and to redesign the cockpit. This accommodated a pair of new CRT multi-function display screens, one usually serv-

ing as a control and display unit, and one as a head down display. These screens augmented a new wide-angle HUD, while the cockpit designers also had to locate new radios and a data transfer cartridge system on the side consoles. The inclusion of a Mirage 2000-style stick-top, with modifications to the throttle, allowed true HOTAS operation. Switching from air-to-air or air-to-ground modes could be achieved by a single button-press.

Canards

Apart from the avionics improvements, the MirSIP Mirage 5 incorporates a host of structural modifications designed to extend service life, and is fitted with canard foreplanes and vortex generators intended to improve aerodynamic performance. The low aspect-ratio tailless Delta configuration of the Mirage III/5/50 family was chosen and optimised for supersonic performance, and the high drag at higher angles of attack resulted in high approach speeds, poor landing performance and poor low-speed manoeuvrability. By adding fixed canard foreplanes total lift is increased, and airflow over the wing remains attached at higher Alpha, while turn performance is improved and take-off run is reduced. The extra lift generated by the canards ahead of the centre of pressure tends to rotate the nose, and also downloads the elevons on the trailing edge of the wing, meaning that they do not have to deflect up as far, reducing drag and increasing overall lift. Instantaneous turn rate and manoeuvrability in general is dramatically improved, and the aircraft can be flown at angles of attack of up to 42° and at speeds down to 105 kt (195 km/h).

Unfortunately, the MirSIP programme was

launched just as the Cold War came to an end, leading to a dramatic reduction of tension and offering West European politicians the chance for some vote-winning (if ill-considered and myopic) further defence cuts. It soon became apparent that a dramatic reduction of Belgian air force frontline strength would be possible, to the extent that even F-16s would be released from the frontline for storage or resale, and against this background, the future of the ancient Mirage 5 (even if upgraded) looked tenuous. No. 8 Squadron, the intended recipients of the MirSIP aircraft, disbanded in 1991 and it was decided that the aircraft would instead directly replace the Mirage 5BRs of No. 42 Squadron. Complete project cancellation seemed impossible, however, since the funds had already been allocated (and largely spent) and since the contract incorporated such severe penalty clauses that cessation would not have produced any financial saving, while a batch of modernised aircraft would be easier to sell than a mixed bag of modernised, partially modernised and unmodified aircraft. Political considerations also supported continuing the programme, since it offered SABCA the opportunity to remain involved in a high-tech military aircraft upgrade programme, a useful learning venture if the Belgian company was to bid for similar upgrade work.

Defence cuts

Thus, the project continued, even while plans were being made for the disbandment of Belgium's remaining Mirage 5 squadrons, and despite the tacit acknowledgment that the upgraded aircraft would never re-enter Belgian air force service. Further defence cuts in 1993 had reduced the scope of the upgrade programme

Right: Cocooned Mirage 5s await conversion to MirSIP standards at Koksijde. Unconverted Mirage 5s retained by the Belgian air force are stored at Weelde. They may be released for resale or conversion.

Below: The MirSIP prototype en route to Le Bourget wears the colour scheme applied for its particiaption in the 1993 Paris Air Salon. All other MirSIP conversions were painted in standard three-tone Mirage 5BA-type camouflage, initially retaining full Belgian national markings.

Left: Intertwined Chilean and Belgian flags were applied to the five aircraft allocated to the MirSIP training flight (known as 'Détachment MirSIP') set up at Brustem/St Truiden in April 1994 for the training of eight Chilean pilots and the first group of Chilean ground crew. This small unit had three Belgian-standard MirSIP two-seaters and two single-seaters, with two Belgian pilots and about 10 ground crew. The Belgian air force took responsibility for training the Chileans on the basic MirSIP aircraft, with SABCA providing training courses on new, specific features of the Chilean aircraft.

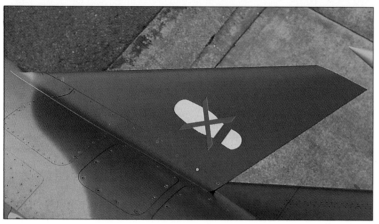

Above: The MirSIP/Elkan uses a fixed composite canard foreplane similar to that fitted to Dassault's own Mirage upgrades.

Right: The MirSIP programme for the Belgian air force included the substitution of Martin-Baker Mk.12 zero-zero ejection seats for the original zero-ninety Mk 4s, and the installation of a Ferranti HUD, a SAGEM-ULISS 92 INS, a SAGEM UTR-90 nav/attack computer, and a LOX breathing system. A Thomson-CSF TMV-630 laser rangefinder was fitted below the nose, and the aircraft had strobe anti-collision lights, single-point pressure refuelling and canard foreplanes.

to only five aircraft (five Mirage 5BAs and five Mirage 5BDs, these comprising BA-04, BA-46, BA-48, BA-60, BA-62, BD-01, BD-03, BD-04, BD-14 and BD-15), while the MirSIP name had evolved from being the Mirage Safety Improvement Programme to being the Mirage System Improvement Programme. Redelivery of the last MirSIP aircraft (straight into storage) was scheduled for November 1993, one month before the disbandment of the last Mirage squadron. In the same year it was announced that the Belgian air force would retain only three unmodified Mirage 5BAs (for ground training duties), and that the remaining 60 Mirages, comprising 32 Mirage 5BAs, 10 Mirage 5BDs and 18 Mirage 5BRs, would be released for sale by SABCA, including the 10 MirSIP conversions.

Belgium's Mirage era

Belgium had originally procured 106 Mirages, comprising 63 single-seat Mirage 5BAs, 16 Mirage 5BD trainers and 27 Mirage 5BR recce aircraft. The first example of each sub-variant was Dassault-built, but the remainder were licence built by SABCA at Gosselies. The type equipped four squadrons at its peak, and for many years formed the backbone of Belgium's tactical fighter and fighter reconnaissance force. Procured as a replacement for the Republic F-84F Thunderstreak and RF-84F Thunderflash, the

Mirage 5BAs began to enter service in July 1970, with 8 Escadrille (alternately known as 8 Smaldeel in Flemish) at Florennes. Mirage 5BAs also entered service with co-located 2 Escadrille in September 1970, and with 1 Escadrille at Bierset in January 1972. The Mirage 5BRs served with 42 Escadrille at Bierset (and Florennes between 1986 and 1988). The rundown of the Belgian Mirage force began in 1987, when 1 and 2 Escadrilles began to convert to the F-16. The Mirage 5's career was far from being over however, and in January 1991 10 aircraft from 8 Escadrille, and five from 42 Escadrille, deployed to Erhac in Turkey to bolster UN forces in Turkey in case of an Iraqi attack on that country during Desert Storm. The aircraft returned to Florennes after the war and disbanded on 13 September 1991, although its aircraft and pilots continued flying for some months. This left only 42 Escadrille with the Mirage, flying a mix of 11 Mirage 5BAs, 18 Mirage 5BRs and five Mirage 5BDs. The intention was to retain this unit with a mix of MirSIPs and recce aircraft, but it disbanded on 22 December 1993, when silver-painted Mirage 5BD BD-12 made the unit's final flight.

Mirage 5BA BA-60 made its maiden flight as the MirSIP prototype on 28 December 1992, in the hands of Lieutenant Colonel Mark d'Espallier at SABCA's Gosselies factory. BA-11

and BD-01 followed soon afterwards, giving SABCA a three-strong flight test and development fleet. All this occurred after Belgian defence minister M. Leo Delcroix had made the decision that all Belgian Mirages would be retired by the end of 1993, and that the MirSIP aircraft would definitely not be taken into service. Initially flown in bare metal finish, with its chemically milled single-piece canard foreplanes in dark green, BA-60 was later painted up in an attractive overall air defence grey, with black, red and gold logos and cheatline for display at the 1993 Paris Air Salon, as part of the effort to find a buyer for the upgraded aircraft. Finding a buyer for these aircraft was not an easy task, since the small market for second-hand combat aircraft was flooded with upgraded A-4s, F-5s, F-16s, Mirages, Kfirs and MiGs being offered by a host of companies, and with other companies offering new aircraft at very favourable terms.

Export prospects

Discussions were reportedly held with the Philippines and with Chile during 1993 and 1994, the talks with Chile eventually leading to the sale of the 10 MirSIP aircraft that had already been converted, and of the other five aircraft originally scheduled for conversion, and to the sale of a further five unmodified aircraft, four reconnaissance aircraft and a trainer.

The negotiations with the Chileans began in 1993, and ended in February, with the signature of a letter of intent to proceed to contract signature in July 1994. At this stage Chile reserved the right to walk away from the deal without any indemnities, and continued to look at other options, reportedly including the purchase of new JAS 39 Gripens or Chengdu F-7Ps, refurbished ex-RAF Jaguars, and refurbished IDF/AF Kfirs, before finally deciding on the purchase of the MirSIP Mirages.

Controversy

This decision generated some controversy in Chile, not least among the Chilean press, the civil service, and elements within the air force. This arose primarily because the aircraft were seen as bordering on obsolescent, and because the contract price was regarded in some quarters as being excessive. In less well-informed circles criticism was levelled at the limited amount of fatigue life remaining (even though this was equivalent to between 12 and 18 years of front-line operation) and fears were expressed as to the advisability of relying on Dassault for spares support. The latter worry was a function of the arms embargoes imposed some years before, during which Chile had experienced difficulties in keeping its existing Mirage 50s serviceable, but such problems were long past. A more serious complaint came from sources within the air force (many of whom had been trained in Britain) that the Jaguar best suited Chilean needs, and was being ignored for political reasons.

The fact that Chile already operated the Mirage 50 was a crucial factor in the eventual selection of the MirSIP aircraft, and effectively narrowed the competition down to the IAI Kfir and the Belgian-modified Mirages. Chile first became a customer for the Mirage in 1980, when Dassault handed over eight low-houred former Armée de l'Air Mirage 5Fs as Mirage 50FCs. These were followed by six new-build Mirage 50Cs with Agave radar during 1982-83. All

Above: The second 'production' MirSIP taxis out for what will be an exhaustive post-conversion shakedown flight, necessitating the carriage of two 1700-litre (374-Imp gal) fuel tanks.

Left: A newly-converted MirSIP two-seater undergoes pre-flight checks, with the new multi-function display screens clearly visible. Two of these are in each cockpit, consisting of a control and display unit and a separate head-down display.

Below: BA-48 is seen under tow to the fuel-system check out facility, prior to final reassembly as a MirSIP aircraft. The MirSIP aircraft are completely rewired, and are structurally refurbished for 12 years further service.

Dassault/SABCA Mirage 5BA MirSIP/Elkan

Above: Détachment MirSIP used only Belgian MirSIP standard aircraft, and not fully-modified MirSIP Plus Elkans. This was dictated by the need for early conversion of Chilean pilots, by convenience, and by the need to use Belgian radios and air traffic control equipment. The aircraft retained Belgian national markings and serials even after Chilean markings (not seen here) were applied in order to make operating in Belgian air space less difficult. They were modified to full Elkan standards when conversion training of the first group of eight pilots was complete. The intertwined flags insignia was used as a unit badge by Détachment Mirsip.

Chilean single-seaters are powered by the more powerful Atar 09K50 engine, although the two twin-stick Mirage 50DC trainers delivered in 1982 reverted to the Atar 09C. One of the latter aircraft crashed and was replaced by a converted Mirage IIIBE, and this may have been re-engined with an Atar 09K50. The Chilean Mirage 50s were used to re-equip Grupo 4, which was re-established at Arturo Moreno Benitez airport, Santiago, on 15 September 1980, and was for-

Mirage 50 identities

Chilean AF Serial	Notes
Mirage 50FC	
501	ex ADLA 01
502	ex ADLA 03
503	ex ADLA 05
504	ex ADLA 08
505	ex ADLA 16
506	ex ADLA 23
507	ex ADLA 28
508	ex ADLA 30
Mirage 50C	
509	new build
510	new build (First 'production' Pantera)
511	new build
512	new build
513	new build
514	new build (Pantera prototype)
Mirage 50CD	
515	new build
516	new build (Written off in service)
Mirage IIIBE	
516	Former ADLA, identity unknown. (Replaced original 516, possibly with 09K50 engine)

mally commissioned as a component of Ala 2, II Brigada Aérea two months later. The unit moved to Base Aérea Carlos Ibanez, Punta Arenas in March 1986, transferring to Ala 3, IV Brigada Aérea.

Pantera

Since 1986, ENAER has been upgrading the 13 surviving single-seat Mirage 50s, and the two Mirage 50DCs under the Pantera programme. Budgetary constraints and technical difficulties have led to extremely slow progress, and only a handful of aircraft have been modified so far. The aerodynamic prototype for the Pantera was Mirage 50C 514, which initially flew with Israeli-designed canard foreplanes (of broader chord and less sweep than those fitted to the Kfir) and nose-mounted vortex generator strakes, but without any other modifications.

Standard wing

The full Pantera upgrade is more significant and far-reaching, with Elta EL/M-2001B radar in a Kfir-type nose, and with other avionics items, including a new INS. The cockpit contains a new computerised HUD, while a new angle of attack sensor vane is mounted on the forward fuselage. The electrical, hydraulic and armament control systems are all modernised, and the indigenous ENAER Caiquen III RHAWS is backed up by Eclipse chaff/flare dispensers. Unusually, the Pantera retains the standard Mirage 50 wing, and does not incorporate any of the Kfir-style wing modifications fitted to other Israeli-derived Mirage upgrades. The same aircraft (514) served as the full-standard Pantera pro-

totype, and the type started to enter service with Grupo 4 during mid-1993. Only a handful of the rest of Chile's Mirages have been modified so far, however. When modified to Pantera standard, the basic Chilean Mirage 50FC is redesignated 50FCN, the Mirage 50C is the 50CN and the Mirage 50CD becomes the Mirage 50CDN. The aircraft will continue to operate in the air-superiority and intercept roles, although it may have a secondary ground attack commitment.

Elkan identities

Chilean AF Serial	Belgian Serial and comments
Mirage 5MA	
701	BA-01 (Dassault-built 5BA prototype)
702	BA-04 (First M5MA Elkan prototype) (Detachment MirSIP)
703	BA-11
704	BA-23
705	BA-37 (Also quoted as BA-27)
706	BA-39
707	BA-46 (Second series production MirSIP)
708	BA-48
709	BA-50
710	BA-52
711	BA-56 (First MirSIP handed over to Chile) (Détachment MirSIP)
712	BA-57
713	BA-59
714	BA-60 (First MirSIP prototype)
715	BA-62 (Détachment MirSIP)
Mirage 5MD	
716	BD-01 (Dassault-built 5BD prototype)
717	BD-03 (Détachment MirSIP)
718	BD-04 (First MirSIP in Chilean markings) (Détachment MirSIP)
719	BD-14 (First M5MD Elkan prototype)
720	BD-15 (Détachment MirSIP)
Unmodernised Mirage 5BR	
721	BR-13
722	BR-25
723	BR-26
724	BR-27
Unmodernised Mirage 5BD	
725	BD-12

Chile's requirement for a new fighter arose from its urgent need to replace the fleet of ageing Hawker Hunter fighter-bombers (known locally as the Aguila). The last Chilean Hunters continue to serve with Grupo 8 at Base Aérea Cerro Moreno at Antofagasta, and include aircraft delivered during 1966, as well as some newer arrivals acquired after the Falklands War. Despite having been carefully looked after, and extensively modernised, these aircraft are beginning to show their age, and their replacement has been an urgent priority for some years. The availability of the MirSIP Mirages came at an ideal time, and the ex-Belgian aircraft represent something of an ideal solution, having enough commonality with the existing Mirage 50s to offer the potential of a degree of uniform spares support, and a reservoir of trained pilots and ground crew.

It was probably these factors, more than any others, that swung the balance in favour of the MirSIP, and a contract was signed on 19 July 1994 by Belgian defence minister Leo Delcroix and Chilean air force chief of staff, General Jaimes Estay Viveros. This contract covered the supply of 25 aircraft, consisting of 15 modernised single-seat MirSIP Mirage 5MAs and five MirSIP Mirage 5MD twin-stickers. The contract also covered the delivery of four unmodified Mirage 5BRs and one unmodified Mirage 5BD, chosen according to condition and airframe life remaining, and was valued at $54 million (with payments spread over the following 18 months).

The four unmodified Mirage 5BRs will be used to replace Grupo 8's handful of Hawker Hunter FR.Mk 71s in the tactical fighter reconnaissance role, while the single unmodified two-seater will give a trainer with the same equipment fit and handling characteristics as the unmodified Mirages. Because the Belgian reconnaissance Mirages were equipped with British-made Vinten 626/636 cameras, there should be little difficulty in employing the processing and interpretation facilities used by the reconnaissance Hunters. It is possible that these aircraft will be modified (either by SABCA or by ENAER) in the future.

Second contract

A second contract apparently followed soon afterwards, but this has not been widely reported and cannot yet be confirmed. For a total of $100 million (payable in instalments until the year 2000) Chile will receive a further five modernised aircraft, and a further five non-modernised aircraft, together with a massive holding of spares and support equipment. This contract, it is hoped, will be financed by expected export sales of the ENAER A-36 and T-36 (licence-built versions of the CASA C.101 Aviojet) and by borrowing. The exact breakdown of variants

Right: Over the top? The MirSIP and Elkan upgrades are relatively modest, and do not add radar, BVR missiles, or night-attack systems. Apart from the addition of canard foreplanes, the equipment fit is little better than that of the Mirage 5E2s delivered to Egypt in 1980. The aircraft will be an excellent replacement for the Hawker Hunter in the ground attack role, however, and was acquired at a bargain price.

Below: Another of the aircraft used by Détachment MirSIP was BD-15, seen here during a conversion training sortie from Brustem/St Truiden. Deliveries of full-standard Elkans took place from February 1995.

Above: Although the nearest aircraft wears full Chilean insignia, it is a basic Belgian-standard MirSIP Mirage 5BD, not a fully-modified Elkan Mirage 5MD. For flights in Belgium a small Belgian fin flash and serial were retained. The triangular Elkan project badge is worn on the tailfin. The Chilean aircraft are retaining the basic three-tone Belgian air force camouflage scheme, with low-visibility unit markings and serial numbers, although the new paint looks much more vivid than the faded and well-worn Belgian aircraft.

A Belgian-marked MirSIP Mirage 5BD trainer accompanies the first of the MirSIP Mirage 5BA single-seaters to be painted in full Chilean markings. Painted up especially for the official handover on 11 October 1994, this aircraft had not then been modified to full Elkan standards, and went back to Détachment MirSIP for training Chilean pilots. The winged bomb insignia of Grupo No. 8 is carried in a small disc on the nose. Delivery of the first Elkans was due to begin in March 1995.

involved in this second contract remains unknown at the present time. There have been suggestions that further contracts will follow, but the pool of available airframes for the second and subsequent contracts remains large, with 17 Mirage 5BAs, three Mirage 5BDs and 14 Mirage 5BRs available for export or modification.

The limits of commonality

Although there is a degree of commonality between the Mirage 50 and the MirSIP Mirage 5, it soon became apparent that the aircraft would have to be further modified to fully meet Chilean requirements, and to be able to operate in the Chilean air defence environment. The aircraft will, for example, have VOR/DME in place of TACAN, and are also receiving GPS. They will also be fitted with a SNAR nav/attack system derived from that fitted to the Chilean Mirage

50, and will receive the same ILS and HUD. Thus modified the Chilean aircraft is officially known as the MirSIP Plus or the Elkan, the latter meaning Guardian in the local Mapuche Indian dialect.

As well as the contract with SABCA, the Chilean air force signed a protocol with the Belgian air force, paying $1.5 million for the provision of technical assistance and training. Under the terms of this protocol, the Belgian air force took responsibility for training pilots and ground crew on the basic Belgian standard MirSIP, with SABCA providing training courses on the new systems and equipment unique to MirSIP Plus.

In order to achieve the training target (of converting some eight Chilean pilots and a group of ground crew) to the aircraft, the Belgian air force established a new unit, known as Détachment MirSIP, at Brustem/St Truiden. Staffed by two

Above: Although high Alpha capability is increased, approach angle of attack (and thus speed and landing speed) is limited by the danger of a tailscrape. No extra braking is incorporated in the MirSIP aircraft, so landing distances remain high.

Right: When the fully modified Elkans arrive in Chile, pilot conversion will switch from Brustem/St Truiden to Cerro Moreno in Chile, although Belgian personnel, from SABCA and perhaps from the Belgian air force, will continue to be involved.

Belgian air force pilots and about a dozen technicians (all drawn from the disbanding Mirage 5 units) the unit was formed in April 1994 and received five Belgian standard MirSIP aircraft, three of them (BD-03, BD-04, BD-15) two-seat trainers, and two of them single-seaters (BA-56 and BA-62). It was decided not to wait for full standard MirSIP Plus aircraft since these would not have been compatible with Belgian ground support equipment and infrastructure, nor would they have been compatible with Belgian ATC systems and procedures. The initial task of the new unit was to receive the already converted MirSIPs from storage at Weelde, and to then transfer them to Gosselies for Elkan conversion. Flying began in September 1994, although this was initially dedicated to staff pilot continuation training and to shake down the long-stored aircraft assigned to the unit, since the Chilean pupils were then still undergoing groundschool.

Handover

The first aircraft (a standard MirSIP and not an Elkan) was formally handed over to the Chilean air force during a ceremony at Gosselies on 11 October 1994. This was 711 (previously BA-56) which was painted in full Chilean markings, although a small Belgian fin flash and serial were added alongside these markings before the aircraft transferred back to to Détachment MirSIP. The aircraft was formally handed over to Chilean air force chief of staff General Ramón Vega Hidalgo by the director of SABCA, Remo Pellichero and Belgian air force chief Lieutenant General Guido

Vanhecke. Conversion training for the Chilean pilots began in November 1994, and lasted until March 1995. The unmodified MirSIP aircraft in use by the conversion unit were then transferred to Gosselies for conversion to full MirSIP Plus/Elkan standard, bringing the number of Elkan conversions to the full 15 contracted for.

Further Chilean pilots will convert to the Elkan at Cerro Moreno, in Chile, although Belgian instructors (from SABCA and perhaps also from the air force) and technical staff will oversee the process, at least initially. Type conversion will then probably be undertaken at squadron level, although there is the faint possibility that all the two-seaters may be concentrated in a single conversion unit supplying pilots for the Elkan, Mirage 5BR, Pantera and Mirage 50.

Deliveries of fully-modified Elkans were scheduled to begin in February 1995 (starting with MirSIP Plus prototypes BA-04 and BD-14), and were to have been completed by the end of the year. The Chilean air force was responsible for its own aircraft deliveries, and in view of the long and difficult transatlantic route opted to

send the aircraft as freight aboard chartered Antonov An-124s, which could transport up to five Mirages at a time. Spares and heavy logistics equipment, including the former Belgian air force Atar engine test facility dismantled at Bierset, were sent by sea. It remains uncertain as to how and when the 10 aircraft purchased under the second contract will be delivered.The service introduction of the Elkan will give the Fuerza Aérea de Chile a potent fighter-bomber to replace the much-loved Hunter, and one which will be easy and cheap to operate, enjoying a degree of commonality with the Mirage 50s already in service. The fact that the aircraft have already been modernised is a distinct advantage, since an indigenous upgrade programme would almost certainly have run into the same delays that have already beset the Pantera modification of the Mirage 50FC and Mirage 50C. The new-generation nav-attack suite will allow a great improvement in bombing accuracy, and will mark a major advance in fighter-bomber and offensive support capability for the Fuerza Aérea de Chile. **Ulrich de Bruyn and Jon Lake**

British Aerospace
Hawk

and McDonnell Douglas/BAe T-45 Goshawk

First flown in 1974, the BAe Hawk retains its reputation as the world's best advanced trainer and light strike aircraft. A fundamentally sound design has been continuously refined, modified and modernised, resulting in a succession of variants. It has even been adapted to fulfil the night/all-weather attack role, and a single-seat derivative is being sold as a multi-role light fighter. The aircraft has even won a market in the USA, traditionally resistant to buying 'foreign' aircraft, where it has had to be adapted for the demanding carrier training role. Excellent performance, maintainability and affordability have been key factors in the Hawk's success, but perhaps most important has been its superb handling characteristics. Above all, the Hawk is a joy to fly, and can turn the heart of even the most jaded pilot. Who is to say that this hasn't been a deciding factor, even in the hands of professional evaluation pilots paid to base their decisions on more concrete factors?

The Hawk 200 RDA and an Omani Hawk Mk 103, seen in formation, represent the current generation of combat-capable Hawks. The Hawk has made the transition from advanced trainer to fully combat-capable fighter and all-weather light strike aircraft, and advanced versions are continuing to attract new orders. Potential customers for the Hawk include India, Australia, Brunei and South Africa, and the aircraft could still crack the 1,000 example barrier.

British Aerospace Hawk

The first four Hawks were essentially the pre-production test and evaluation batch, although only the first of these was officially classified as anything other than a production standard aircraft. They are seen here flying in formation during a sortie from Dunsfold. The changing ventral fin configuration of the early Hawks is noteworthy. The aircraft closest to the camera ship was the first camouflaged Hawk and has served in a variety of test roles. It was the only camouflaged Hawk with light grey undersides, later aircraft having camouflaged undersides as well. It remains in service today, currently flying with the test fleet at Boscombe Down. The red and white training colour scheme remained virtually unchanged for many years, but is now giving way to overall gloss black.

The RAF started thinking about replacing its 105 diminutive Folland Gnat tandem-seat advanced jet trainers during the early 1960s, while the first of these agile aircraft were entering service as Vampire T.Mk ll replacements with No. 4 FTS at RAF Valley. The short-coupled but transonic Gnat T.Mk 1 soon began to establish new standards as 'a pilot's aeroplane', with phenomenal roll rates (aileron stops were soon added to slow down the rate of roll) and a reputation for precision handling in formation. This made it an ideal choice as the mount of the RAF's first national aerobatic team, the Red Arrows, and it marked a clever adaptation of Teddy Petter's brilliant and original lightweight jet fighter,

As an advanced trainer, however, it had some problems, quite apart from being rather unreliable and extremely labour-intensive to maintain. Instructor visibility was limited from the cramped rear cockpit since not only was the rear seat not raised, but the instructor also had to peer around the large headrest of the student's lightweight ejection seat. Its longitudinal control system was complicated although effective, with a tailplane datum shift during

undercarriage retraction and extension, the latter also involving partial movement of the landing gear legs and fairings as airbrakes. It was not cleared by the RAF for spin training. But one of the Gnat's biggest drawbacks, so far as the RAF was concerned, was its lack of armament training capability, since the instructor's rear seat had no weapons-sight line, which meant that about 45 Hunter FGA.Mk 9s and two-seat T.Mk 7s had to be retained for operational conversion and weapon training.

Apart from being expensive to operate, and representing yet another aircraft type in the inventory, the Hunter was itself already long overdue for replacement. Moreover, it was further proposed that a new advanced trainer should undertake some of the top-end syllabus scheduled for the RAF's 105 pressurised and uprated Jet Provost T.Mk 5s, themselves only ordered in early 1969. The aircraft originally intended to replace the Gnat in the RAF's advanced training role was the twin-Adour, two-seat Anglo-French Jaguar B, but this was rejected on cost grounds. It was cancelled in favour of a proposed new type, which a later UK Defence White Paper claimed (in 1973) would allow the RAF to receive an extra three squadrons of the single-seat Jaguar S version.

In any case it was then envisaged that the Gnat T.Mk 1 would not have much more than a 10-year service life, so it was unsurprising that ideas for a new advanced jet trainer started to circulate within the UK industry. In its initial rationalised form, this then comprised the British Aircraft Corporation (combining Bristol, English Electric, Hunting and Vickers), and Hawker Siddeley Aviation (formerly Avro, Armstrong Whitworth, Blackburn, de Havilland, Folland, Gloster and Hawker).

Plans for a new trainer were endorsed by the Society of British Aerospace Companies in its long-term industry plan for the 1970s, which, when issued in early 1969, specifically included provision for Gnat, Hunter and Jet Provost replacements. Even before then, in 1968, prior to the issue of an official Air Staff Requirement, Hawker Siddeley Aviation had started design studies of new jet trainers at its historic Kingston premises. Ralph Hooper led the design team which undertook these studies, including among its leading members Gordon (K. G.) Hodson, who had previously been the design engineer in charge of the Gnat project and of Folland's ejection seat systems at Kingston. It was Hodson who set out a draft specification for a low-cost jet trainer with weapons capabilities for training or close support, from which Ron Williams, then head of preliminary design

The fitting of four underwing pylons immediately marks this aircraft as not being a standard RAF Hawk T.Mk 1 or T.Mk 1A. It is in fact the first prototype, seen here demonstrating the tremendous bomb-carrying capacity of even the basic Hawk, which was an important factor for many of the aircraft's early export customers. RAF Hawks were delivered without provision for outboard underwing stores, although inboard hardpoints were used by TWU aircraft for the carriage of practice bomb carriers and SNEB rocket pods. The centreline pylon could be used to carry conventional stores, or as the mounting point for a 30-mm ADEN cannon pod.

at Kingston, completed the first outline drawings.

These drawings actually showed a tandem-seat shoulder-mounted straight-wing basic trainer, known as the SP.117-1, but provided the initial basis for further studies within Hawker Siddeley's company-funded P.1182 programme, for which Gordon Hodson was appointed Head of Preliminary Design in 1969. Detailed analyses followed of 20 different trainer configurations, covering both tandem and side-by-side seating, with 12 different engines, and with various wing locations.

Initially these designs were aimed at replacing the Jet Provost, which was also the declared aim of the MoD's Air Staff Target 397, issued on 1 October 1968, although this was written around what was then described as an advanced trainer. Its intention was to equip the RAF, for the first time, with an aircraft designed from the outset for advanced training and weapon instruction, as an alternative to pro-

curement of the Jaguar Trainer originally designed for these roles in the joint Anglo-French programme. Considerable licence was left to industry by the MoD specification, which allowed for single or twin engines, with jet or turbofan; tandem or side-by-side seating; straight or swept wings and powered or manual flying controls. It was specified that the aircraft should weigh no more than 10,000 lb (4536 kg) for take-off.

AST 397 performance requirements called for an exceptionally wide speed range, clean, ranging between a maximum operating figure of about Mach 0.84, or 500 kt (926 km/h) at sea level, and less than 100 kt (185 km/h) at the stall, to cover the broadest possible training spectrum. Also included was a climb requirement to reach 30,000 ft (9150 m) in seven minutes from brake-release, as well as a service ceiling of 43,500 ft (13250 m), and a four-turn spin capability with standard recovery techniques.

This family protrait was taken to celebrate the integration of Hawker Siddeley and BAC into the new British Aerospace. A pre-production Hawk is joined by Scottish Aviation's Bulldog demonstrator, the prototype Jet Provost T.Mk 5 and a Scottish Aviation Jetstream.

An early No. 4 FTS Hawk flies over Wales. Black codes and tiny fin badges were used by No 4 FTS and the CFS initially.

British Aerospace Hawk

A specified 6,000-hour fatigue life represented a requirement of unprecedented severity for any previous RAF aircraft, particularly as it was based on 1,100 counts of $4g$ every 100 flying hours (11 per hour), plus one count of $6g$ every flying hour. Although the AST left engine options entirely open, UK sentiment at that time was strongly inclined towards a single powerplant, on the grounds of economy and adequate reliability. Some have suggested that this was a brave decision, made at a time when other manufacturers were opting for twin engines, but the RAF had years of experience of single-engined jet trainers, from the Vampire and Jet Provost to the Gnat, and British industry was confident of being able to produce a single engine of sufficient reliability.

On the basis of its experience with the Gnat, and with the Meteor T.Mk 7 before it, the RAF was happy to stay with tandem seating for its follow-on trainer, to give a more representative environment for its fast-jet students, and to gain the higher performance, reduced drag and greater economy which resulted from the lower (frontal) cross-sectional area.

Competitive trainer designs

Confirmation of "a decision to replace the (RAF) Gnat and the Hunter with a new jet trainer, less sophisticated and expensive than the Jaguar" came in the 1970 Defence White Paper. This accompanied the finalisation of two competing industry proposals. International collaboration was a strong feature of the British Aircraft Corporation's submissions from Preston, which incorporated design inputs from Aermacchi (as a result of a joint trainer development agreement) as well as from the Commonwealth Aircraft Corporation in Australia. BAC studied numerous designs

with Adour, Viper or RB.199 engines, and also explored the prospects of a collaborative project in Europe, possibly through Panavia with its new aircraft proposals (PANNAP).

BAC originally offered two variants of a similar shoulder-wing design – the P.59, with the latest 15.2-kN (3,420-lb) Bristol Siddeley Viper 623, and the P.62, with a more advanced 23.13-kN (5,200-lb) Rolls-Royce/Turboméca Adour turbofan. Its final AST 397 submission, however, involved only the P.59, since BAC considered the cost of developing and purchasing a non-reheat version of the contemporary Jaguar's Adour as being excessive.

Unlike BAC's broadly multi-national approach, Hawker Siddeley's ideas had firmly and unilaterally crystallised in the shapely form of its tandem-seat single-engined Project 1182, similarly powered either by the Viper 623 turbojet (the HS 1182 was effectively a re-engined, bigger-winged Gnat), or the Adour. The latter powerplant was specified by HSA for its formal low-wing HS 1182AJ submission, for optimum performance and load-carrying capabilities, although the RAF was also given the final option of a stripped, lower-cost 1182AT with no close support capability. Both projects then were regarded by Hawker Siddeley as Gnat – as well as Jet Provost – replacements.

Competitive evaluations were also made by the MoD of such foreign contenders as the Northrop T-38, the Aermacchi MB.326G, the uprated SAAB 105XT, and the Breguet/Dornier Alpha Jet. Even the option of conducting pilot training overseas was examined. The Alpha Jet advanced trainer programme, which slightly preceded the RAF's AST 397 proposals, was offered to the UK as a possible collaborative project to follow the late 1960s Anglo-French helicopter package and the Jaguar and AFVG projects initiated by Britain's previous Labour government. On

the basis of that experience, however, the new Conservative administration decreed that the UK would join in future collaborative programmes only if it was assured of design leadership. Rejection of the Alpha Jet was also inevitable, although it remained a useful baseline datum, because of its 'substantial divergence' from the AST 397 specifications, and because of its much lower fatigue specification.

HS 1182 selection

Submissions to meet AST 397 were invited by the MoD before the end of 1970. This Air Staff Target envisaged the procurement of up to 180 aircraft, and thus represented a potentially vital programme for whichever company's aircraft was chosen. Although neither the BAC P.59 nor the HS 1182, which shared similar performance and capabilities, fully met the Air Staff Target specifications, a letter of intent for the latter type went out to Hawker Siddeley in October 1971. This slightly unusual MoD procedure ended the need for further government and company funding for the BAC P.59, while accepting the limitations resulting from still incomplete detailed design work on the HS 1182. A final decision had not then been made on engine choice, for which contract finalisation was extended by about three months for Hawker Siddeley to quantify in more detail the relative merits of the two alternative powerplants. By this time, P.1182 design was being handled by Kingston's mainstream organisation under the similarly-named Gordon (G. T.) Hudson as chief designer, and Gordon (K. G.) Hodson as assistant chief designer – both former Folland personnel.

While the new twin-shaft Adour, as a turbofan, was about twice the initial £60,500 price of the well-tried and reliable Viper, with estimated unit costs of £125,000 including R&D, it was favoured by the RAF because it offered better overall fuel economy than the older turbojet. It also had about 95 per cent commonality with the Jaguar's Adour 101, plus more power and greater development potential. These latter qualities were regarded as particularly important in view of Hawker Siddeley plans from the out-

Above: One of No. 1 TWU's first Hawks ripples off two full pods of SNEB rockets on the Pembrey range. This is highly unrepresentative, since maximum training value was achieved by firing a pod of rockets singly, during multiple passes. The unit used the badge of No. 229 OCU (its forerunner) until that unit reformed with Tornado F.Mk 2s.

Left: The camouflaged undersides of a No. 1 TWU Hawk T.Mk 1. The continuation of camouflage onto the undersides of RAF tactical aircraft was intended to prevent the phenomenon of 'blinking' as aircraft manoeuvred hard at low level. Underwing serials were deleted during the early 1980s.

set to market armed versions of the HS 1182 for export. HSA had also proposed an HS 1182 version with two SNECMA Larzac turbofans which it was prepared to develop if required by overseas customers, although this would have resulted in an even greater head-to-head confrontation with the twin Larzac-powered Dassault Alpha Jet, already the main export competitor. With a two-stage low-pressure and five-stage high-pressure compressor, each driven by a single-stage turbine, plus an annular combustion system, the Adour 151 was a relatively simple engine with a limited number of parts, and was of compact modular construction.

Its main features include a compression ratio of 11:1; 0.9

No. 1 TWU adopted the same shadow unit designations for its constituent squadrons as had previously been used by No. 229 OCU for its Hunters. This aircraft wears the distinctive red diamonds on black of No. 234 Squadron, with the sword and crossed torch badge of No. 229 OCU on the nose.

British Aerospace Hawk

by-pass ratio; a length of 1.953 m (6.41 ft); 0.567 m (1.86 ft) diameter; a specific fuel consumption at max take-off power of 0.74; and a dry weight of 533 kg (1,175 lb). It made its first run at Rolls-Royce's Derby factory in February 1973, some two weeks ahead of schedule, by which time Adour orders totalled over 800 engines worth more than £100 million for the Jaguar and similar Mitsubishi T-2, as well as for the HS 1182.

Other factors influencing RAF selection of the HS 1182 included the need to keep Hawker Siddeley busy, in view of the disproportionate amounts of work facing the two UK aerospace groups at that time. BAC was then committed to the recently-launched Anglo-French Jaguar development and production programme, as well as to initial feasibility and design studies for the tri-national Multi-Role Combat Aircraft project (later to become the Tornado), apart from its other major collaborative preoccupation with Concorde and ongoing Canberra refurbishing work. BAC was thus perhaps slightly lukewarm about the P.59, which was not seen as being crucial to the company's survival. Australian interest in the possible joint development of an advanced trainer had been the subject of prolonged negotiations with BAC, and the Canberra government was thought likely at that stage to contribute up to about 30 per cent of the estimated £80 million R&D budget. Australia eventually switched its attentions to Hawker Siddeley.

When the HS 1182 was selected the MoD laid down strict timescales for project milestones. These included a required first flight by 1974, and initial service with No. 4 FTS at Valley two or three years later. The design was finalised following confirmation of the RT.172-06 Adour Mk 151 turbofan as the new trainer's powerplant. Rolls-Royce guaranteed a sea level ISA thrust of 23.13 kN (5,200 lb) in March 1972, and this swung the selection. This in

turn allowed the finalisation of an estimated £90 million MoD fixed-price contract on 21 March 1972, for 175 HS 1182s, plus a single pre-production example, due to make its first flight in the spring of 1974. The HS 1182 was still somewhat misleadingly described as an 'all-through' jet trainer, although by then it had been decided that the Jet Provost would be replaced somewhat later, by a totally different aircraft.

To minimise programme costs, HSA proposed that the HS 1182 should be built from the outset on production tooling, with no prototypes. Pre-production HS 1182 01 (XX154) would be used, together with up to the first five off the line, as part of the development programme and, with 02 (XX156), would be the only examples not scheduled for delivery to the RAF. The service was also to receive, from orders placed at a later stage, five mobile Hawk simulators. These were bought from Redifon of Crawley at a cost of about £2.5 million.

Main design features

Even at this stage, however, details were still being refined. Changes from wind-tunnel testing included the transfer of the simple semi-annular intakes from the upper centre-section fuselage behind the cockpit to a position over the forward wingroots, and the introduction of marked (10°) anhedral on the variable-incidence slab

tailplane. This was to ensure stabilator effectiveness with the flaps extended, while yet another change was deletion of the original Hunter-type 'pen-nib' fairing above the Adour jet-pipe.

Officially named the Hawk by the RAF in August 1973, the HS 1182 was a landmark in being the first British aircraft to utilise the SI (metric) system of measurements throughout, apart from on some of its internal equipment. It also represented a remarkably successful compromise between high performance and the docility of handling essential for the protection of inexperienced pilots, while at the same time reproducing the general characteristics of advanced combat aircraft. Most of these qualities derive from its sophisticated wing design which was optimised for high subsonic speeds, and which reinforced continuing British predominance in this area. Hawker Siddeley's 1957 Trident airliner had incorporated the world's first supercritical wing on a production aircraft, and this had been closely followed by the Harrier, which also used a supercritrical wing section. The use of a similar advanced aerofoil section on the Hawk gave minimum induced drag and was to confer a transonic performance capability with an ultimate drag limit of almost M=1.2/572 kt (1060 km/h) on the HS 1182, despite its leading-edge sweep of only 26° (21.5° at quarter-chord), and fat 10.9 to 9 per cent thickness/chord ratio. The excellent wing design contributed towards a 15 per cent decrease in overall induced drag compared with design predictions and a 5 per cent reduction in profile drag,

Wide-span, one-piece, double-slotted, trailing-edge flaps, each with three external hinges, ensured correspondingly good low-speed performance. A low wing position was selected to allow a wide undercarriage track for maximum cross-wind landing capability, and this had the added benefit of minimising oleo length and simplifying servicing access. At the same time, the long-stroke levered-arm suspension main oleos (stressed for a rate of descent of up to 13 ft/sec/3.96 m/sec) gave ample clearance for a centre-line stores pylon with 1,000-lb (454-kg) capacity. This also positioned all components that needed to be reached during first line servicing within 5 ft 6in (1.67 m) of the ground.

Built from the beginning at HSA's Brough factory, the one-piece wing was attached to the fuselage by only six bolts. The two-spar wing effectively comprised a machined-skin structural box, providing ample room for a single 184-Imp gal (836-litre) integral fuel tank extending over most of the span, as well as stowage forward of an auxiliary spar for the inward-retracting, wide-track mainwheel legs. Built to service release load factors of +8g and -4g, the wing was required by the RAF to have two hardpoints for stores of up to 500 lb (227 kg) each (for armament training), with optional plumbing for external fuel tanks (although this provision was later deleted by the RAF). HSA made provision from the beginning, however, to upgrade the mainplane stressing at its own expense to accommodate four pylon attachments, each of 1,000-lb (454-kg) capacity. In ground static load tests, the equivalent of +12g was applied without any permanent deformation to the airframe, which reached 15.5g before any failure.

Fuselage design was dominated by the substantial height differential required between the two cockpits. These were

British Aerospace Hawk

separated by a full internal screen with a canopy bracing frame, to protect the backseater from windblast if the integrity of the front cockpit was compromised by a bird-strike. The stepped cockpits provided the instructor in the back with adequate visibility at all attitudes, especially to see the touch-down point, and enabled both occupants to use the same sighting index. This ensured a field of view of 15° from the horizontal over the nose (through the one-piece stretched acrylic windscreen) for the front occupant and of 5° for the instructor in the rear. Enough width was also designed into the canopy to allow some lateral head movement, to increase forward and downward visibility from the rear seat. Space was also needed to accommodate twin Martin-Baker Mk 10B zero-zero rocket-boosted automatic ejection seats, which require the occupant's weight in kilos to be dialled on a vernier control on the seat pan when strapping in. This information is used to align the rocket thrust through the CG of the potential ejected mass. The seats were installed on rails inclined aft at 21° from the vertical.

Bird-strike testing for the steeply-raked, rain-shedding windscreen included a 1-kg (2.2-lb) bird impacting at 450 kt (840 km/h). Miniature detonating cord (MDC) is used to shatter the large, side-hinged, one-piece cast-acrylic canopy. The command ejection system can be initiated from the rear seat ensuring that the front occupant follows the instructor after 0.5 second, with full escape clearance for both within 0.7 seconds. Alternatively, each occupant may eject individually using the seat-pan handles, which also actuate the MDC. Cabin pressurisation is provided automatically above 5,000 ft (1520 m), and reaches the full differential pressure of 4 psi (27.6 kN/m²) at 40,000 ft (12190 m).

The Hawk's cockpit equipment and avionics were fairly basic, with full dual installations of electro-mechanical analog flight and engine instruments, plus VHF and UHF transmitter/receivers, TACAN, ILS and IFF/SSR.

TACAN was thus the sole onboard navigational equipment, and the Hawk did not have a sufficiently comprehensive avionics fit to fly on civil airways, although airways navaids were, of course, later installed in HSA's civil-registered demonstrator (G-HAWK), and were offered to prospective export customers.

The centre fuselage accommodates a 181-Imp gal (823-litre) flexible bag fuel tank, which is virtually on the CG and extends between the bifurcated intake trunks, with short runs to the aft-mounted Adour turbofan. Engine changes can be achieved within 1.5 hours through two large doors in the semi-monocoque lower fuselage, with no airframe split required and with no disturbance to the actuating systems for the non-powered rudder, hydraulically-boosted all-moving stabilator and rear-mounted 'Hunter-type' ventral air brake. Duplicated hydraulic systems operating at 3,000 psi (21.1 MN/m²) serve the airbrake and tailplane, as well as the ailerons, flaps, undercarriage (including the forward-retracting nose-stowed non-steerable nosewheel leg), wheel brakes and anti-skid system. The flying controls are actuated via push/pull rods with appropriate servos. An additional back-up system is provided using an automatic, pop-out, ram-air turbine just forward of the fin. While the rudder has a conventional direct electrically-operated trim tab, trimming of the ailerons and all-moving tailplane is achieved by electrical adjustment of the earthing points of their spring feel units. A thumb-switch on the stick controls pitch trimming. Additional stick force per g inputs are provided in the longitudinal control circuit by means of a bob-weight.

A Microturbo 047-MK2 gas turbine APU above the Adour confers independence from ground facilities for starting, and may also be similarly used for air-starts at heights up to 25,000 ft (7620 m). A key feature of the empennage design was positioning the swept vertical tail well forward of the horizontal surfaces to minimise rudder blanketing during spins. Two small ventral fins were also added beneath the rear fuselage at an early stage in the flight-test programme, to improve directional stability.

Flight development begins

The sole pre-production Hawk, XX154, began to take final shape at Kingston in early 1974, from wing, tailplane and fin sections produced at Brough, and from rear fuselage sections, nosecone, canopy and windscreens built at Hamble. Anticipated Australian interest began to fade because of other Commonwealth defence funding priorities, and it became apparent that the HS 1182 was likely to become Britain's last non-collaborative major military aircraft programme. The project was also threatened by similar UK

defence economies following the return of a minority Labour government but, despite delays of two or three months because of industrial problems, XX154 was rolled out only slightly behind schedule on 12 August 1974 after final assembly at Dunsfold.

XX154 made its maiden flight on 21 August, in the hands of HSA Dunsfold chief test pilot Duncan Simpson, following ground-running of the Adour 151, final systems checks and low- and high-speed taxiing trials. The flight lasted 53 minutes, and drew the inevitable report that the Hawk handled "beautifully". In fact, initial aileron control had proved distinctly disappointing, although that was soon remedied by changing the circuit gearing from non-linear to linear.

Climbing initially to 5,000 ft (1524 m), Simpson retracted the undercarriage and take-off flap, increasing speed to 250 kt (463 km/h). The climb was continued in unfavourable visibility conditions to 20,000 ft (6096 m), where approaches to the clean and all-down stall were completed, handling down to 100 kt (185 km/h) proving "very good". After descending to 10,000 ft (3048 m), more general handling to an IAS of 310 kt (574 km/h), just

below the initial limit of 325 kt (602 km/h), was performed. Simpson reported that the approach and landing were very easy, and the first flight was completed with full serviceability in readiness for the next sorties.

These followed, in fact, on the next day, when in just over an hour and a half Duncan Simpson climbed the Hawk to 27,000 ft (8230 m), achieved an indicated speed of 400 kt (741 km/h), a Mach number of 0.8, and pulled 4g in tight turns. Project pilot Andy Jones was at the controls for the third flight, which lasted just over an hour, and was also "a complete success". By 28 August, slightly more than 11 hours had been completed of the flight-test programme in nine sorties, including full and half-rolls; inverted flight up to 12 seconds; sustained 5g turns; and airbrake operation up to M=0.8 at 35,000 ft (10668 m), and 400 kt (741 km/h) at 1,000 ft (305 m). Because of its aft location and rapid actuation, the relatively small ventral airbrake initially resulted in a pronounced nose-down pitch change on extension at the upper end of the speed scale, and this prompted investigation.

Further trials were then halted so that the Hawk could be flown into Farnborough for its scheduled daily appear-

A TWU Hawk breaks away from the gunnery banner target towed by another Hawk. This photo is obviously posed since in real gunnery training the firing aircraft would never approach so close to the banner, nor would it approach the target-towing aircraft with so little angular displacement! In real life this Hawk pilot would have just scored a kill against the tug!

Loaded for 'Bear' a No. 151 Squadron (No. 2 TWU) Hawk T.Mk 1A takes off from Chivenor. Chivenor reopened as a TWU primarily because it enjoyed better weather than Lossiemouth and Brawdy.

as little as 88 kt (163 km/h) IAS at light weights, although the break-away was initially described as "unforgiving", with a lack of warning aerodynamic buffet and a pronounced wing drop. The stall warning problem was fixed simply enough by the time-honoured addition of two 8-in (20-cm) triangular section strips along the inner leading edges to provide some aerodynamic buffet over the stabilator at high angles of attack, at the cost of increasing the stalling speed at half-fuel weight by about 5 kt (9 km/h).

Reducing the tendency of the wing to drop at high angles of attack required a little more work, including the fitting of wool-tufts to the upper surface of the wing and filming these with cameras installed on the rear cockpit weapons sight bracket to study the low-speed airflow break-away at the three flap settings. This helped to determine the ideal size and position of the remedial leading-edge wing fences, the Hawk's original small inboard fences proving unsuccessful. A straight stall from all attitudes was soon achieved, however, using a longer-chord fence of some 4 in (10 cm) depth, located further outboard.

Flap-induced stall problems

Another low-speed control problem emerged later in the test programme with the pre-production Hawk. This revealed a possibility of completely stalling the stabilator, thereby putting the Hawk into an apparently uncontrollable dive, in one particular configuration, with full 50° flap extension and with the undercarriage retracted. Fortunately, Duncan Simpson discovered this phenomenon when exploring Hawk stalling behaviour with Dunsfold test pilot Jim Hawkins at a height of around 32,000 ft (9760 m), and was able to regain control after flap retraction. This tailplane stall was attributed to the powerful downwash from the double-slotted flaps at high angles of attack, made worse by the large negative deflection angles of the stabilator. Rectification included deleting the outer section of the flap slot, to reduce the downwash, and limiting the maximum negative tailplane incidence from 17° to 15°. Low-

A Canberra TT.Mk 18 of No. 100 Squadron peels away from one of the squadron's first Hawks. The Hawk does not carry the sophisticated Rushton target system used by the Canberras, but is rather less expensive to operate, and is better able to simulate modern threats in the silent target role.

ance in the 1974 SBAC air show programme, having been cleared for general handling, except into the possible flutter regime. The Hawk had experienced no technical failures or unserviceabilities of any kind during its pre-Farnborough flight tests, the last of which was the first with two pilots on board (a CFS instructor occupying the rear cockpit). It had also demonstrated a better than expected fuel consumption, giving a safe endurance on internal fuel of about three hours, or rather more than the Hunter T.Mk 7 with two 100-Imp gal (454-litre) drop tanks.

Continued flight development was delayed for several months (until 19 December) for completion of the test instrumentation installation. XX154 was then used for further general handling, flutter clearance and load measurement trials. In the low-speed regime, it was flown down to

Two Canberras (an E.Mk 15 leading a TT.Mk 18) and four BAe Hawks fly in formation on the occasion of the Canberra's retirement from No.100 Squadron. Despite its age, the Canberra's superb high-altitude performance, and long endurance made it an excellent target facilities aircraft, while its challenging handling characteristics gave it a unique capability as an advanced trainer. Many student pilots chopped at TWU stage were able to rejoin the fast-jet stream after a tour or two on Canberras. The Hawk, however, offered considerably lower operating costs. This, coupled with the availability of spare Hawk airframes after the end of the Cold War when the RAF reduced its throughput of trainee pilots, made its selection as a Canberra replacement inevitable. The Hawks of No. 100 squadron have not been painted with the traditional yellow and black target towing stripes.

speed handling of the Hawk proved completely innocuous thereafter.

At the other end of the speed scale, the Hawk's somewhat unexpected transonic capability originally presented slight control problems with uncommanded longitudinal trim changes from about Mach 0.83-.84 due to compressibility effects. These were eventually resolved by the addition of two rows of four vortex generators on each side of the upper wing fence, opposite the flap/aileron junction. The inner group improved longitudinal control from about Mach 0.82 by optimising shock-wave location, while the outboard vortex generators improved aileron effectiveness in the transonic flow region above M=0.98. After successful trials, it was found that the second row of vortex generators was unnecessary, and therefore removed.

With the 'dressed' wing, only about half aileron was needed to remain laterally level going through Mach 1, instead of almost full stick deflection with the original 'undressed' wing. Transition through Mach 1 proved completely smooth, with no untoward trim changes and, like the Hunter before it, the Hawk proved self-limiting at 1.15TMN in a steep dive. At low altitudes, the normal maximum level speed of the Hawk was found to be around 540 kt (1000 km/h). Among the few other changes deemed necessary during flight development was the installation of higher-force centring springs for the aileron and rudder circuits. Airbrake pitch-change and pitch-oscillation problems were solved by several small modifications, including reducing the actuating speed, balancing the stabilator control rods, and by transferring the lateral strakes on the brake surface to the adjacent lower fuselage, where they serve as ventral fins, with a small increase in size, improving directional stability.

More development aircraft

Of the nine other Hawks on the Kingston final assembly line at the time of XX154's first flight, five were earmarked for the flight development programme. The requirement to build them in production jigs and to full production standards delayed the first flight of a second Hawk until 22 April 1975. XX157, actually the third aircraft off the line, flew in the hands of project pilot Andy Jones, with Jim Hawkins in the rear seat. The aircraft was earmarked for armament and avionics development, transferring to Boscombe Down by September 1975. The second Hawk (XX156) had been briefly grounded for structural resonance testing after completion. Initially allocated to engine, systems and intake development trials, it finally flew on 19 May 1975.

At that time, the first two Hawks had flown only about 115 hours instead of the 180 originally programmed. Since 75 hours had been achieved in only 72 sorties by the pre-production aircraft between 5 February and 30 April, the HSA team was confident of getting back on schedule by the third quarter of 1975. By then, the Hawk development fleet had been augmented by XX158, first flown on 1 July 1975. This aircraft was scheduled for performance and spinning trials, the latter following model testing in the French vertical wind-tunnel at Lille. More than 150 spins had been flown by late 1975 with no problems anticipated for final clearance. The two remaining development aircraft XX159, nominated for service and CA release trials with the Airframe & Armament Experimental Establishment at Boscombe Down, and assisted by XX160 – joined the programme after first flights on 17 June and 19 November.

These six Hawks were required to complete some 500 hours of development flying to clear the way for initial deliveries to the RAF by October 1976. All except the pre-production aircraft were then scheduled for refurbishment before RAF service, as part of the overall contract for 175. With output building to four aircraft per month during 1976, this total was due to be completed by late 1980. HSA retained the eighth Hawk off the line as a sales demonstra-

tor and for 100 flying hours of private venture light ground-attack development with no fewer than nine weapons stations for potential export markets. It was registered as G-HAWK (later ZA101). Making its initial flight from Dunsfold on 17 May 1976, the aircraft was given a Mk 50 export designation, and subsequently enjoyed a colourful and eventful career.

First overseas flights

Rapid progress allowed Hawk XX156 to fly to Malta for three weeks of hot weather trials in June 1975, during which 25 sorties were flown at ground temperatures up to 33°C (91°F), proving satisfactory operation of the pressurisation and air-conditioning systems. On 18 July XX156 went on to Cairo for the Hawk's first export demonstration, following the announcement of Egyptian plans to licence build advanced trainers and light strike aircraft by the newly-formed and Gulf States-funded Arab Military Industrial Organisation.

During the four-day visit, Hawker Siddeley test pilots Jim Hawkins and Don Riches flew with four EAF officers, including a MiG-17 squadron commander. The sorties were undertaken from Almaza air base in even higher ambient temperatures of up to 40°C (104°F) (ISA+25°C),

The commanding officer of No. 100 Squadron flies this specially marked Hawk, with a black spine and fin, blue and yellow cheatline, and a much enlarged squadron skull-and-crossbones insignia. The small blue and yellow checkered pod is a Luneberg lens radar reflector, used to enhance the Hawk's radar cross-section. This allows trainee radar operators to see the aircraft more clearly during practice intercepts and the like.

This smartly decorated No. 1 TWU aircraft, flown by a No. 79 Squadron pilot, was used as the Solo Hawk display aircraft during 1987, until a senior officer ordered that the colour scheme should be removed.

By 1991, anniversary colour schemes and special markings for CO's aircraft or display aircraft were becoming increasingly common. Here a No. 4 FTS Hawk, painted to celebrate the unit's 70th anniversary, flies formation with No. 25 Squadron's display aircraft. The Tornado/Hawk combination would have been used in wartime in mixed fighter force operations.

and demonstrated the Hawk's performance and combat manoeuvrability with and without external stores on its five pylon attachments, before the Defence Minister and EAF Commander in Chief. The Hawk was also demonstrated at the government aircraft factory at Helwan, and flew twice the number of planned sorties, with excellent serviceability under extreme climatic conditions. XX156 later completed successful cold weather trials in Canada in early 1978.

In some 400 hours of development flying achieved by November 1975, 99 per cent of the aerodynamic trials had been accomplished, rockets had been launched, practice bombs dropped, and the weapon aiming programme was well under way, mostly with the third Hawk, XX157. For weapons training, RAF Hawks were scheduled to carry normal loads of a MATRA 155 rocket-pod, containing 18 68-mm (2.7-in) projectiles under one wing pylon and ML CBLS 100 carriers containing Portsmouth Aviation 4-lb (1.8-kg) or 28-lb (12.7-kg) practice bombs under the other. Provision was also made for an underfuselage 30-mm ADEN Mk 4 gunpod with 120 rounds, similar to the pods carried by RAF and RN Harriers, with a Ferranti F.195R ISIS gyro gunsight in each cockpit. After more than 1,000 rounds had been fired from the Hawk's gunpod on the

ground at Dunsfold, and after aerodynamic trials with an inert pod had been completed, air firing followed in October and November of 1975, resulting in full clearance.

During 1976, further testing included 350 erect spins in a four-week period, some of them extending to 14 turns. Eight-turn spins were also demonstrated with inboard stores and the underwing ventral cannon pod. No RAF requirement was expressed for inverted spinning, which had been so successfully demonstrated by the Hunter Trainer. The Hawk proved to be extraordinarily spin resistant when mishandled, but showed consistent classic spin entry and recovery characteristics. Its spin characteristics can be varied by applying pro-spin or out-spin aileron, the first resulting in an accurate simulation of the accelerating oscillatory rotation typical of most swept-wing jets.

Such a high-oscillation spin can result in engine surge and rocketing jet pipe temperatures if the throttle is not maintained at idling thrust, but the Adour is otherwise tolerant of most low-speed manoeuvres. It also has a particularly wide relight envelope, ranging from 165 kt (306 km/h) to Mach 0.85 below 25,000 ft (7620 m). At high speeds, a windmill relight is possible but, because of the turbofan's relatively slow rotation, the Hawk's Microturbo

047-MK2 gas-turbine APU can be used up to 25,000 ft (7620 m) to feed the Adour's air starter.

HSA's contract called for delivery of the first six aircraft to the RAF by October 1976, and for delivery of 10 by the year's end. The seventh Hawk off the line, XX161, was described at the time as the "first production aircraft", and was completed to definitive standards. This aircraft was used for the "final conference" at Dunsfold with the Ministry of Defence Procurement Executive and by the RAF for service acceptance. It therefore represented the last opportunity for any hardware changes to be made before the aircraft entered service.

Having survived this final hurdle, XX161 became the first Hawk to be delivered to the RAF, on 1 April 1976. This was technically ahead of the specified schedule, although its initial role was a non-flying one, being used for maintenance familiarisation training. At that stage, the award of full MoD Controller of Aircraft (CA) clearance awaited the completion of A&AEE trials at Boscombe Down. This was finally achieved in October 1976, after some 600 hours of flying by the six development aircraft. This clearance was for the clean aircraft only, operating in the flying training role, with a maximum take-off weight of 11,023 lb (5000 kg). Maximum landing weight was 10,250 lb (4650 kg), using the limiting undercarriage absorption rate of 13 ft/sec (3.96 m/sec).

Somewhat surprisingly, in the absence of an RAF requirement for supersonic capability, the CA release included a maximum speed of $M=1.05$ at altitude (instead of the originally-planned 0.9), with a maximum level speed limitation of $M=0.875$, and a low-altitude limit of 530 kt (982 km/h) IAS. Take-off and landing operations had been satisfactorily demonstrated in 90° cross-winds of up to 28 kt (52 km/h) on a wet runway, despite the deliberate omission of nosewheel steering. Clearance was also included for four-turn erect spins, but the first Hawks had an altitude limitation of 30,000 ft (9144 m) because of a vibratory engine buzz, eventually cured by spring-loading the low-pressure compressor disc assembly. CA clearance was later extended to 48,000 ft (14630 m), the Hawk having already flown at heights of up to 50,000 ft (15240 m) during its development programme.

Deliveries

With the original clearances issued the delivery of two follow-on production Hawks, XX162 and XX163, marked the true service entry of the type. These were delivered to No. 4 FTS at Valley on 4 November 1976, enabling the RAF Air Member for Personnel, Air Chief Marshal Sir John Aitken, to praise HSA and Rolls-Royce for "not only meeting a delivery date set five years earlier, but also for providing an aircraft likely to meet or exceed all its specifications with no cost overruns". All was not completely rosy, however, since the RAF had received only six of the 10 Hawks due for delivery by late 1976.

Output built up and deliveries were soon back on track. In contrast, although the first of four prototypes of the rival Alpha Jet flew some 10 months before the first Hawk, the complications of the Franco-German programme meant that the first production example – a French trainer – did not fly until November 1977.

Among the 11 performance-guaranteed specifications exceeded by the RAF Hawks was the time to 30,000 ft (9144 m), which was reduced from seven minutes to six minutes and 20 seconds, probably because the Adour 151-01 was apparently then delivering 5,340 lb (23.75 kN) for take-off instead of the lower output originally guaranteed. Acceleration response could be further improved by the simple expedient of a speed switch in the engine fuel system. Such a switch was incorporated in the Adour Mk 851 fitted to export Hawks, but the sole RAF Hawks with this feature were the 12 Adour 151X-engined aircraft of the Red Arrows. Since these aircraft rotate between Valley and

the Red Arrows, a number of aircraft have been modified, but all are demodified when they leave the team.

Many of the Hawk's most important characteristics are only apparent from the cockpit, flying the aircraft. An internal battery is more than ample to spin up the Micro-turbo APU, fed from the aircraft's fuel supply. This provides enough power to start the Adour, which then idles at about 55 per cent rpm. This provides adequate power for the cockpit conditioning system and is also sufficient for taxiing. Differential toe brake application is used for steering on the ground. An unmatched all-round view is available from either seat through the one-piece canopy, making the aircraft easy to taxi. In RAF service, pilots learn routine checks by heart, and run through them from memory, without looking at the Flight Reference Cards stowed in a flying suit pocket.

On the runway brake release follows a full-power check, and the pilot checks RPM and TGT as the aircraft starts to roll. Acceleration is brisk. The aircraft is initially steered using differential braking, although the rudder becomes effective at about 50 kt (93 km/h). The nosewheel is raised at 90-100 kt IAS (167-185 km/h), and a further gentle rearward stick movement would lift the Hawk off at 100-105 kt (185-196 km/h). In RAF service, however, the aircraft is deliberately flown off the runway at 120 kt (222 km/h). Unstick occurs some 12 seconds after brake release and after a typical ground roll of about 2,000 ft (600 m). Undercarriage and flaps need to be quickly raised before reaching their limiting speed of 200 kt (370 km/h). 'Cleaning up' is accompanied by minimal associated trim changes. General handling is delightful, since the fighter-like controls have been fine-tuned to what must be near perfection even compared with the Hunter. Postings from the front line to Hawk navigator instructor or Qualified Weapons Instructor jobs are highly sought after, largely due to the Hawk's handling and sheer fun value. The low cockpit noise level allows relaxed communication between instructor and student throughout the flight envelope, even at

No. 79 Squadron celebrated its 75th Anniversary in 1992, decorating one of its Hawks with a large version of the squadron badge on a red disc on a black fin. The squadron's 75th anniversary was to be its last, since the unit did not survive the 1992 closure of RAF Brawdy. When the RAF decided that one of the TWUs would be closed, Brawdy was the obvious choice, since the Welsh airfield had never enjoyed good weather conditions.

British Aerospace Hawk

Specification
McDonnell Douglas T-45A Goshawk

As for Hawk T.Mk 1A except in the following particulars
Powerplant: one 5,845-lb (26-kN) Rolls-Royce/Turboméca Adour F405-401 turbofan
Wingspan: 30.75 ft (9.39 m)
Overall length: 39 ft 3.98 in (11.988 m)
Height: 13 ft 4.74 in (4.083 m)
Wheel track: 12 ft 9.52 in (3.899 m)
Empty weight: 8,756 lb (3972 kg)
Empty weight, equipped (service): 9,834 lb (4461 kg)
Maximum take-off weight, clean: 12,750 lb (5783 kg)
Maximum fuel: 2,893 lb (1312 kg)
Maximum catapult launch weight: 13,704 lb (6216 kg)
Maximum level speed: M= 0.85
High-speed cruise: M=0.74 at 33,000 ft (10058 m), using 1,100 lb/h (499 kg/h)
Stalling speed, landing configuration: 93 kt (172 km/h) IAS
Carrier approach speed: 118 kt (218 km/h)
Catapult launch speed: 121 kt (224 km/h)

The front (left) and back (right) cockpits of the T-45A Goshawk, with the pre 'Cockpit 21' analog instruments. A digital cockpit with F/A-18 style displays will be installed from the 73rd aircraft, and may be retrofitted to surviving earlier airframes. The existing T-45 cockpit would be immediately familiar to any Hawk pilot.

British Aerospace Hawk T.Mk 1 (Red Arrows)

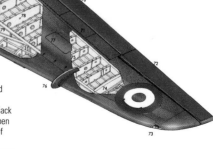

1 Pitot head
2 Landing lamp
3 Nose undercarriage wheel bay
4 IFF/SSR aerial
5 Avionics equipment bay
6 Fresh air intake
7 One-piece frameless windscreen panel
8 Shrouded instrument panel
9 HUD mounting, not fitted to display aircraft
10 Cockpit canopy cover, hinged to starboard
11 Miniature detonating cord (MDC) canopy breaker
12 Pilot's Martin-Baker Mk 10D ejection seat
13 External canopy latch
14 Side console panel with throttle and flap controls
15 Ejection seat rocket pack
16 Lower UHF aerial
17 Personal equipment connectors
18 Rear instrument panel console
19 Internal windscreen panel
20 Rear (instructor's) ejection seat
21 Boarding step
22 Engine air intake
23 Smoke generator fuel tank
24 Pressure refuelling connection

25 Wing spar attachment joint
26 Fuselage frame and stringer construction
27 Boundary layer spill duct
28 Cockpit pressure bulkhead
29 Oxygen bottles (2)
30 Fuselage bag type fuel tank
31 Air conditioning system equipment bay
32 Heat exchangers
33 Anti-collision light
34 Heat exchanger air intakes
35 Vortex generators
36 Wing fence
37 Starboard navigation light
38 Starboard aileron
39 Double-slotted flap
40 Upper UHF aerial
41 Heat exchanger exhaust ducts
42 Gas turbine starter
43 Starter exhaust
44 Emergency ram air turbine
45 Ram air turbine doors
46 Hydraulic reservoir, port and starboard

47 Engine bay venting air intake
48 Two-spar tailfin construction
49 Fin tip VHF aerial fairing
50 Rudder
51 Rudder trim tab
52 Tailplane hydraulic actuator
53 All-moving tailplane centre-section and control quadrant
54 Tail navigation light
55 Smoke generator nozzles (3)
56 Port all-moving tailplane
57 Tailplane multi-spar construction
58 Tailplane attachment main frames
59 Tail bumper
60 Heat-shrouded exhaust duct
61 Ventral fin, port and starboard
62 Airbrake hydraulic jack
63 Ventral airbrake, open
64 Engine bay fireproof bulkhead
65 Rolls-Royce/Turboméca Adour 151 turbofan engine
66 Engine bay fire extinguisher access

67 Accessory equipment gearbox
68 Generator
69 Wingroot fillet
70 Double-slotted flap
71 Trailing-edge control access panels
72 Port aileron
73 Port navigation light
74 Wing tank end rib
75 Wing rib construction
76 Port wing fence
77 Wing tank access panel
78 Port wing integral fuel tank
79 Main spar
80 Auxiliary front spar
81 Undercarriage leg pivot fixing
82 Hydraulic retraction jack
83 Port main undercarriage wheel bay

Cockpit
The tandem stepped cockpits give the backseater an unparalleled view forward over the nose, making the aircraft unequalled in the advanced training role. The cockpits each accommodate a Martin-Baker Mk 10B zero-zero ejection seat, and the single side-hinging acrylic canopy incorporates MDC (Miniature Detonating Cord) which explosively fragments the canopy immediately prior to ejection, which may be command-initiated from either seat. The MDC may be detonated from outside the aircraft, to aid ground rescue of the crew. An improved windscreen has been retrofitted to RAF Hawks, this improving birdstrike tolerance enough to withstand an impact by a 1-kg (2.2-lb) bird at a speed of up to 528 kt (607 mph; 978 km/h). The previous screen had been able to withstand the impact of a 0.9-kg bird at speeds of up to 454 kt (523 mph; 841 km/h). The instructor's cockpit has a separate windscreen inside the canopy. The entire cockpit is pressurised, heated and air conditioned using engine bleed air, which is channelled through a BAe cockpit air conditioning and pressurisation system.

BAe Hawk T.Mk 1A
No. 92 (Reserve) Squadron
No. 7 Flying Training School
RAF Chivenor
1994

Although nominally 'only a trainer' in RAF service, the Hawk has won an enviable reputation among both pilots and engineers for its mix of performance, handling characteristics and maintainability. Front-line Tornado pilots covet a Hawk QWI/QFI/Nav instructor tour, and the aircraft has proved to be a great display aircraft, in the hands of the 'Red Arrows' and various solo display pilots. The Hawk has also become one of the great success stories of post-war British military aviation, winning many important export orders in the face of stiff competition from a wide variety of jet and turboprop trainers. This aircraft is seen in the markings which it wore while serving in the tactical weapons training role at RAF Chivenor, and is seen in full 'War role' fit with AIM-9L Sidewinders and centreline gun pod. In such a configuration, the backseater would probably be acting as a navigator. The advanced tactical weapons training role was initially undertaken by the two tactical weapons units at Lossiemouth (later Chivenor) and Brawdy. These units effectively acted as fighter/ground attack lead-in schools, preparing aircrew prior to their posting to front-line (type-specific) operational conversion units. With the adoption of the Mirror Image training scheme in 1991, No. 2 TWU at Chivenor disbanded to reform as No. 7 FTS, with Nos 19 and 92 Squadrons effectively adopted as 'Shadow' unit identities, although nominally designated as Reserve squadrons in their own right. Under the new scheme, advanced flying training (hitherto the province of No. 4 FTS at Valley) and tactical weapons training were amalgamated into a single course, split between No. 4 FTS at Valley and No. 7 FTS at Chivenor. The drawdown in flying training which accompanied Options for Change led to pressure to centralise Hawk flying training at a single base, and Valley was selected as the survivor. On the disbandment of No. 7 FTS, No. 19 Squadron's identity passed to the CFS Hawk squadron at Valley, while No. 92 Squadron disbanded, all of these events occurring on 1 October 1994. This aircraft, XX157, went on to serve with the Royal Navy's Fleet Requirements and Air Direction Unit at RNAS Yeovilton (HMS *Heron*), remaining under MoD ownership but being serviced, operated and maintained by Flight Refuelling, now known as Cobham.

Colour schemes
Initially, the RAF's Hawk fleet wore two distinctively different colour schemes, with red, white and grey on the advanced training aircraft, and the standard low-level camouflage of sea grey and dark green on the TWU aircraft. Wraparound two-tone camouflage was adopted on the TWU aircraft when it was found that the light grey undersides (which showed up when aircraft manoeuvred hard at low level) led to a 'blinking' effect. Only the second prototype had light grey undersides, production aircraft having wraparound camouflage from the start. This was in turn replaced by the same overall two-tone air superiority grey colour scheme that was worn by RAF Phantoms and Tornado ADVs from 1984. Trials on four aircraft compared a medium sea grey top surfaces and barley grey lower surfaces scheme with a scheme using dark sea grey topsides and medium sea grey undersides during 1983, the lighter grey scheme being preferred. The aircraft were given black 'false canopies' below the nose, but these proved more confusing and dangerous to wingmen than they were to the adversaries. The end of the Cold War brought an increased emphasis on flight safety and it was decided to adopt a fleet-wide high-conspicuity colour scheme. Trials, named Long View Two, compared the original red, white and grey colour scheme with the old grey/green camouflage and the newer air defence greys scheme and with aircraft painted matt black, and dark sea grey overall. The trials were sponsored by the Inspectorate of Flight Safety, and the Central Trials and Tactics Organisation, and Farnborough's Department of Human Factors also made major inputs into the trials. Matt black was preferred, with its low reflectivity, proving easiest to see clearly and without distortion. Weathering was not taken into account during the trials, which ran from 19 November 1992 to 27 November 1992, even though the matt black aircraft in the trials quickly began to lose its finish, with the base red, white and grey paint soon starting to show through. No. 7 FTS at Chivenor had already painted a pair of aircraft gloss black (with chevrons in white or yellow) as display aircraft for the 1992 season, and it was soon noticed that these shared many of the attributes of the matt black aircraft, with few of the disadvantages. It came as no real surprise when an all-black colour scheme was adopted to replace both the red, white and grey and air defence grey colour schemes, and this is now being introduced fleet-wide. The red, white and grey colour scheme has also changed slightly since the Hawk entered service, with the deletion of underwing serials, and the addition of coloured fins and spines (initially on display aircraft, but later spreading to the training fleet). No. 100 Squadron's target facilities Hawks wear an overall grey colour scheme, with squadron markings, although the CO's aircraft has a black fin. Underwing target-towing stripes have not been applied to these aircraft. All Hawk units apply unit markings, and these have become progressively larger and more colourful in recent years. Other specially marked aircraft have included a pair of overall gloss roundel blue Hawks used as display aircraft by No. 7 FTS at Chivenor.

Main undercarriage
The main gear was developed by AP Precision Hydraulics and the oleos were extended by 8.5 in to provide a longer stroke. The undercarriage was of high tensile steel to improve corrosion resistance and to reduce the danger of fracture. The oleos support larger mainwheels. The attachment points are moved 8.5 in outboard to compensate for their increased length, thereby increasing wheel track. The mainwheel doors are sequenced to close after the gear has been extended.

External stores
Like the RAF's Hawk T.Mk 1s, the T-45 has five hardpoints, but the outboard pair (stations one and five) are not used, wired or tapped, but could be activated for an export customer, or in the future. The centre station is suitable only for carrying a travel pod, since it is neither wired nor plumbed for bombs nor plumbed for drop tanks. The inboard underwing pylons, stations two and four, are wired for the carriage of practice multiple bomb racks (PMBRs) and can be plumbed for fuel, although they have not yet been so modified, and the T-45A has not flown with external fuel.

Airframe
A significant degree of airframe strengthening was necessitated by the need to operate from a pitching, rolling carrier deck (which may pitch rapidly up to meet a descending aircraft, resulting in an extraordinarily high cumulative rate of descent), and to withstand the rigours imposed by catapult launches and arrested landings. Most of the vertical landing and horizontal catapult launch stresses are transmitted to the aircraft via the undercarriage, while the arrested landings impose stresses on the attachment points for the arrester hook. The most extreme loads on the undercarriage are imposed by an inadvertent airborne engagement of the arrester wire, which snatches the aircraft back onto the deck giving a rate of descent of 25 ft/sec and a peak download on the nose gear of 75,000 lb. This is equivalent to simply dropping the aircraft onto its undercarriage from a height in excess of 10 ft. For realism, the 79 actual drop tests included drops with the aircraft 12.8° nose up and 2° banked right. Undercarriage modifications are detailed separately, while the tail-hook parallel mounting beams pick up on modified fuselage frames (Nos 30 and 31) with an associated area of thicker, strengthened skinning. The addition of leading-edge slats necessitated strengthening of the adjacent wing leading edge. Longitudinal members in the forward and rear fuselage are modified for greater strength, and in some areas new materials are used, for improved resistance to stress, corrosion and fractures. Structural changes account for much of the T-45A's 1,000-lb increase in empty weight over the 'vanilla' Hawk. The nose and forward fuselage of the T-45A is US built, but the rear fuselage and wings are built in England.

McDonnell Douglas (BAe) T-45A Goshawk VT-21 'Red Hawks', Training Wing Two, Naval Air Station Kingsville, Texas, 1995

Yaw damper
An integrated full-envelope digital yaw damper was added to the anti-float rudder to improve stability on the final approach, while the aircraft was flying in the turbulent air in the wake of the carrier's superstructure. An aileron rudder interconnect improved low-speed/high-Alpha handling characteristics.

Arrester hook
A modified F/A-18 type arrester hook was installed below the rear fuselage, necessitating some local airframe strengthening around the attachment points.

Colour scheme
The T-45A wears the standard US Navy training colour scheme of white with high-conspicuity orange patches on the nose, wingtips and tail unit.

Airbrakes
The basic Hawk's ventral airbrake would have interfered with the location of an arrester hook, so the decision was taken to relocate it, moving to twin brakes on the fuselage sides. These caused a pitch-down when actuated, and had to be redesigned to minimise this pitching moment. They also had to be redesigned for actuation at speeds of up to 340 kt. In addition, a compensator was designed which limits pitch-up to 0.25 *g* by sensing Mach number and speed brake angle.

Aileron

Flight tests revealed inadequate directional stability, a tendency to Dutch roll and towards excessive adverse yaw. These deficiencies were compensated for by adding a ventral fin to the arrester hook fairing, by designing a no-float rudder, by changing the yaw damper control system, and by adding 6 in (originally 10 in) to the fin height. Aileron deflection has been increased from 12° to 15° and aileron gearing has been changed to improve roll response.

Smurfs

Small lateral fuselage strakes are fitted immediately in front of the tailplane leading edge. These help to offset the effects of flap downwash on the tailplane, also helping to maintain pitch authority with flaps extended and gear retracted.

Flaps

The slot was restored across the full span of the flap on the T-45, but this was only achieved at the cost of greater wing drop at the stall, necessitating a redressing of the wing.

Powerplant

The T-45A is powered by a single Rolls-Royce/Turboméca Adour 871 turbofan. The Adour 861-49 (F405-RR-400) originally specified for the T-45 was a de-rated version of the Adour version used by the Hawk 60, with JPT reduced to prolong engine life to meet naval low life-cycle cost requirements, with a consequent reduction in thrust, from 5,700 lb st (25.4 kN) to 5,450 lb st (26 kN). The more powerful Adour 871 is designated F405-RR-401 in US Navy service, and was adopted from the fourth aircraft to provide extra thrust for hot-and-high operations and faster throttle response on approach. The engine control amplifier is especially 'hardened' to withstand the danger of electromagnetic interference on carrier decks. An extra fuel control system has been added for improved single-engined safety during extended overwater operations. The Adour is exceptionally economical, and gives a fuel burn equivalent to 35 per cent of that of the TA-4J or 55 per cent of that of the T-2. Before the number of T-45s on order dropped to its present level, there was much talk of replacing the Adour with the Garrett F124-GA-100 (a non-afterburning version of the F125 (TFE1042-70) which powers the Taiwanese Ching Kuo). Although Rolls-Royce then had a contract to provide engines for the first 24 aircraft, it was felt that the Garrett engine offered certain advantages, chiefly in its use of newer technology (including a digital fuel control system), its higher thrust rating and its slightly reduced unit price. McDonnell Douglas planned a competition (which was to have included a fly-off) before the Secretary of the Navy directed that the Adour should be used because the reduced number of aircraft being procured did not justify a change.

T-45 Training System

The T-45TS designation covers an entire training system, and not merely the airframe/engine combination. This overall system includes academic classroom and computer material, a variety of simulators and ground-based trainers, a training management system and an integrated logistics support system for all elements of the T-45TS. The original contract called for 302 aircraft, and no less than 32 simulators, with Sperry as prime contractor for the latter.

Wing

Against the advice of BAe, McDonnell Douglas decided to dress the T-45A wing for maximum lift, ignoring the effect on handling characteristics. This led to considerable problems and an extended flight development programme. The T-45A wing thus gained full-span leading-edge slats and new squared-off wingtips. It is understood that the T-45 wing is still less effective than the third-generation wing fitted to BAe-built Hawk 100s and Hawk 200s.

Leading-edge slats

Development of the T-45A's leading-edge slats began with the installation of aerodynamically representative fixed slats in the extended and retracted positions. Actuation of the slats is linked to movement of the trailing edge flaps.

Cockpit

The cockpit of the baseline T-45A was redesigned by McDonnell Douglas to allow the critical instruments to be scanned more readily, but retains most of the same analog instruments. A Smiths Industries mini HUD was added to the front cockpit to allow for the simulation of gun-firing, and to prepare for the possible later addition of a hybrid digital cockpit (the so-called Cockpit 21, scheduled for incorporation in the 73rd production aircraft). Apart from the revised layout, changes to the T-45A cockpit included the provision of a cable-operated emergency landing gear extension system, a new weapons control panel, and an emergency flap extension system using hydraulic pressure from the braking system instead of pressurised gas. Other additions include a standard US Navy-style landing gear selector, a radar altimeter and a tail hook actuator.

Nose gear

The entire nose section is reprofiled to accommodate the new dual-wheel nose undercarriage. This is manufactured by Cleveland Pneumatic, and replaces the Hawk's single small nosewheel with two larger wheels which straddle the catapult shuttle. The nose undercarriage unit incorporates a standard catapult launch bar. The nosewheel doors are sequenced to close after the gear has been extended.

Armament

All Hawks can be fitted with a centreline gun pod, containing a single 30-mm ADEN Mk 4 cannon and 120 rounds of ammunition, or a centreline pylon. Finnish Hawks have a 12.7-mm (0.5-in) VKT machine-gun in the same position. Two underwing pylons are fitted as standard, but most Hawk series can be fitted with four underwing pylons. RAF Hawk T.Mk 1As have provision for underwing Sidewinders, and have the provision (seldom used) for reactivation of the outboard underwing hardpoints. In service they are usually limited to external loads of 1,500 lb (680 kg), carrying CBLS practice bomb carriers or SNEB rocket pods. The uprated Hawk 60 and Hawk 100 can carry up to 3000 kg (6,614 lb), including a wide range of weapons and even including wingtip AAM launch rails.

War role

A January 1983 contract provided for the conversion of 89 Hawks to T.Mk 1A standard, with provision for the carriage of underwing AIM-9L Sidewinder AAMs under the inboard underwing pylons and for the reactivation of the unused outer wing hardpoints. Some 72 of these aircraft were declared to NATO as point-defence aircraft, and for use in mixed fighter force operations with RAF Tornado F.Mk 3s. In such operations, the Tornados would have effectively acted as BVR killers and as mini-AWACS platforms, sending in the small, agile Hawks against close-in targets. The aircraft would have been flown by experienced instructors during wartime, and by the pilots of the 'Red Arrows' aerobatic display team, whose aircraft were all T.Mk 1As. The number of aircraft declared to NATO was reduced to 50 in 1993, as a result of Conservative government defence cuts.

Cannon pod
The detachable pod contains a single ADEN Mk 4 cannon. This can be loaded with training ammunition (ball, Practice Round Mk 4) or high-explosive (Mk 6) or armour-piercing (Mk 1) shells. Muzzle velocity is 790 m (2,592 ft) per second, and rate of fire is 1,200-1,400 rounds per minute. The pod has a removable rear section to allow for the rapid insertion of the 130-round magazine during operational turnarounds. Reloading the cannon pod and both pylons can be achieved in 10.3 minutes. The basic cannon pod fairing serves as the basis for the dye and oil tanks used by the 'Red Arrows' to produce the coloured smoke which is an integral part of the team's displays.

Fuel
Although the Hawk has provision for carrying external fuel tanks of 100- or 130-Imp gal (455- or 591-litre) capacity on its inboard underwing pylons, this option is little used by RAF aircraft, for which the internal fuel capacity of 364 Imp gal (1655 litres) is adequate. This is housed in a single bag tank in the fuselage (183 Imp gal/823 litres), with an integral wing tank accounting for the rest.

Avionics
By comparison with some of its more exotic, attack-roled export brethren, the RAF's Hawks have a relatively primitive avionics fit. Most aircraft have a simple weapons aiming sight, although this is not fitted to some of the T.Mk 1s allocated to the Central Flying School's Hawk squadron. About 90 RAF Hawks have a more advanced GEC-Marconi F.195 weapon sight and camera recorder in both cockpits. All RAF aircraft have a pair of Honeywell RAI-4 4-in (10-cm) remote attitude indicators and a magnetic detector unit, and have GEC-Marconi gyros and inverter, a Smiths-Newark compass system, Sylvania UHF and VHF, Cossor CAT.7000 TACAN, CILS.75/76 ILS localiser/glideslope receiver and marker receiver and IFF/SSR.

British Aerospace Hawk

Inflight-refuelling probe
The Royal Malaysian Air Force specified that its single-seat Hawks should be capable of inflight refuelling (like the new F/A-18 Hornets and MiG-29s) even though the air force currently lacks tanker aircraft. This deficiency will probably be addressed by the conversion of the air force's Lockheed C-130H Hercules transports of No. 14 Squadron. Inflight-refuelling capability has been provided by the simple expedient of plumbing the aircraft to accept a bolt-on, non-retractable inflight-refuelling probe below the starboard windscreen. As the first Mk 208, this aircraft was transferred from Warton to Boscombe Down for clearance trials of its new inflight-refuelling probe. It made inflight refuelling contacts with an RAF VC10 K.Mk 3 while carrying a wide range of external stores, including bombs, drop tanks and wingtip Sidewinders. Omani single-seat Hawks reportedly have provision for the same inflight-refuelling probe.

Nosewheel steering
Most Hawks have a simple castoring nosewheel, and are steered using differential braking. The Malaysian Hawk Mk 108s and Mk 208s have nosewheel steering. This makes manoeuvring on the ground rather easier, but adds to weight, complexity and cost.

Advanced Combat Wing
The Hawk 100 and Hawk 200 are fitted with the so-called 'combat wing', this incorporating double-slotted trailing-edge flaps and a fixed leading edge with slight droop to increase camber. The flaps can be manually selected to perform as combat flaps (at less than one quarter of the usual extension angle) below 350 kt (403 mph, 649 km/h). The stall buffet strips are reduced in size and the leading edge is re-dressed. The original fence level with the flap/aileron intersection is removed, and is replaced by a much smaller fence just inboard from the wingtip, while three similar mini-fences are added to the leading edge inboard, between centre span and wingroot. Behind these, extending out to the wingtip, is a row of 16 vortex generators approximately at quarter-chord. In all, the new wing dressing added 30 per cent to the overall lift coefficient at speeds between Mach 0.2 and 0.6, and adding 50 per cent at Mach 0.8. This extra lift gives a 0.5 *g* increase in turn performance. The advanced combat wing also features wingtip missile launch rails, raising the number of weapons stations to seven and allowing the carriage of four AIM-9 Sidewinders, together with a centreline gun pod and underwing fuel tanks.

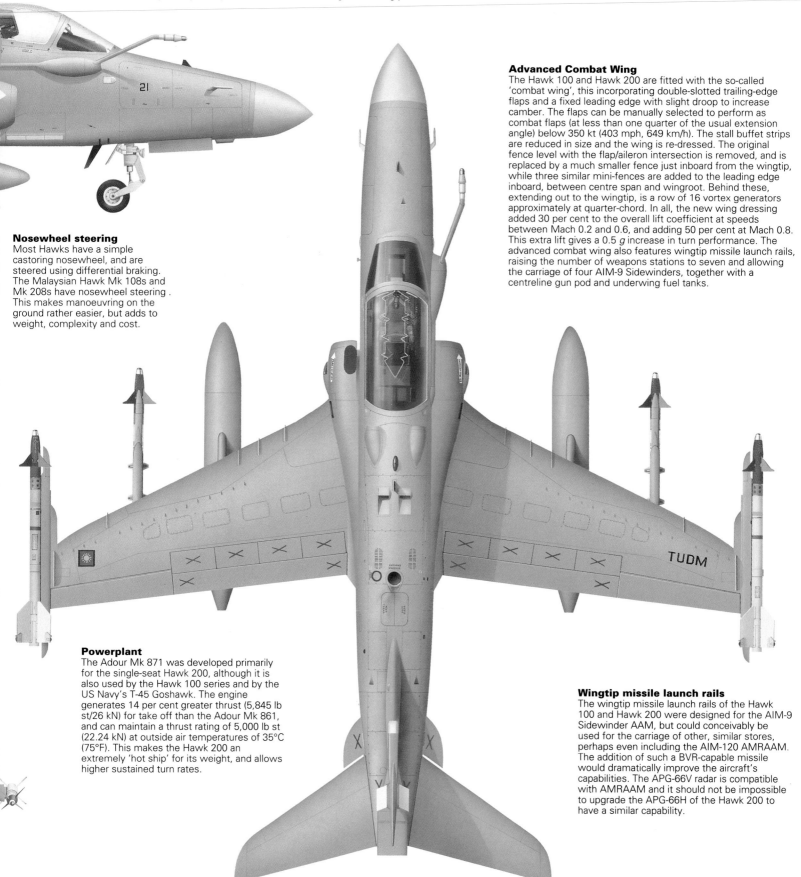

Powerplant
The Adour Mk 871 was developed primarily for the single-seat Hawk 200, although it is also used by the Hawk 100 series and by the US Navy's T-45 Goshawk. The engine generates 14 per cent greater thrust (5,845 lb st/26 kN) for take off than the Adour Mk 861, and can maintain a thrust rating of 5,000 lb st (22.24 kN) at outside air temperatures of 35°C (75°F). This makes the Hawk 200 an extremely 'hot ship' for its weight, and allows higher sustained turn rates.

Wingtip missile launch rails
The wingtip missile launch rails of the Hawk 100 and Hawk 200 were designed for the AIM-9 Sidewinder AAM, but could conceivably be used for the carriage of other, similar stores, perhaps even including the AIM-120 AMRAAM. The addition of such a BVR-capable missile would dramatically improve the aircraft's capabilities. The APG-66V radar is compatible with AMRAAM and it should not be impossible to upgrade the APG-66H of the Hawk 200 to have a similar capability.

Radar warning receiver
All Hawk 100 and Hawk 200 series aircraft are fitted with a fin leading-edge fairing which accommodates the forward hemisphere antenna for the radar warning receiver. On Omani and Abu Dhabi aircraft, this is a GEC-Marcon Sky Guardian 200, but details of the defensive avionics equipment fitted to the Malaysian Hawks remain shadowy.

Chaff/flare dispenser
A chaff/flare dispenser is located in the box-like fairing at the base of the tail fin. *Jane's All the World's Aircraft* state that this is a Vinten Vicon Srs 300 or equivalent, though customers and potential suppliers remain tight-lipped. The dispenser is ideally located, close to the jet pipe and clear of the bulk of the airframe.

Unit markings
This Hawk Mk 208 carries the chess-piece (Knight) insignia of No.3 Flying Training Centre, superimposed on a red white and blue lightning flash. No.9 Squadron's aircraft wear a golden eagle badge in the same position, superimposed on three red lightning bolts.

Formation lights
Low-intensity strip lights (inevitably known as slime lights because of their green colour) are fitted to the fin, rear fuselage and forward fuselage of Malaysian Hawk Mk 108s and Mk 208s. When not in use these appear as simple pale buff strips. Similar formation lights are common on most US-built aircraft types, including the F/A-18s currently being acquired by Malaysia. With its radar and advanced avionics, the Hawk 200 series enjoys a considerable measure of night/all-weather capability.

British Aerospace Hawk Mk 208
No. 3 Flying Training Centre
Royal Malaysian Air Force
Butterworth, Malaysia 1995

The Hawk Mk 208 introduced a number of customer-specified modifications, including the addition of nosewheel steering and a detachable, non-retractable inflight-refuelling probe. This aircraft was the first Hawk Mk 208 for Malaysia, and first flew on 4 April 1994. It left Warton on the first stage of its delivery flight on 25 July 1994. In Malaysian service the Hawk Mk 208 will equip at least one front-line squadron (No. 9, converting from the McDonnell Douglas A-4PTM during early 1995) and will augment Hawk Mk 108s, PC-7s and MB339s with No. 15 Squadron, also known as No. 3 Flying Training Centre. Both of these units were initially based at Kuantan, although No. 3 Flying Training Centre later moved to Butterworth. Both units will have a primary responsibility of providing lead-in training for the new McDonnell Douglas F/A-18D Hornets and MiG-29SD 'Fulcrum-Cs' being procured by Malaysia. It is unlikely that any RMAF pilots will convert directly to the new aircraft types without having completed a tour on the F-5E, A-4 or Hawk 200. The unit is also probably provide training for Hawk pilots from Brunei, likely to be the next Hawk customer. In Malaysian service the Skyhawk served in the ground attack role, but had an important secondary air defence commitment, and could be armed with a wide variety of weapons, including AGM-65 Maverick ASMs and AIM-9 Sidewinder AAMs. The Hawk 208 will fulfil the same roles, using an expanded range of weapons.

Radar
The BAe Hawk 200 is equipped with a powerful multi-mode pulse-Doppler radar in its redesigned nose. This is the Westinghouse AN/APG-66H, derived from the AN/APG-66 fitted to the F-16A/B and further developed for a range of applications, from the Japanese F-4EJ Kai Phantom upgrade to the A-4K Kahu upgrade for the RNZAF. The radar offers 10 air-to-surface modes, including ranging, real beam ground mapping, expanded real beam mapping, Doppler beam sharpening, fixed target tracking and maritime targeting. It also has nine air-to-air modes, with a look-up search range of 35 miles and a look down range of 27.5 miles. The air-to-air modes include useful ACM modes to provide auto-acquisition of manoeuvring targets.

Cockpit
The cockpit of the Hawk 200 has been entirely redesigned to allow operation by a single pilot, with HOTAS controls and new multi-function displays. The pilot sits on a Martin-Baker Mark 10LH zero-zero rocket-powered ejection seat. The seat is mounted high up on the fuselage, allowing an excellent all-round view, even forward over the long nose. The Hawk 200's agility, firepower and handling characteristics make the aircraft an extremely popular pilot's aircraft , and would make its cockpit very much a dream posting for pilots in air forces lucky enough to have ordered the type.

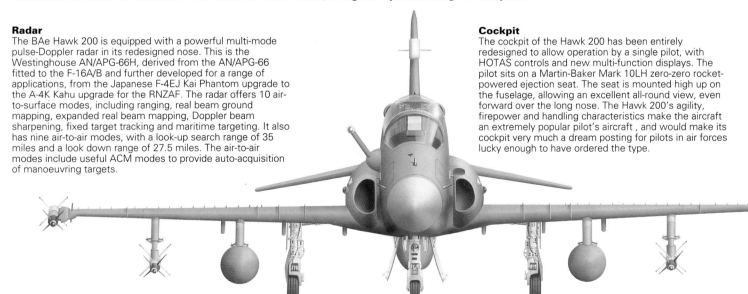

No. 92 Squadron
One of the RAF's premier fighter units, No. 92 'East India' Squadron formed in September 1917, and subsequently flew a variety of scouts over the Western Front. Disbanded in 1919, the unit re-emerged as a Spitfire unit in 1939, participating in the Battles of France and Britain before transferring to North Africa. It supported the Eighth Army throughout its long push through Italy. Postwar, the squadron flew Meteors, Sabres, Hunters and Lightnings in the air defence role, transferring from Leconfield to Geilenkirchen in 1965 with its Lightning F.Mk 2s. A move to Gütersloh followed on 22 January 1968, and the unit moved to Wildenrath on 1 April 1977 when it re-equipped with Phantom FGR.Mk 2s. The end of the Cold War led to a dramatic downscaling of the RAF presence in Germany, and the two Phantom squadrons at RAF Wildenrath were among the first units to disappear. No. 92 Squadron stood down on 30 June 1991, disbanding on 5 July. It was resuscitated as No. 92 (Reserve) Squadron in September 1992, as part of the Chivenor-based No. 7 Flying Training School. The squadron, along with former Phantom partner No. 19 Squadron, was effectively no more than a shadow identity for one of the squadrons of what had been No. 2 TWU, replacing Nos 63 and 151 Squadrons. No. 92 Squadron did not survive the closure of No. 7 FTS in September 1994, although its historical importance will ensure that if a numberplate is needed, No. 92 Squadron may again rise Phoenix-like from the ashes, and there are still reports that it may become the second Eurofighter squadron. No. 92 Squadron adopted its distinctive red and yellow checkers during the 1950s, while the cobra and maple-sprig badge dates back further.

Specification
British Aerospace Hawk T.Mk 1A

Powerplant: one Rolls-Royce/Turboméca Adour Mk 151-01 turbofan rated at 5,200 lb st (23.13 kN) also quoted as 5,340 lb st (23.672 kN); bypass ratio 0.8, SFC 0.7 lb/lb st/hr
Wing span: 30 ft 10 in (9.39 m)
Wing area: 180 sq ft (16.9 m²)
Overall length: 38 ft 11 in (11.85 m)
Height: 13 ft 1 in (4.00 m)
Wheel track: 11 ft 5 in (3.47 m)
Wheel base: 14 ft 9 in (4.5 m)
Empty weight, equipped: 8,013 lb (3635 kg)
Maximum take-off weight: 18,390 lb (8340 kg)
Maximum landing weight: 17,000 lb (7650 kg)
Internal fuel: 2,970 lb (1347 kg), 375 Imp gal (1705 litres)
Maximum external fuel: two 190-Imp gal (860-litre) fuel tanks
Maximum external load: tested up to 6,500 lb (2948 kg)
Maximum level speed: 560 kt IAS (1040 km/h; 646 mph) Mach 0.88 at sea level
Maximum speed (shallow dive): 572 kt IAS (1060 km/h; 658 mph), Mach 1.2 at 3,000 ft (914 m)
Demonstrated Mach No: 1.20 IMN
Service ceiling: 50,000 ft (15240 m)
Maximum endurance: 5 hours 30 minutes
Maximum rate of climb: 9,300 ft (2835 m) per minute
Time to 30,000 ft (9144 m): 6 minutes
Take off roll: 1,600 ft (488 m)
g limit: -4 to +7.5 g (service limit, cleared to 9 g); sustained turn 4.7 g at 1,600 ft (487 m)
Ferry range, internal fuel: 1,300 nm (2400 km; 1,491 miles)
Endurance, internal fuel: 3.5 hours
Ferry range, external fuel: 1,700 nm (3150 km; 1,957 miles)
Endurance, external fuel: 5 hours
Combat radius: 500 nm (930 km; 578 miles) hi-lo-hi with gun, four 1,000-lb bombs and two fuel tanks
Weapon load: up to 6,800 lb (3100 kg) on export versions
Maintainability: 5.6 MMH/FH (RAF demonstrated 4 MMH/FH for first, second and third line); demonstrated turnaround 8.75 min; engine change 1 hr 40 min demonstrated
Life: 6,000 flying hours allowing 11 4g counts and one 6g count per hour

Powerplant
The Hawk is available with a range of versions of the Rolls-Royce Turboméca Adour turbofan. This engine is a non-afterburning version of the engine originally developed for the Anglo-French SEPECAT Jaguar (which was, interestingly, developed to meet the same advanced/weapons training role now fulfilled by the Hawk). The Adour is an exceptionally robust two-shaft turbofan, of modular construction. It has a two-stage fan, a five-stage compressor, an annular combustion chamber with 18 spray fuel nozzles and two igniter plugs, and with single stage low-pressure and high-pressure turbines. The engine has a bypass ratio of between 0.75 and 0.8 and an overall pressure ratio of 11. Specific fuel consumption is 0.74 lb/h/lb st). Assembled in both Britain and France, the engine uses parts from single sources, with Turboméca producing compressors, casings and external pipework. The RAF's Hawks are powered by the 5,200-lb st (23.13-kN) Adour 151-01 engine (although 'Red Arrows' aircraft have the 'tweaked' Adour 151-02). A similar engine, the Adour 851, powered the Hawk 50 series, while the Hawk 60 has the more powerful 5,600-lb st (25.35-kN) Adour 861. The Hawk 100 and 200 Series are powered by the 5,845-lb st (26-kN) Adour 871. Starting is by an integral Microturbo gas turbine starter.

Flying controls
The Hawk has conventional hydraulically actuated ailerons outboard and one-piece all-moving tailplanes, with a mechanically actuated rudder. The small rudder trim tab at the base of the rudder is electrically actuated. The double-slotted trailing-edge flaps inboard are also hydraulically actuated, as is the large airbrake under the rear fuselage, between the fixed ventral fins. All flying controls are fully duplicated in the front and rear cockpits. What look like spoilers or lift dumpers at the leading edge of the flaps are in fact merely access panels. Twin ventral strakes on each side of the airbrake enhance directional stability, while small fences on the outboard part of the wing reduce the tendency of the boundary layer to migrate spanwise across the wing, generating unwelcome induced drag and producing a risk of the wing dropping at the stall.

Specification
British Aerospace Hawk Mk 208

As for Hawk T.Mk 1A except in the following particulars
Powerplant: Rolls-Royce/Turboméca Adour Mk 871 turbofan, with a max sea level ISA thrust of 5,730 lb (25.5 kN)
Wingspan (with missiles): 32 ft 7⅜ in (9.94 m)
Overall length: 37 ft 2½ (11.34 m)
Height: 13 ft 6¾ in (4.133 m)
Empty weight: 9,810 lb (4450 kg)
Maximum take-off weight: 20,062 lb (9100 kg)
Maximum internal fuel: 364 Imp gal (1655 litres), 3,000 lb (1360 kg)
Maximum external load: 7,000 lb (3175 kg)
Maximum level speed: 549 kt (1017 km/h) at sea level
Maximum speed (VNE): 575 kt (1065 km/h); Mach 0.87 at sea level
Maximum speed (VNE): 575 kt (1065 km/h); Mach 1.2 above 17,000 ft (5,180m)
Maximum initial climb: 11,510 ft/min (58.46 m/sec)
Service ceiling: 44,500 ft (15256 m)
Climb to 9150 m (30,000 ft): 7.5 min
Maximum sustained *g*: 5.8
Combat radius: with 7,000 lb (3175 kg) of stores, hi-lo-hi/lo-lo, and 515 kt (955 km/h) dash speed, 104 nm (192 km)
Ferry range, internal fuel: 1,313 nm (2433 km)
Ferry range, two 190-Imp gal (864-litre) tanks: 1,400 nm (2964 km)
Take-off run: 1,800 ft (550 m) SL/ISA, clean
Take-off run at max TOW: 5,400 ft (1645 m)
Landing ground roll: at 9760 lb (4428 kg) landing weight, 2,570 ft (785 m)

Above: The cockpit of the Hawk 200 Series is dominated by a pair of CRT multi-function display screens, with two smaller screens on the left hand side of the cockpit. Miniature conventional analog back-up instruments are located on each side of the central screen. There are few differences between this cockpit and that of the Hawk 100 Series front cockpit. This cockpit is believed to belong to the Hawk 200 RDA, and may not be fully representative of the cockpits of any specific export customer's aircraft.

Left: This neat detachable refuelling probe can be fitted to Malaysian (and reportedly Omani) Hawk 200s. The probe was proved using the aircraft illustrated opposite, which refuelled from a No. 101 Squadron VC10, ZA149. The Hawk was itself then still painted only in primer, and wore the British military serial ZH778. No two-seat Hawks have been adapted to use this refuelling probe, although it could presumably be an option.

Below and below left: The front (left) and rear (right) cockpits of the generic Hawk 100, with ejection seats removed. The rear cockpit has only one CRT multi-function display, and lacks other controls. In place of a HUD it has a HUD repeater screen, with a separate control panel on the right hand side of the main panel. The Hawk's origins as a trainer mean that the occupant of the rear cockpit enjoys an unrivalled view forward over the nose.

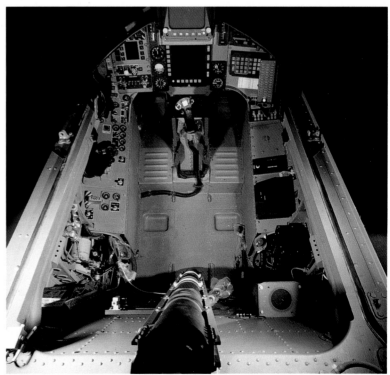

No. 63 Squadron's redecoration of XX255 in matt black during 1991 pre-dated the Longview 2 trials of different Hawk colour schemes. Matt black was found to offer high conspicuity but very poor durability, and a compromise solution of gloss black was eventually adopted. XX255 is seen here in company with a pair of No. 2 TWU's standard Hawks, which also had matt black tailfins.

maximum continuous power. The optimum initial climb is undertaken at 300 kt (556 km/h), the datum changing to M 0.7 with increasing height. Maximum rate of climb is 9,300 ft/min (47.3 m/sec). No. 4 FTS used to climb at 350 kt (649 km/h), giving an initial rate of climb of about 4,000 ft per minute (1220 m).

A comfortable training height of around 30,000 ft (9144 m) is reached in little more than six minutes from brake release. A height of 40,000 ft (12192 m) could be reached in under 10 minutes, using only about 44 lb (200 kg) of fuel. An optimum cruise speed of M=0.69 is achieved at altitude for a very low fuel consumption of about 11 lb/min (5 kg/min), depending on aircraft weight. If a maximum range profile is to be flown, the cruise begins at 42,000 ft (12802 m), drifting up to 46,000 ft (14021 m) as fuel burns off. Ferry range with normal reserves and no external fuel is a remarkable 1,400 nm (2594 km).

In transonic flight, as speed increases past the normal maximum level of M=0.86-0.87 to M=0.88, a progressive light buffet becomes apparent. In the M=0.9-0.92 range some reduction in aileron effectiveness becomes evident. This improves by the time the speed reaches M=0.95, when buffet also disappears, as the wing airflow becomes fully supersonic. No handling difficulties occur up to M=1.2, or 572 kt (1060 km/h), which is the self-limiting maximum achievable speed in a vertical dive from 50,000 ft (15240 m). There is therefore no risk of the student losing control at high Mach numbers. BAe claims that this can be a real hazard in other advanced trainers – "past and present" – as the result of their often unpleasant high-speed handling, thus making the Hawk's full flight envelope available to inexperienced pilots with complete safety, as evidenced by the lack of cockpit placard limitations.

Behaviour is equally benign at the stall. The aircraft stalls at speeds of 75-90 kt (139-167 km/h) in the landing configuration, depending on weight. A natural airframe buffet starting at 14 units of Alpha on the AoA indicator (fitted to all except RAF Hawks) provides adequate warning, becoming progressively more pronounced with further increases in angle of attack. This is accompanied by a small amount of lateral and directional unsteadiness, although with no tendency to depart. The angle of attack finally settles at about 20-22 units with the stick hard back as the Hawk nods into a gentle oscillatory pitch forward. Recovery is immediate on relaxing aft stick pressure, and some lateral control remains. Behaviour is similar in the clean configuration, at speeds of 90-110 kt (167-204 km/h).

Classic spin characteristics can be demonstrated by a standard academic 'full aft stick, full rudder, ailerons neutral' entry from a normal height of 25,000-30,000 ft (7620-9144 m). The aircraft departs at an airspeed comfortably above the straight and level stalling speed at the selected altitude. In this mode, rotation is fairly slow at about four seconds per turn, and rapid recovery follows within one turn simply by centralising the controls. Although spin rates and characteristics vary with different stabilator, rudder and aileron inputs, rotation can always be stopped by simply centralising the rudder, even if full outspin aileron and full aft stick are maintained – a useful safety feature for students.

For aerobatics, the Hawk combines precise and responsive controls with a high level of agility, good stall/departure warning, and unrestricted engine handling throughout the normal flight envelope between +8*g* (limits are +9.2) and -4*g*. The aircraft's low induced drag and specific excess power margin allow sustained low-level turns of 6*g* at 450 kt (834 km/h), and prolonged 8*g* turns with only modest descent rates or speed loss.

Aerobatics and spinning are not without risks, of course, and these are minimised by careful planning and good airmanship. The engine is more likely to surge or flame out, than in 'normal flight', although the Adour has proved remarkably surge-resistant. If the engine does surge or flame out, it can usually be relit easily, but if it does not relight, the aircraft has a good gliding range at its best glide speed of 180 kt (334 km/h).

Low fuel burn allows the Hawk to range further from base than either the Gnat or the Hunter could, even with external tanks, or to undertake long-duration sorties. Alternatively, the Hawk can mount consecutive training sorties without refuelling, speeding turnaround time.

The most usual method of rejoining the circuit is through a visual run in and break. The pilot chooses an initial point 30 seconds out on the extended centreline of the runway in use, descending to 500 ft and running in at 360 kt (667 km/h). About one third of the way down the runway he closes the throttle, extends the airbrake and pulls 4*g* in a hard break upwards and to the left, arriving at the start of the downwind leg at 1,000 ft and, hopefully, with the airspeed reducing to below 200 kt (370 km/h), allowing the pilot to lower the undercarriage and partial flaps. Power is set at about 78 per cent, allowing airspeed to decay further. The pilot runs quickly through his downwind vital actions (lowering the landing gear, setting mid flap, checking brake pressure and crew harnesses, and calculating threshold speed). The 180° final turn is made abeam the runway threshold, using between 45° and 50° angle of bank and entering the turn at about 150 kt (278 km/h). Full flap is selected. The aircraft comes out of the turn at 125-135 kt (232-250 km/h), and the pilot maintains an AoA of 8-10 units down to the flare. This gives an excellent view of the runway from the rear cockpit. The target threshold speed is 110 kt (204 km/h), depending on fuel weight, with a 1 kt addition for every 100 kg over the base weight figure. The light aircraft pilot might be surprised to learn that the Hawk pilot controls his airspeed using the throttle, and his rate of descent with the control column. Ground roll is a typical 2,000 ft (610 m) at normal landing weights, although the Hawk is now cleared for service use to land at the clean maximum training take-off weight of 11,000 lb (4990 kg). Landings have also been demonstrated, presumably fairly gingerly, at a weight of 16,500 lb (7484 kg), carrying full internal fuel and nine 550-lb (250-kg) bombs. This gives the pilot confidence that he can safely go around and land immediately if problems are experienced on take-off or during the climb-out, without having to wait to burn off fuel to get down to landing weight.

Into service at Valley

At Valley, the Hawks began replacing the surviving Gnat T.Mk 1s and 20 or so Hunters, including about a dozen two-seat trainer versions. The first Valley unit to re-equip was Gnat-equipped No. 1 Squadron (the CFS squadron), responsible for instructor training and standardisation. The Hawk then went on to replace the Hawks and Hunters operated for advanced flying training courses, about a year earlier than planned. By October 1979, when re-equipment was complete, the 46 Hawks operating from Valley demonstrated a 36 per cent reduction in defect rates and 32 per cent less maintenance man-hours per flying hour (MMH/FH) compared with the Gnat, and a 70 per cent reduction in defect rate and a 40 per cent reduction in MMH/FH compared with the Hunter. Some criticised the

Hawk for having handling characteristics that were insufficiently challenging, especially by comparison with the Gnat and Hunter, but others felt that this supposed limitation was more than compensated for by the much-reduced operating costs and by the flight safety implications of the instructor's much improved forward view.

Student pilots arrived at Valley with some 175 flying hours (some ex-UAS pilots having amassed up to 150 hours more on the SAL Bulldog) having successfully completed basic training on the mild-mannered and rather sedate Jet Provost (and more recently on the Shorts Tucano). The No. 4 FTS syllabus covered 74 hours and 45 minutes of General Handling (GH), Instrument Flying (IF), low-level navigation and academic (as opposed to tactical) formation flying. This was programmed to last for 18 weeks, following a gruelling two weeks of ground school, the latter being enlivened only by eight simulator sorties. The flying side of the course was neatly divided into two phases, the first

being a CONVEX (conversion exercise) and the second being an applied phase. The CONVEX culminated in a progress check at Exercise 28, and the Instrument Rating Test at Exercise 30. Successful completion of the latter allows the award of a White instrument rating. Wings were awarded at the end of the Valley course, following completion of the 46-exercise applied phase and culminating in the Final Navigation Test (FNT) and Final Handling Test (FHT). The school had two constituent squadrons, each with two intakes (or courses) between six and eight weeks apart. On average, during the late 1980s, about one in five student pilots was 'chopped' at Valley, a relatively low failure rate after the vicious 'weeding out' of student pilots in the basic and elementary stages. Poor performance on three consecutive trips resulted in a pilot being put on review, during which his progress was carefully monitored, and during which he would fly only with the most experienced instructors, perhaps

The 1993 Valley display aircraft was painted gloss black overall, and carried the station badge of a dragon and portcullis on its tailfin. Its roundels were not outlined in white, unlike current black Hawks. The Hawk is an excellent display aircraft, big enough to be easily seen, and agile enough to be entertaining. All RAF Hawks used in the training role are now being repainted gloss black, as they come up for overhaul.

A pair of Hawks wearing the markings of Nos 19 and 92 Squadrons. These units (latterly equipped with Phantom FGR.Mk 2s at RAF Wildenrath in Germany) are among the RAF's oldest and proudest fighter squadrons, with distinguished histories including a magnificent record in the Battle of Britain. On the retirement of the Phantom the unit's identities were saved from oblivion by being assigned to the Hawk training squadrons of No. 7 FTS at Chivenor as de facto shadow designations, replacing Nos 63 and 151 Squadrons. No. 92 Squadron did not survive the amalgamation of the two mirror training schools into a single unit, however, disbanding on 30 September 1994. Rumours suggest that No. 92 Squadron may be the first squadron to form with the new European Fighter Aircraft, presently known as Eurofighter 2000 following changes to meet German political needs.

British Aerospace Hawk

The Hawk T.Mk 1 in plan view, nosed over into a vertical dive. With the adoption of an all-black colour scheme, many within the Hawk community hope to be given the chance to loop 22 in formation (preferably at Farnborough) to equal the record set by No. 111 Squadron in their shiny black Hunters. The Hawk's resemblance to the Hunter is particularly noteworthy in plan view. In RAF service the Hawk has proved a great success, and looks set to enjoy many more years of profitable service.

Opposite page: A formation of four Hawks from No. 4 FTS demonstrates the new gloss black colour scheme, with national insignia thinly outlined in white. Although these freshly painted aircraft do not wear squadron markings such insignia started to reappear almost as soon as aircraft emerged from the paintshop. Formation flying forms a vital element of the training course at RAF Valley.

For the 1994 SBAC air show at Farnborough, black-painted Hawks of No. 4 FTS were decorated with the national flags of the Hawk's overseas customers, and flew a 12-ship formation alongside two BAe demonstrators, a Hawk 100 and a Hawk 200. The aircraft carried BAe's patriotic triangular Union Jack logo on their noses and above one wing. The 12 No. 4 FTS aircraft are seen here lined up at Valley.

being given an extra flying hour or two to help him overcome his problems. If no improvement occurred, the student would then fly with his squadron commander who would decide whether or not to recommend suspension from flying training. If such a recommendation was made, the student pilot would fly with the school's Chief Flying Instructor who would decide whether or not to 'chop' the student.

While replacement of Valley's Gnats and Hunters was clearly the major priority, the Hawk was also scheduled to replace the massive fleet of Hunters in use by the Tactical Weapons Units for what amounted to pre-OCU fighter/ground-attack lead-in training. Weapons would clearly have to be carried to fulfill such a role, and full CA clearance for weapons training was finally achieved in July 1977. This cleared the aircraft to operate at take-off weights of up to 12,750 lb (5783 kg), with a maximum RAF external load of up to 1,500 lb (680 kg) on two underwing and one ventral fuselage station. With or without its ventral gunpod, the Hawk was recleared to a self-limiting diving speed of M=1.2 or a level speed of 550 kt (1019 km/h), and for gun firing at altitudes up to 20,000 ft (6096 m) and in turns of up to 5g. It had also been dived to M=0.9 while carrying two MATRA rocket pods on its underwing pylons. All this occurred some 10 weeks after the Hawk became a British Aerospace product. This resulted from the full absorption of HSA into the newly-formed and initially nationalised BAe group from April 1977.

Hawk variations

Hawk deliveries continued at a rate of about four per month to Nos 1 and 2 Tactical Weapons Units at RAF Brawdy and Chivenor from July 1977. The TWU course built on the advanced phase of the No. 4 FTS course, and aimed at turning the competent fast-jet pilot who emerged

from Valley into a military fast-jet flier. Thus the course encompassed more GH and IF, but with added Cine weave, and tactical formation flying. The student also learned the rudiments of Air Combat Tactics (ACT) and Air Defence (AD) in one-versus-one and two-versus-one sorties. Simulated attack profiles were planned and flown, increasing in difficulty, complexity and realism. Air-to-air and air-to-ground weaponeering was taught, with 10° dive and level deliveries. Eleven further aircraft were delivered to the Central Flying School's Red Arrows formation team at RAF Kemble in August 1979. Early in the Hawk's busy career, the RAF drew up a requirement for a small additional batch as attrition replacements, despite an accident-free record of over 50,000 hours set by the 130 delivered up to early 1980. A £48 million order for another 18 RAF T.Mk 1s was actually announced during a Parliamentary defence debate on 28 April 1980, but the necessary funding was axed in the ensuing moratorium on new defence contracts.

First combat Hawks

In 1977 approval was finally attained for a 15-year programme costing more than £1.5 billion to rebuild UK air defences, which had been seriously run down by successive British governments, Labour and Conservative. Concern had eventually been expressed over the capabilities of British forces to meet their NATO commitments and to provide adequate home defence, particularly against a growing Soviet supersonic manned bomber threat. The RAF's home defence force then comprised five Phantom interceptor squadrons, and two squadrons with ageing BAC Lightnings, though these could be augmented by the RN's remaining Phantoms and growing force of Sea Harriers, and by the various RAF Lightning and Phantom conversion units.

Measures immediately implemented for the reorganisation of UK air defence included $119 million of orders for 1,709 AIM-9L Advanced Sidewinder all-aspect air-to-air missiles, these being intended principally to re-arm the F-4s, which hitherto relied on obsolete AIM-9Gs. The successful use of TWU Hawker Hunters as point-defence fighters during exercises prompted examination of the Hawk as a point defence fighter. Sidewinder installation development started in early 1980 at Kingston, and was also extended to optional activation of outboard pylon fittings, plus replacement of the original non-aerobatic attitude reference system by a Newmark-adapted Lear Siegler 6000S twin gyro platform (later to become standard in the Hawk), which was less likely to 'topple' during manoeuvring. Aerodynamic trials of the Sidewinder-armed Hawk were started on XX160, with first launches in 1980. After resolving potential problems of engine ingestion of the missile plume, a useful firing envelope was approved in May 1983.

This examination resulted in an MoD contract of 31 January 1983 for the conversion of 89 TWU Hawks (also including those aircraft assigned to the Red Arrows) to Hawk T.Mk 1A standards with provision for two AIM-9Ls on their underwing pylons, in addition to their ventral ADEN cannon pod. This was intended to allow the aircraft to operate in supplementary air-to-air roles in times of emergency.

Work on the first T.Mk 1As started at Dunsfold in February 1983, and the 89th, in the form of XX256, was handed back to the RAF on 30 May 1986, some 12 weeks ahead of schedule. Some 72 of the Hawk T.Mk 1As were NATO-declared as part of the RAF's Mixed Fighter Force, and still constitute a valuable low-level low-cost visual interceptor element for point defence, and for emergency use against enemy transport aircraft and helicopters. Mixed fighter force operational tactics have been developed using the Hawk T.Mk 1A in conjunction with radar-equipped Tornado F.Mk 3s.

Three Hawks (XX341-343) from the total RAF order

British Aerospace Hawk

G-HAWK lets rip with two full cans of SNEB rockets. As BAe's demonstrator and development hack, G-HAWK was used to clear a huge range of stores for carriage on the type, and was used to demonstrate the aircraft to countless potential customers. The seventh Hawk built, this aircraft has been heavily used, but remains in regular use with British Aerospace at Warton, currently as a Hawk 100 demonstrator.

One that got away: test pilot Duncan Simpson (in flying kit) and Danny Norman (in raincoat) host a party of senior JASDF and JMSDF officers, and their RAF escorts, during a 1977 visit to Hawker Siddeley at Dunsfold. The Japanese were extremely impressed by the Hawk, but political considerations meant that an indigenous design had to be ordered, as history records. An early T.Mk 1 destined for service with the RAF, still scruffy in primer finish, serves as the backdrop.

were allocated by the MoD's Procurement Executive to replace Hunters at the Empire Test Pilots' School (although Hunters were retained for their unique inverted spinning clearance). In mid-1984 the first of these went to Cranfield for conversion as a variable stability research and demonstration aircraft, following a competitive £2.6 million MoD PE contract.

The Advanced System Training Aircraft (ASTrA) project began with a 1981 feasibility study contracted to the Cranfield College of Aeronautics, by the ETPS, under the direction of David Williams, head of the Flight Systems Laboratory. This was to examine the modification of an ETPS Hawk as a variable stability aircraft to supplement (and eventually replace) the varistab Beagle Basset then in use as an airborne simulator of different aircraft's handling characteristics. The Basset had proved to be an excellent simulator of a wide range of aircraft types, but had been limited by the basic aircraft's rather limited envelope. The varistab Basset could be made to handle like a Lightning, for example, but the realism of the simulation was somewhat limited by the Basset's 200-knot top speed.

The Hawk modification involved installing a discrete fly-by-wire control system with variable artificial feel in the front cockpit, incorporating the latest in microprocessor, display and control system technology. This was linked, via twin digital simulation computers, a flight safety monitor, a system controller and electrically-signalled actuators to the primary flying control surfaces. The rear cockpit retained the Hawk's conventional flying controls (which could be

used to override the controls in the front cockpit) and was intended to be occupied by a safety pilot or instructor.

The rear seat has a multi-function display with a VDU mode and menu options, and from here the ASTrA Hawk can be selected as a configurable airframe to simulate the handling characteristics of specific or invented aircraft, with variable feel, differing degrees of stick motion and response, stick force per g, alpha and g limits. It can also demonstrate in flight the effects of altering the size or shape of the Hawk's aerodynamic surfaces, although the system incorporates fail-safe automatic protection to maintain the aircraft within the limits of its normal flight envelope.

Its primary role at ETPS is to allow student test pilots to experience inflight simulated aircraft with very different stability and handling qualities, over a wide range of flight conditions. The first flight of the ASTrA Hawk took place at Cranfield on 21 August 1986, in the hands of BAe Dunsfold chief test pilot Chris Roberts, and redelivery to the ETPS eventually followed on 13 July 1988.

Further role diversification for the RAF's Hawks came in late 1991, when twelve T.Mk 1As were transferred to replace the Canberras of No. 100 Sqn at Wyton for target towing and silent target duties. For the latter role, the Hawks frequently carry a podded Luneberg lens radar reflector, in order to increase their radar signature. Six Hawk T.Mk 1s were also allocated to No.6 FTS at Finningley to provide fast-jet navigator students with high-speed low-level training after their initial Dominie and Tucano experience. Two Hawk T.Mk 1s were provided to RAE Llanbedr for drone-chase duties, and further aircraft were supplied to the Royal Navy's civilian-operated Fleet Requirements and Air Direction Unit at Yeovilton to replace Hunters used in the target facilities role. More Hawks are held in reserve at St Athan.

One of the few setbacks in the Hawk's otherwise triumphant progress came in the late 1980s, with the discovery of small fatigue cracks in some of the mainplanes of the aircraft assigned to the TWUs. Although the original 6,000-hour fatigue life had included 2,400 hours of low-level operation, the Hawks' built-in recording accelerometers had shown greater-than-anticipated g applications resulting from changes to low-altitude tactical training. T.Mk 1A modifications had also resulted in increased operating weights and training in the air combat role had resulted in more high-g manoeuvres. The damage required the retrofit of redesigned and strengthened mainplanes to the RAF Hawks before they had flown 75 per cent of their design fatigue lives.

In mid-1988, BAe was awarded an MoD contract for the first 85 wing sets, on which work was due to begin at a relatively slow rate in the following year. BAe was awarded a follow-up contract, after competitive tender, for a further 59 wing sets. All these new wings were virtually identical to the original T.Mk 1 wings, apart from slight reinforcement. No attempt was made to incorporate any of the aerodynamic advances incorporated in the next-generation Hawk 100s and 200s, then under development. In 1986, under a separate contract BAe's Hamble factory received an RAF fixed-price contract for the supply of 201 new Hawk windscreens reinforced to withstand the impact of a 1-kg (2.2-lb) bird at speeds of up to 528 kt (978 km/h).

The entire Hawk training syllabus was given a major shake-up in 1992, when the two separate Tactical Weapons Units at Brawdy and Chivenor, and the single Flying Training School at Valley were amalgamated into two units (at Valley and Chivenor). Brawdy was closed and the Strike Command TWUs were effectively disestablished, passing their role to the two new units, which reported to Support Command (and now Personnel and Training Command). Thus No. 4 FTS at Valley and the new No. 7 FTS at Chivenor each used a new, shorter, 102-flying hour seamless syllabus which combined advanced flying and tactical weapons training at a single base, under the so-called mirror image system. The units do not operate separate advanced and tactical squadrons, students instead remaining with their shadow squadron throughout the whole course. Wings are now awarded at the end of the course (effectively after the tactical phase of training). The adoption of the scheme allowed the closure of RAF Brawdy, giving a massive cost saving. Subsequently, the reduced throughput of trainee pilots allowed the disbandment of No. 7 FTS at Chivenor, leaving Valley as the RAF's sole advanced fast jet training base. RAF sources have admitted some disadvantages, primarily that Valley's remoteness from the Pembrey range has necessitated maintaining a detachment at St Athan for air-to-ground weapons training. Valley remains known as No. 4 FTS, although an alternative title is the Advanced Training and Tactical Unit.

Hawk exports begin

From the start of the Hawk project, the aircraft was designed for export especially for the light attack role, albeit with the proviso that such efforts would not impair its ability to meet RAF requirements. Hawker Siddeley was looking for a minimum 30 per cent share of an estimated overseas market for about 3,000 light attack and advanced training aircraft world-wide. With the Alpha Jet as the main competitor in its top-of-the-line category, the export Hawk was initially developed privately, and was marketed at a typical 1976 fly-away cost of around $2.25 million for the standard version (with one centreline and four underwing pylons carrying up to 5,000 lb (2268 kg) of stores over a 280-nm (520-km) combat radius).

From the beginning studies were also made of a single-seat light strike version for potential export customers, with considerably more room for additional fuel and equipment, including advanced avionics and ECM. A full-scale mock-up had been built at Kingston by early 1975. A sales point put forward by HSA at an early stage in its export campaign was that with a claimed maximum low-level speed of around 550 kt (1020 km/h), the Hawk was fast enough to evade the widely-available SA-7 shoulder-launched infantry SAM.

With Australia having faded from the picture as a prospective partner or initial customer for the Hawk, the Middle East was seen as the most likely area in which the export Hawk would find a customer. Egypt was then looking for up to 200 advanced jet trainers and light ground-attack aircraft, and seemed on the brink of signing for 250 Westland Lynx helicopters, to be built mainly by the newly-established Arab Organisation for Industrialisation in Cairo, funded by the Gulf States. After several years of negotiations, however, and another Hawk Middle East demonstration tour in 1978, Egypt was persuaded by Dassault, with French government backing, on 17 September of that year, to contract for the procurement and AOI co-production of up to 160 Alpha Jets.

This order survived the crash two days earlier of Dassault's Alpha Jet demonstrator in Cairo after a double engine failure, probably through a lubrication problem after prolonged inverted flight. Dassault test pilot Jean-Marie Saget did well to crash-land the crippled Alpha Jet and receive only relatively minor injuries, after his senior EAF officer passenger had ejected. Funding shortages, rather than this unfortunately-timed accident, resulted in the eventual EAF order being confined to 30 Alpha Jet MS.1 trainers in 1981, followed a year later by 15 MS.2 ground-attack versions with enhanced nav-attack avionics, and a laser designator.

First customer

With Egypt and Australia out of the picture, it fell to Finland to become the first Hawk export customer, placing an initial £128 million order for 50 T.Mk 51 versions on 30 December 1977, in a 100 per cent reciprocal trade deal. Only the first four Finnish Hawks were to be British-built and only the first two would be assembled and flown by BAe, with Valmet in Finland responsible for some component manufacture and final assembly of the remainder. A few weeks later, on 9 February 1978, a second Hawk export order was announced from "an unspecified African country", which proved to be Kenya. This involved 12 Hawk Mk 52s, which were the first to be equipped with a tail brake parachute. The initial brake chute design was of 7-ft (2.13-m) diameter, although G-HAWK later completed trials with one of 8.5-ft (2.59-m) diameter, giving almost 50 per cent more drag. A third Hawk export order followed on 4 April, with an initial Indonesian air force (TNI-AU) contract for eight Mk 53s (increased to 20 on 18 May 1981), for use in the advanced flying and weapons training roles.

Although generally similar to the RAF Hawks, with similar Adour engines (designated Mk 851 for export), the Mk

Kenyan Hawk Mk. 52s on the break over their home airfield. In 1978 Kenya became the second overseas customer for the Hawk, buying 12 aircraft for use in the advanced training and light strike roles. Kenya's Hawks were the first to be fitted with a braking parachute, this being housed in the box-like fairing above the jet pipe.

A view of the final assembly line for the Hawk at Dunsfold. The nearest aircraft is destined for Zimbabwe, and already wears that country's bird insignia on its tailfin. The small African nation took delivery of an initial batch of eight Hawks in 1982, but one was destroyed and three were damaged by sabotage only twelve days after their arrival. Two of the aircraft had to be returned to the UK for repair, so severe was the damage inflicted. A batch of five further Hawks was delivered in 1992. The aircraft seen here is virtually complete.

This view of a Dubai Air Wing Hawk clearly shows the revised wing dressing applied to the Hawk Mk. 60 series, with three inboard mini-fences. The Mk. 60 also offered greater engine thrust and other improvements. Dubai took delivery of eight Hawks from March 1983, and subsequently received a single attrition replacement.

A Saudi Arabian Hawk, carrying long range fuel tanks, flies over some spectacularly rugged and arid terrain.

50 series incorporated several improvements gained from extensive RAF experience. Stronger wheels, tyres and brakes allowed a 30 per cent higher max take-off weight of 16,200 lb (7348 kg) and a 70 per cent greater disposable load. Bigger drop tanks of 130-Imp gal (591-litre) capacity could be carried on the inner (wet) pair of the five stores pylons, giving a 30 per cent increase in ferry range. Cockpit improvements included a Lear Siegler twin-gyro attitude and heading reference system (AHRS), plus a revised weapons control system incorporating a Ferranti Isis D126R lead-computing gyro sight, and more comprehensive flight instrumentation. Finnish Hawks used an Avimo/SAAB RGS-2 sight. The Finnish aircraft also had provision for a Vinten reconnaissance pod, while the ADEN cannon was replaced by an indigenous 12.7-mm (0.5 in) machine gun in an almost identical underfuselage pod.

A typical export avionics fit, based on the RAF installation, included Sylvania or Collins VHF (20B), Sylvania or Magnavox ARC-164 UHF, Cossor CAT7000 or Collins ARN-118 TACAN and VIR31A VOR/ILS, Cossor 2720 Mk 10A IFF/SSR, CDC five-pylon weapon control system, and Ferranti C121 camera recorder. Vinten Military Systems was also awarded a BAe contract in late 1989 to equip export Hawks with its new Vicon 78 Srs 300 passive countermeasures suite using a microprocessor and MIL-STD1553B databus to interface a chaff and flare dispenser, located in a square box above the tailpipe, directly into the aircraft's radar warning receiver.

These orders entailed increasing Hawk production to six aircraft per month in 1978, as production for the RAF was nearing 100. In fact the 100th aircraft was delivered to the RAF in March 1979. Export deliveries were then able to start, with Kenya becoming the first recipient on 11 April 1980. Indonesia received its first aircraft on 1 September, and Finland followed with delivery of its first Hawk on 16 December.

Engine improvements resulted in a new generation of export versions, known as the 60 series, and Finland, Indonesia and Kenya remained the only customers for the 50 series Hawk. Improvements to the Adour resulted in the RT.172-56 Adour Mk 861, and this engine was used to power the new Hawk variants. The new engine featured a refined LP compressor and a 50°K increase in permissable turbine-inlet temperature (to 1,500°), plus refinements to the engine control system. Together these improvements raised maximum dry thrust to 5,588 lb (24.85 kN), and represented a 21 per cent increase at Mach 0.8. An Adour of this improved standard first flew in G-HAWK on 30 April 1979 and, as the Mk 861, achieved full flight clearance about two years later.

The Mk 861 engine was immediately adopted for installation in all future export Hawks, which became known as the Mk 60 series. The new engine allowed a further increase in maximum take-off weight to 18,960 lb (8600 kg), which marked a 50 per cent improvement over the original T.Mk 1, making it possible to carry a disposable

load of 10,703 lb (4855 kg), a 125 per cent improvement. It also allowed a 65 per cent increase in ferry range to 2,176 nm (4032 km) with the carriage of bigger drop tanks (of 190-Imp gal (860-litre)) capacity. Limiting TOW was 20,062 lb (9100 kg), for a basic mass empty of 8,845 lb (4012 kg). The wing of the 60 series was refined as a result of continuing BAe development work, with changes to the wing dressing (this entailing revision in the size and location of the wing fences), and the provision of a fourth flap position at 37.5°. The improvements gave improved take-off and stalling performance, and improved agility.

Zimbabwe was the first customer for the Hawk 60 series, placing a 9 January 1981 order for eight Mk 61s. These were fitted with the larger-diameter tail parachutes. The Zimbabwe order was followed on 30 June by a contract for eight Mk 61s from the Dubai Air Wing of the United Arab Emirates air force. In subsequent years, five more Mk 60As were ordered by Zimbabwe; 16 Mk 63s and four Mk 63Cs went to Abu Dhabi; 12 Mk 64s were bought by Kuwait; 30 Mk 65s were purchased by Saudi Arabia (this total excluding 20 aircraft recently ordered under Al Yamamah II); 20 Mk 66s were bought by Switzerland; and 20 Mk 67s

were purchased by South Korea, which has requirements for at least 20 more. The latter aircraft featured the extended nose of the Hawk 100, with a small radome for radar. Fifteen surviving Abu Dhabi Hawks were later rebuilt to Mk 63A standards, with several improvements designed for the 100 series, including the newly developed 'combat wing', provision for four underwing stores pylons, wingtip AAM rails and aerodynamic improvements, plus Adour Mk 871 turbofans.

As the RT.172-86C, the Adour Mk 871 was developed between 1984-1987, primarily for the single-seat Hawk

Wearing Zimbabwe's new multi-coloured roundels overwing, a Hawk Mk 60A overflies the Victoria Falls. The brown and green camouflage is unique to Zimbabwean Hawks, and is similar to the colour scheme previously used by the country's Hunters, Vampires and Canberras.

An Abu Dhabi Hawk Mk 63 toting a pair of Rockeye cluster bombs under its outboard underwing pylons. The Hawk is cleared to carry a very wide range of stores, including weapons of US, French and British origin.

British Aerospace Hawk

200, and was intended to provide 14 per cent more thrust (5,845 lb/26 kN) for take-off, but also to maintain over 5,000 lb st (22.24 kN) at outside air temperatures of up to ISA+35°C (275°F). Seven Hawk Mk 60As were ordered from BAe by Finland in December 1990, as attrition replacements, at a cost of £210 million. These aircraft had similar modifications as the improved aircraft for Abu Dhabi, although they retained Adour Mk 861 engines,

Next-generation Hawks

G-HAWK was used by BAe for intensive flight development as well as for customer demonstrations. The staged development of further mainplane improvements during the late 1970s, resulted in the progressive finalisation of the new 'combat wing' required for the long-planned Hawk fighter line. Apart from a return to full-width double-slotted flaps, the new wing incorporated slight fixed leading-edge droop to provide increased camber. The stall-buffet strips were reduced in size, and the large wing fence formerly located forward of the aileron/flap intersection was replaced by a mini-fence just inboard of the wingtip. This was augmented by three small fences outboard of the wing-root, and by a row of 16 vortex generators along the approximate quarter-chord line extending out almost to the wingtips. In all, these changes effected a 30 per cent increase in lift coefficient between Mach 0.2 and 0.6, increasing to nearly 50 per cent at M=0.8 which, with a partial-flap combat manoeuvre setting, conferred a 0.5g increase in turning performance.

These changes eventually became standard throughout the entire Hawk family and provided the improved agility required by the new combat versions, while also reducing stalling speeds close to those achieved by the USN's slatted T-45 version. Seven stores attachment points were provid-

ed, with the addition of wingtip rails for Sidewinder (or similar) air-to-air missiles. The four underwing pylons were also each cleared for the carriage of a dual weapons carrier, allowing the Adour Mk 871-powered combat Hawks to lift, for example, nine 550-lb (250-kg) Mk 82 HE bombs. Weapons options for the Hawk now encompass almost 100 alternative weapons types within the Hawk 100/200's 6,800-lb (3100-kg) maximum external load capability.

Initial production and export Hawks had very limited, training-optimised avionics with beacon-homing navigation systems, but this would clearly not be adequate for frontline versions. BAe had started development of an Enhanced Ground Attack (EGA) version of the Hawk during the early 1980s. This was designed around a range of autonomous nav/attack systems which were intended to allow full exploitation of the aircraft's load-carrying capabilities and performance. These systems were supposed to turn the aircraft into a "a trainer with teeth".

The Hawk 100 programme was launched in 1982, and evolved gradually as new systems were examined and sometimes incorporated. The new variant gained an integrated F-16-type Singer Kearfott SKN 2415 (later BAe LINS 300 ring laser-gyro) INS, and this was linked, via a dual-redundant MIL STD1553B digital databus, with a Smiths 263/1500 HUD/Weapons Aiming Computer, a Smiths radar altimeter, a new stores management system, and an air data sensor for precise low-level navigation and weapons delivery. Provision was also made for a nose-mounted Ferranti 105H laser rangefinder, with overall control of all new systems through hands-on-throttle-and-stick (HOTAS) input buttons.

As these systems were developed in the early 1980s, they were augmented by a Marconi forward-looking infra-red (FLIR) sensor in the nose, this giving a wide-angle image

A Swiss Hawk leads a Vampire T.Mk 55 and a Northrop F-5E Tiger II. Swiss student pilots amass 100 hours on the turboprop-powered PC-7 before they undertake a 115 hour course on the Hawks of Fliegerschule 1 at Emmen before transitioning to the F-5E/F for tactical training at the same base. In service, Swiss Hawks wear a similar colour scheme to that originally applied to the Hawk T.Mk 1s of No. 4 FTS. Some sources have suggested that Switzerland could be a possible customer for the Hawk 100 and 200, to replace its Hunters, which have been retired and replaced in the short term by ill-suited F-5Es.

superimposed on the HUD. Other new equipment included a pair of Smiths 3000 series central colour multi-purpose display screens incorporating electronic flight instrumentation, although these have since replaced by GEC Ferranti units. Provision was also made for night-vision goggles. The Hawk's already extensive range of ordnance was also further widened to include such weapons as the BAe Sea Eagle anti-ship missile, flown on the underfuselage pylon but not further integrated, or up to four Marconi Sting Ray homing torpedoes on the underwing pylons. Most weapons combinations were developed, flown and demonstrated using G-HAWK. Another standard fitting on the Hawk 100/200 was an upper-fin fairing for the radar-warning receiver of defensive sub-systems. BAe Military Aircraft Division's Hawk project chief John Scutt has since confirmed plans for the integration of further precision-guided munitions for air-to-air and air-to-surface use in the Hawk 100/200, including the AGM-65 Maverick.

Single-seat development

Avionics developed for the Hawk 100 were also applied to the single-seat Hawk 200. Launch of the Hawk 200, as "a more affordable fighter" was finally, reluctantly announced by BAe at the September 1984, Farnborough air show, following continued pressure from prospective overseas customers. Such reluctance was understandable since BAe's eventual R&D investment in the Hawk 100 and 200 exceeded £150 million from company funding. This has subsequently been more than returned from the £12 billion or more in export sales achieved by Hawks of all variants by early 1994.

Using the same basic weapons systems avionics as its two-seat predecessor, those of the Hawk 200 were further integrated to cope with the single-pilot workload. A multimode coherent pulse-Doppler radar system (with an antenna width, or diameter of up to 24 in/61 cm) was offered as an optional alternative to FLIR/laser sensors. The aircraft had a completely new single-seat front fuselage, forward of the original aft cockpit bulkhead. Of the available radars, a derivative of the F-16's radar, the powerful Westinghouse APG-66(H) was eventually selected, its installation in the Hawk 200 being made possible by the integration of two previously separate components into a single lightweight signal data processor. Air-to-air and air-to-surface modes included an ability to detect moving targets at sea, and the radar can provide guidance data for the BAe Sea Eagle or for other long-range anti-ship missiles.

The Hawk 200 was originally designed to accommodate a powerful fixed internal armament of two 25-mm versions of the ADEN revolver cannon, with 100 rounds per gun.

This was to have been replaceable by the 27-mm Mauser, 30-mm ADEN or other similar weapons, if required. Only one cannon could be fitted if radar was carried, however. This would have left the centreline pylon free for additional optional stores, up to a revised maximum stores weight with two double stations beneath each wing of 7,700 lb (3500 kg). Provision for the internal cannon was subsequently deleted, however, in favour of the original ventral gun pod, perhaps as a result of the development problems that have bedevilled the 25-mm ADEN.

The Hawk 200 prototype made its maiden flight at Dunsfold on 19 May 1986, in the capable hands of Mike Snelling. This aircraft (ZG200) flew without radar but with the Phase 3 combat wing and Adour 871 engine two days before schedule. Its career was regrettably brief, however, since after only 28 hours of flight test it crashed in a tragic G-LOC (g-induced loss of consciousness) accident at Dunsfold on 2 July killing Jim Hawkins, who was demonstrating the extreme agility of the aircraft. Certainly the Hawk 200 is an incredibly agile aircraft. Using combat flap, the Hawk 200 can sustain turns at greater than 6g, with the speed stabilising at about 320 kt (593 km/h). Its low-level turning performance is quoted as 21°/sec at 420 kt (778 km/h) with two air-to-air missiles on the wing pylons.

Construction of a second Hawk 200 prototype (ZH200) had already been planned, and the crash of the first flight led to its first flight being brought forward ahead of schedule. Chris Roberts took the new aircraft aloft from Dunsfold for 1 hour 27 minutes on 29 April 1987, again without radar fitted. On 21 October a rebuilt G-HAWK (ZA101) joined the Hawk 100/200 test programme, having been fitted with the extended 100-series FLIR/laser-range nose. This increased the overall length to 40.78 ft (12.43 m). BAe's Hawk demonstrator had previously flown with fixed leading-edge droop in September 1986, and the aircraft continued to be involved in the aerodynamic development programme for the Hawk 100 and 200. The aircraft finally flew with the full 'combat wing', including wingtip missile rails, in April 1990, in the hands of Paul Hopkins.

Aerodynamically, at least, it was then virtually fully representative of the Hawk 100, although lacking its full weapons systems avionics, which continued development on electronic ground rigs. Both G-HAWK and the second prototype Hawk 200, were also fitted with lateral fuselage strakes known as 'smurfs' (side-mounted unit root fins) just forward of and below the stabilator leading edge, these also being applied to the T-45A Goshawk. These strakes were found to be necessary following the restoration of the full-width flap slot vanes on the new wing, helping to offset the effects of flap downwash on the tailplane and to maintain

One of four Hawk Mk 63Cs delivered to Abu Dhabi, to complement some 18 Hawk Mk 102s and 16 Mk 63 trainers. The Mk 63C is a unique hybrid, a trainer airframe with the combat wing of the 100 and 200 series. The aircraft thus retains the wingtip AAM hardpoints and has the full high-lift wing dressing of later Hawk variants. This makes it particularly useful for advanced tactical and ACM training, and for weapons training. There have been suggestions that the aircraft were delivered as an incentive for Abu Dhabi to order Tornados from BAe.

The long-serving BAe demonstrator, G-HAWK, has been used to test most Hawk improvements, and flew with the advanced combat wing dressing some time ago, although it then reverted to a standard 50 series wing. The aircraft also received a military serial number in order to allow it to carry and use live weapons. As ZA101 the aircraft was converted to serve as the aerodynamic prototype for the Hawk 100, initially just receiving the new nose shape and increased height tailfin but successively gaining SMURFs, a tail-mounted RWR fairing and the various wing improvements. It was eventually converted to full Hawk 100 standards and continues in use as a development workhorse and demonstrator.

pitch-control authority when the flaps are extended with the undercarriage retracted. They also minimise pitch-change effects when selecting flaps. In effect, the 'smurfs' operate as king-sized vortex generators, re-energising the airflow over the tailplane and preventing the stabilators from being blanked.

Final assembly of all Hawks was moved from Dunsfold to Warton between 1988 and 1991. About 85 per cent of the production programme, including the fuselage, wings, stabilator and vertical fin, remained at BAe's Brough factory on Humberside which is also the Hawk's design and engineering centre. Aerostructures Hamble Ltd in Hampshire continue to manufacture windscreens, cockpit canopies, nose cones and some role equipment.

The first pre-production Hawk 100 (PV102D), also the 359th Hawk, was rolled out at Warton on the occasion of the official reopening of the final assembly line in October 1991, after its two-year transfer from Dunsfold. PV102D was retained by BAe as the Hawk 102D demonstrator, serialled ZJ100. A further extensive programme of systems development was shared with the equally new first production standard single-seat Hawk 200 (ZJ201), also completed at Warton at about the same time. This aircraft made its maiden flight on 13 February 1992 from Warton, flown by Phil Dye. With the Westinghouse APG-66H radar finally installed, together with wingtip missile rails, ZJ201 was initially operated as the radar development aircraft (RDA). It was followed on 29 February by the first two-seat Hawk 102D, which introduced a taller vertical tail, leading-edge crank and a yaw-damper and q-feel added to the powered rudder control circuit.

Combat Hawk exports

An early 1989 order gave Abu Dhabi the status of launch customer for the Hawk 100. It received the first of its 18 new Mk 102s in 1993. Three other countries have so far bought combat versions of the Hawk, each ordering a mix of Hawk 100 and Hawk 200 sub-types. Oman was the launch customer for the Hawk 200 attack/interceptor, placing a contract for 12 Mk 203s on 30 July 1990, and ordering four two-seat Mk 103s at the same time.

The second customer for the Hawk 200 was Malaysia,

which placed a 1.2 billion Ringgit (£400+ million) order on 10 December 1990. This covered the supply of 12 Mk 208s and 10 two-seat Mk 108 advanced systems trainers, plus spares, ammunition, support and training. The first Mk 108 was formally handed over to the RMAF on 25 January 1994, and deliveries of both variants continued through 1994 and 1995. There have been allegations that the Malaysian deal was clinched after Britain signed an aid deal with Malaysia, undertaking to fund and build the Pergau Dam. The deal resulted in a great deal of business for Britain, however, and was as easily defensible as the now common demands for huge offsets for defence contracts. RMAF Hawks incorporate several customer-specified modifications, including the addition of nosewheel steering, while the Mk 208s also have provision for a fixed flight-refuelling probe. This was based on the trial probe installation flown in 1991 on the first pre-production Hawk 200 (ZH200). A similar air-refuelling capability is also planned by Oman for its Hawk Mk 203s. Both air forces will need suitable tanker aircraft, possibly by the installation of drogue pods and associated fuel transfer equipment in their C-130s or in other transport types.

Indonesia, already a Hawk customer, placed a $500 million order during June 1993. This was for eight Hawk Mk 109s and 16 Mk 209s and followed a co-production agreement signed between BAe and IPTN at the 1991 Paris air show. The contract included an option for an additional 20 aircraft, and offset contracts amounted to about 35 per cent of the total cost. Large-scale longer-term TNI-AU requirements for up to 69 Hawk 100/200s have also been mooted by Indonesian ministers, to equip six more squadrons, and $676 million has already been allocated in planned FY1996-97 funding for the first 20 of these.

A number of nations continue to express serious interest in the Hawk, which is seen as the optimum solution to meet a number of firm requirements. Brunei, for example, has been talking for some years about buying eight BAe Hawk 100s and eight 200s. Although no contracts have yet materialised, Malaysian Defence Minister Najib Abdul Razak said in early 1994 that an RMAF Hawk squadron would be based in East Malaysia at Labuan, and would be used for joint training with the adjacent Brunei air force.

Brunei, he added, would receive its Hawks after Malaysia, and the two countries would work together on training their pilots.

In early 1991, BAe signed an MoU with Aerospace Technologies of Australia (AsTA) for co-production of the Hawk 100 if the aircraft was selected to meet an RAAF requirement (Air Force Project 5367) for 35-45 new lead-in fighter trainers. These will replace ageing MB.326Hs by the turn of the century. In Australia, MDC's T-45A

Goshawk is in direct competition with the Hawk 100, for the first time, both aircraft having been short-listed for this contract along with the Aermacchi MB.339FD, Aero L-59, Alenia AMX-T and the Alpha Jet. RFPs are expected later in 1995. A similar competition between the T-45 and the Hawk is likely in Israel to meet a parallel requirement.

India has been looking to buy at least 60 new advanced jet trainers for many years, and has evaluated both the Hawk and the Alpha Jet. So far, the IAF has been unable to

Korea's Hawk Mk 67s are unique in combining the standard 60 series airframe with the extended nose of the 100 series. This nose contains extra avionics, rather than a radar as might be expected by the black tip. These aircraft, seen on a pre-delivery test flight, carry their own national insignia in outline form, to help painters locate them, with tiny RAF roundels superimposed.

In 1988 the Hawk 100 demonstrator (ZA101/G-HAWK) and the Hawk 200 prototype (ZH200) conducted a major sales tour of Asia, visiting Egypt, Saudi Arabia, Bahrain, Dubai, Oman, India, Thailand, Malaysia, Singapore, Indonesia, Australia, and the Philippines. This Hawk 102D later re-visited Australia where it is seen in company with an example of the ageing Aermacchi MB.326 which BAe hope the Hawk will replace. The BAe Hawk 100 would give the RAAF a useful light strike capability to augment the service's Hornets.

The Hawk 100 Series demonstrator and aerodynamic prototype (G-HAWK/ZA101) lets fly with a Bristol Aerospace CRV7 rocket. The centreline pylon carries a test camera pod.

The Hawk 100 demonstrator has worn a variety of colour schemes in its long career. It is seen here with the rear cockpit full of test equipment, and with the wingtip and outboard underwing hardpoints carrying missile launch rails for the AIM-9 Sidewinder IR-homing air-to-air missile.

66 radar, but current reports refer only to further orders for the Mk 65.

Strong interest is also being shown in the Hawk range in the Far East and elsewhere, and the current planned world procurement of around 712 of all variants, including development aircraft, is expected to increase steadily. Equipment, engine and systems improvements are expected to continue well into the next century, maintaining the aircraft's appeal on the export market. Further upgrading of the Adour is being undertaken through the Mk 881 programme. The use of FADEC and component design changes will increase maximum output to around 6,295 lb (28 kN), which is equivalent to 17 per cent more thrust at high ambient temperatures than is produced by the Mk 871. Plans are also already in hand through BAe's New Jet Trainer programme for a Hawk successor for development by about 2010. In the meantime, it has been proposed to install a cropped fan version of the RB.199 developing some 49 kN of thrust. This would allow current performance levels to be retained even with maximum external load under hot and high conditions.

The USN's Hawk programme

American requirements for new training aircraft emerged during the early 1970s. The requirement for a new advanced trainer was initially envisaged as being potentially a joint USAF/USN programme involving 800 aircraft or more. These would be required to replace a wide range of aircraft including the Lockheed T-33, Northrop T-38, Rockwell T-2C and Douglas TA-4J. Replacement of the Buckeye and Skyhawk was a priority by 1975, and the US Navy's VTX undergraduate pilot training programme was formulated around this requirement. It was felt that the existing fleet of 500 T-2C Buckeyes and TA-4J Skyhawks could be replaced by some 300 examples of a single new aircraft type for carrier pilot training and fast-jet fighter/attack conversion. It was envisaged that the new aircraft would enter service during the late 1980s, as one part of the five-component VTX-TS integrated training project. As its VTX-TS (Heavier than air Training aircraft Experimental – Training System) acronym indicated, this was planned to cover complete training systems, including 32 flight simulators, 49 computer-aided instructional aids, four mainframe training integration computers, 200 terminals, training management and integrated logistic support, as well as aircraft. The aim was to produce 600 qualified naval pilots per year.

By adopting the VTX-TS the US Navy was looking for substantial economies in USN training budgets as well as for a new generation training aircraft. It hoped to achieve savings through reductions in flight hours, fuel requirements, maintenance hours and personnel totals. It was hoped that the costs of naval pilot training would be cut by around 48 per cent, with 46 per cent fewer support personnel and 58 per cent reductions in fuel usage.

BAe gave briefings on the Hawk in the USA during 1977 and May 1978, and these may have been influential in shaping the baseline VTX aircraft specifications drawn up by the US Naval Air Development Center soon afterwards. These required stepped tandem seating, a maximum speed of around M=0.8, and a normal take-off weight of about 12,000 lb (5443 kg). One requirement, which was to prove a major factor in the conversion of Hawk to US Navy Goshawk, was for an approach speed below 115 kt (213 km/h).

Although the British aircraft faced plenty of competition from US and foreign contenders, including, inevitably, the Dassault Alpha Jet (Dassault teaming with Lockheed), a teaming agreement soon linked BAe and Douglas Aircraft. This was signed in January 1988 and established that the Kingston-Brough Division of BAe, and the Douglas Aircraft Company of MDC at Long Beach, would co-operate on developing the Hawk to fulfil the VTX requirements.

fund trainer procurement, although the protracted negotiations with BAe and Dassault are expected to reach finalisation over the next few months. Dassault has offered India the entire Alpha Jet programme, with all jigs, tools and support equipment, if required, but the Hawk is believed to be the IAF's preferred aircraft, and finalisation of an order is understood to now be very close. South Africa may also prove a good Hawk export prospect, having at last been released from its previous UN embargo. The newly respectable nation is expected to issue requests for proposals for its New Jet Trainer programme during late 1995, initially involving 20 aircraft.

South Korea has been discussing the purchase of more Hawks, possibly including Hawk 100/200 versions, but the December 1994 go-ahead for the indigenous KTX-II supersonic advanced trainer/light-strike aircraft by the early 2000s could provide strong competition. The local industry team is led by Samsung Aerospace, with Daewoo and Korean Air. In early 1992, BAe said that some of the follow-up Hawks in the second phase of the Al Yamamah II contracts with Saudi Arabia would be Mk 205s with APG-

By then, the Hawk had a proven record of reliability and low life-cycle costs, while BAe and McDonnell Douglas were familiar partners, having demonstrated their capability to jointly develop and produce high-quality, cost-effective and high-performance military aircraft through the successful AV-8 Harrier programme for the USMC. Gordon Hodson – one of the prime instigators of the overall Hawk programme – was appointed as BAe's Project Manager (and later became BAe Project Director).

The British Aerospace/MDC agreement, in which Rolls-Royce and Sperry Systems joined as sub-contractors, did not preclude Douglas Aircraft from continuing its own VTX design studies, and actually allowed for future joint development of a Douglas-derived trainer for service into the 21st century. McDonnell Douglas did submit its own VTX proposal, designated the D-7000. This was, like several other US industry proposals, a twin-turbofan type, of mid-wing layout. Other competitors were headed by the Dassault/Dornier/Lockheed navalised Alpha Jet and included proposals from Aermacchi/Advanced Technology Systems, GD/American Airlines, Grumman/Beech, Gulfstream Aerospace, Northrop/Vought and Rockwell International.

In late 1978, BAe and Dassault/Dornier were both awarded two-month study contracts by the Naval Air Development Center to review the engineering changes required by the Hawk and Alpha Jet for carrier operation. From the six submissions reviewed by NADC in 1980-81, the navalised Hawk proposals emerged on 18 November 1981 as the US Navy's clear preference, on the basis of performance, experience, technology and cost projections. MDC then became prime contractor for the joint VTX-TS submission, with BAe responsible for the airframe, Rolls-Royce for the engine, and Sperry for the simulators.

It was originally envisaged that the navalised Hawk would be powered by an Adour Mk 861-49 turbofan, designated the F405-RR-400 in the US. This offered a miserly specific fuel consumption by comparison with the twin 2,950-lb (13.12-kN) J85-GE-4 turbojets of the T-2C or with the TA-4J's single 8,500 lb (37.81 kN) thrust J52-P6 turbojet. The Adour Mk 861-49 is similar to the Adour 861-56 powerplant used by 60-series export Hawks, although maximum take-off thrust was derated from 5,700 lb (25.35 kN) to 5,450 lb (24.24 kN) in order to meet US Navy engine life requirements.

A Sustaining Engineering contract was signed to complete the project definition phase of the VTX training system, and this was followed, from September 1982, by a pre-FSD phase. This in turn led to full-scale development by mid-1984, this entailing the construction and flight-testing of four 'prototypes' (actually pre-production aircraft, but nevertheless misidentified as YT-45s in some quarters), with an in-service date set at 1988. Physical changes to the standard export Hawk were to be confined to those which were deemed "essential to satisfy carrier suitability standards of the VTX programme", which although extensive were not then considered to be excessively demanding.

Navalisation changes

Perhaps the most important of the changes required to navalise the Hawk were the modifications to the undercarriage. This had to be significantly strengthened in order to meet the 24 ft/sec (7.3 m/sec) vertical velocity limits required for deck-landing operations, while the similarly strengthened Cleveland Pneumatics nose unit also had to be stressed to accommodate a catapult launching bar, and to incorporate power steering for its twin wheels. A deeper nose-section was required to accommodate the T-45's redesigned forward-retracting nosewheel. To allow the longer-stroke A.P. Precision Hydraulics mainwheel units to be stowed within the wing, their attachment points had to be moved outboard by 8 in (20 cm) from rib 6 to rib 7, and the inner fairing doors had to be bulged to cover the thicker wheels.

A modified F/A-18-type arrester hook was installed in the strengthened rear fuselage. This allowed the aircraft to be safely brought to a halt even during power-on, no-flare carrier landings. The hook installation on the underside of the rear fuselage required the removal of the single ventral airbrake and its replacement by twin airbrakes on the sides of the rear fuselage. Airframe reinforcement also included increasing the thickness of the lower wing-skins from 0.16

ZJ100 acts as the primary Hawk 100 demonstrator and test aircraft, although it is officially described as a Hawk Mk 102D. The Hawk 100 is the most likely variant to be ordered by India, South Africa and some of the other potential purchasers of the aircraft. Brunei has signed a Memorandum of Understanding for the Hawk 100, but has yet to finalise an order.

British Aerospace Hawk

in (0.4 cm) to 0.67 in (1.7 cm). The Adour engine casings and other components had to be strengthened to withstand deck-landing impact loads. No wing folding was required for the carrier training role, but the USN called for revised cockpit layouts and avionics installations. Structural changes apart, the US Navy still had to assess whether the standard Hawk's approach and stalling speeds would be satisfactory for deck operation.

On 28 September 1982, McDonnell Douglas received a $15.6 million contract for pre-FSD work on the Hawk-based VTX-TS T-45 aircraft. To speed up service entry, the procurement of 54 land-based T-45Bs (essentially standard Hawks with US cockpits and equipment but without modifications for deck-operation) was to have preceded the main batch of 253 carrier-compatible T-45As. The first flight of the T-45B was planned for 1987, for entry into the USN training programme a year later. The T-45A was due to start flight tests in 1988, and to begin training operations in 1991. Some 50 per cent of T-45 production was to be undertaken in the UK, with all final assembly and flight testing completed in the US, mainly at the Douglas Aircraft Long Beach plant. BAe's workshare also included design and support analysis. Douglas undertook manufacture of the forward fuselage and cockpit, and was responsible for overall systems integration, and contractor support.

In late 1983, the USN abandoned its plans to start procurement of the cheaper T-45B 'dry' Hawks, although this would have allowed advanced training to start some two years before the carrier-equipped or 'wet' T-45A could even be delivered. Congressional deletion of the initial $4.9 million T-45B programme funding was part of a change in naval combat aircraft procurement priorities, but did not result in any appreciable saving in the total number of T-45s required. Procurement of up to 300 carrier-capable T-45As was thus expected to go ahead, within the T-45TS training system. The planned in-service date was advanced by a year to 1990, to help meet an anticipated shortage of USN training aircraft which was expected to become apparent from 1986 onwards.

By early 1988, two of the planned four pre-production T-45s planned had been cancelled as part of continuing US defence economies and the target in-service dates were starting to slip as a direct result. On 26 January 1988, even though the first aircraft had yet to fly, the development programme had reached a stage where the USN felt able to award MDC a $429.4 million initial production contract for the first 12 aircraft and their associated training aids.

The same fiscal year 1988 contract also covered the first of 22 planned operational flight simulators, and the first of 10 instrument flight simulators. These were being supplied by Hughes Simulation System, as were the first set of academic training materials, 16 computer-aided training devices, the first mainframe computer and 60 terminals for the Training Integration System. The contract also included

$64.5 million released by the USN in 1987 for long-lead items for the production and procurement of further aircraft and systems.

A few weeks after the initial USN production contract was placed, the prototype T-45A Goshawk, BuAer. 162787 (c/n 01, known within MDC as T-001 or 'Ship 1'), was formally rolled out under its own power at Douglas Aircraft's Long Beach factory on 16 March 1988, making its initial flight there in the hands of DAC test pilot Fred Hamilton on 16 April. It then went to MDC's test facility at Yuma, to continue its full flight-test and development programme. During November 1988 it was joined there by the second Long Beach-assembled prototype (162788, c/n 01, T-002 'Ship 2'). Both aircraft accumulated 310 hours in 283 flights by mid-1989 before they moved to the US Naval Air Test Center at Patuxent River.

In December 1989, mainly due to the growing civil airliner workload at the Douglas plants in California, design authority for the T-45 was transferred to St Louis from Long Beach, while final assembly was also transferred to St Louis, this time from Palmdale. BAe continued with its share of the design and integrated logistics work and continued to supply all airframe components except the forward fuselage. Planned USN procurement then stood at 300 T-45s, with 96 more required, subject to funding. 12 T-45As had been funded in 1988, and allocations for 24 more T-45s were included in the FY89 and FY90 budgets, with long-lead funding for another 12 approved for FY91. These were to operate from NAS Kingsville, Texas, NAS Chase Field, at Beeville, Texas, and at NAS Meridian, Missouri. McDonnell Douglas were understandably upbeat and optimistic, since they anticipated export orders for the aircraft, and even considered that the USAF could have a potential need for 'at least' 350 similar trainers.

Hawk carrier shortcomings

The first USN evaluation flights of the T-45 were made in November 1988, and the aircraft's handling was severely criticised in a subsequent NATC report. The T-45's shortcomings were listed under five main categories, later known as 'the Big Five'. It was felt that more thrust was needed for operation in high ambient temperatures, and that the engine also needed a faster power response rate for the critical carrier missed approach case. The aircraft was also criticised for its unsatisfactory stalling speed, and for its poor low-speed handling. This latter complaint was a general heading, covering specific slight longitudinal control problems and an unacceptable degree of lateral/directional instability in the approach configuration. The last complaint was of airbrake ineffectiveness, with criticism of the pitch changes which accompanied airbrake actuation. Some of the 'Big Five' problems were inter-dependent, and none proved straightforward to solve. Some of the problems were further complicated by the simultaneous economies

The first Hawk 200 prototype was destined to be short-lived, making its first flight on 19 May 1986, and crashing less than two months later, on 2 July 1986, when test pilot Jim Hawkins experienced **G-LOC** (g induced loss of consciousness) during a display practise. By the time it crashed, ZG200 had exchanged the air defence grey colour scheme seen here for a sinister coat of matt black. Despite this inauspicious start, the Hawk 200 has become an export success, and a capable, agile and cost-effective fighter aircraft for those nations far-sighted enough to buy it.

imposed on US defence spending by successive administrations.

The Adour 861-49 turbofan, for example, had been derated by setting lower JPT limits, in order to achieve a longer life and overhaul interval, and to obtain the lowest possible specific fuel consumption. This worked, but in the T-45 the limited engine was considered gave inadequate initial climb performance in an aborted deck landing or 'bolter'. It was therefore replaced from the fourth development aircraft, by the 'hot-and-high' export Adour 871 (designated F405-401 in the US), which extended the flight-development programme by five months or more. It also contributed to the growing programme costs, and was accompanied by the first of many arguments as to whether the extra expenditure should be paid by the contractor or customer.

Although rated at only 5,845 lb (26 kN) for take-off, the Adour 871 maintains this output at higher temperatures (ISA+15°C (+59°F)), and thus actually delivers about 30 per cent more thrust in the hot and humid southern USA where the T-45 was scheduled to be based. Modifications were made to the Adour 871's fuel control system to reduce acceleration times, and a fast-idle stop was added to the power control lever (PCL). This automatically engages on the approach and provides an improvement of about one second in engine spool-up response time, thereby minimising the danger of students undershooting on the approach. Rolls-Royce/Turboméca began delivering the first Adour 871 (F405-401) engines to MDC in July 1990. Six production Adour 861s delivered previously were uprated to interim F405-400A standards for the flight development programme.

The second Hawk 200 prototype flies chase as John Farley, former Dunsfold Chief Test PIlot, eases the MiG-29UB into the Farnborough circuit. In Malaysia, the Hawk 200 and the MiG-29 are destined to serve side-by-side. The Hawk 200s major inherent weakness as a fighter lies in its lack of thrust, which makes it impossible to sustain very high turn rates.

The most important Hawk 200 prototype made its maiden flight on 13 February 1992, from BAe Warton. This was ZJ201, the so-called Hawk 200RDA (Radar Development Aircraft). It was the first Hawk to carry radar, and was effectively a production-standard single-seater. Despite its significance, the aircraft flew with little fanfare, although a Hawk 200 logo was applied to the nose, on top of the aircraft's primer finish.

Although BAe's Hawk 200 RDA flies in RAF markings, serving Royal Air Force frontline pilots will have to wait until the introduction of the EFA before they can sample the delights of an optimised single-seat fighter aircraft. But the Hawk 200 is far more than a fighter-pilot's toy. With its powerful APG-66 radar and multiple hardpoints, the aircraft represents an excellent basic short range air defence fighter, and would be a remarkably good lead-in trainer pending the arrival of EFA, allowing aircrew to develop new practises, procedures and tactics for use in single-seat, BVR radar-equipped fighters like the Eurofighter.

The basic Hawk's stalling speed and low-speed handling were quite adequate for standard airfield approaches at 130-140 kt (241-259 km/h), and gave target threshold speeds of 110 kt (203 km/h), plus 1 kt (1.85 km/h) extra for each 100 kg (220 lb) of fuel remaining. This was, however, regarded as being quite unsuitable for carrier landing training. It would clearly be necessary to increase the amount of lift being generated by the wing from the basic aircraft's CL_{Max} of 1.5. Restoring the slot across the full span of the flaps achieved the required lift increase but only at the cost of more than 30° wing-drop at the stall. USN T-45 specifications, in fact, required a CL maximum of at least 1.9, which MDC tried to achieve by using fixed leading-edge camber and by redressing the wing. During parallel research and flight tests at Dunsfold, BAe restored the full span of the original double-slotted flaps on XX156, while making its own changes to the wing dressing which showed an increase of over 30 per cent in CL maximum, with the main undercarriage D-doors retracted. This was a remarkable performance from a brief flight development programme, and demonstrated that the USN's lift/stall performance goals could be easily achieved.

T-45 wing development, however, remained completely independent from that of the BAe-built Hawk, and McDonnell Douglas felt it necessary to install complicated full-span hydraulically-retractable leading-edge slats. Actuation of these was linked with trailing-edge flap movement, and gave lift in reserve to allow for future growth in aircraft weight. With an increase from eight to 20 vortex generators on each wing and other aerodynamic changes the T-45 eventually achieved reasonably straight stalls with only a slight wing-drop. At about mid-weights the stall occurred at about 110 kt (204 km/h) and 25° Alpha in clean configuration, and at 93 kt (172 km/h) at 30° with everything down. Natural aerodynamic warning of the approaching stall was artificially (and unnecessarily) augmented by a rudder-pedal shaker, as in other US military aircraft.

The design and development of the extensively-modified wing, which also received squared-off tips, imposed further

delays on the VTX programme despite the addition of a third T-45 to the Patuxent-based test fleet from 10 October 1990. As c/n A-001, BuAer. 163599 ('Ship 3') was the first aircraft to be assembled at Palmdale and on 15 November was soon joined at Patuxent by a fourth T-45 (163600, c/n A-002 'Ship 4'). These were actually the first T-45s from the initial production contract, but since neither incorporated all the planned design changes, they were used to supplement the original two test fleet pre-production T-45s. This effectively made them replacements for the second pair of pre-production test aircraft cancelled several years before.

The slatted wing was first represented on 'Ship One' by incorporating the leading-edge profile of a retracted slat. The next stage was to fit a temporary fixed slat representing the extended position. In this configuration the aircraft carried out low-speed handling and carrier-suitability trials. Other changes to the test aircraft included the installation of the uprated Adour engine, and the incorporation of rebalanced longitudinal control rods. The required low-speed stability was eventually achieved by a combination of a 6-in (15-cm) increase in fin height, a bigger ventral fin, and a 4-in (10-cm) increase in stabilator span. An anti-float rudder with integrated full-envelope digital yaw-damper was also added, and some changes were made to aileron gear ratios, while an automatic aileron/rudder interconnect 'kicked in' at speeds below 217 kt (402 km/h).

Redressing the 'Big Five'

In order to address the last of the original 'Big Five' criticisms, airbrake effectiveness was improved by increasing their travel. Pitch-change was minimised by the addition of an automatic trimmer, interconnected to the stabilator. The T-45 was also fitted from the beginning with the 'smurf' lateral fuselage strakes forward of the stabilator leading edges. These had been found to be necessary on the more recent UK Hawks which also featured restored full flap-span slot vanes. All these modifications naturally incurred more weight penalties, the original design empty weight of 8,756 lb (3972 kg) increasing to about 9,700 lb (4400 kg) in 2787 ('Ship 1'), including test equipment. This was offset to a large extent by the extra thrust of the Adour 871 and by the additional wing lift.

Flight tests of a production standard slatted wing began in September 1990, this being fitted to 'Ship 1' and 'Ship 2'. These demonstrated a CL maximum of 2.1 in the powered approach configuration, with a useful 10 kt (18.5 km/h) reduction in stalling and approach speeds. This allowed the aircraft to meet the USN-specified 115 kt (213 km/h) IAS approach speed requirement. Catapult launch

speeds were reduced to 121 kt (224 km/h), despite the extra weight. Further improvements were incorporated at this stage. Among these were the introduction of a viscous damper in the stabilator control circuit to increase the 'snatch' stick forces per *g*. The nosewheel doors were sequenced to close again after landing-gear extension, to minimise drag in the approach configuration.

After receiving the slatted-wing modifications 'Ship 2' was used for structural and performance trials, while 'Ship 3' was mainly concerned with stores and weapons separation, since the T-45 retains the RAF Hawk's twin inboard underwing hardpoints. No provision is made for the under-fuselage gun in the USN specification, although the T-45's continuously computed impact-point weapons system, combined with the recording video of its Smiths Industries mini head-up display and the rear-cockpit CAI Industries weapons-sight, does allow the Goshawk to be used for simulated gunnery training. After its weapons trials, 'Ship 3' was equipped with an anti-spin parachute and a production Adour F405-401 engine for low-speed handling, stalling and spinning tests, although the Goshawk is not spun in the USN training syllabus.

Static testing

Ground testing of static airframes also continued to precede carrier trials, and included 79 drop tests of the non-flying static test airframe assembled at Long Beach after Ships 3 and 4. These trials simulated landing loads well beyond the specified 25 ft/sec (7.6 m/sec) vertical velocity absorption limit of the undercarriage. These tests were conducted at fuselage attitudes varying between 2.5° nose-down and 13° nose-up, with measured nose gear sink rates of up to 30 ft/sec (9.14 m/sec). Prior to Goshawk sea trials, the four test aircraft had completed more than 500 hours of flying, including about 100 hours in simulated land-based carrier operations.

The big day arrived on 4 December 1991 when 'Ship 1' flew from MCAS Beaufort, North Carolina, to make its first deck-landing aboard the carrier USS *John F. Kennedy* in the Atlantic. The T-45 prototype, with its wing slats then still fixed in the deployed position, also completed its first catapult launch at sea on the same day. The aircraft went on to complete 32 more launches and 33 arrested deck landings in a total of over 12 hours' flying during six carrier deployment periods. In the course of these trials, however, the aircraft unfortunately suffered damage to its rear fuselage and engine tailpipe from a 'tailhook slap', requiring

local reinforcement modifications on production T-45s. A tendency towards intermittent nosewheel oscillations after touch-down was rectified by making a change from analog to digital operation in the dual-gain steering system.

Eighteen months behind schedule, with the T-45TS running about $280 million over budget, the first true production Goshawk finally made its maiden flight. The fifth Goshawk built (BuAer. 163601, c/n A-003) made its 1.1 hour first flight on 16 December 1991. This aircraft was the first St Louis-built T-45 and was regarded by its manufacturers as the first production example of the 268 then required. It was formally handed over to the USN at what was described by MDC as a 'roll-out' ceremony on 23 January 1992. It incorporated all the improvements specified by the USN in 1988 and validated by early 1991, including the slatted square-tipped wings, the extended span stabilators, the increased height fin and the more powerful Adour 871 engine. It also had the improvements which gave better longitudinal control, low-speed stability and the airbrake changes.

Deck trials were concluded on the 60,000-ton USS *Forrestal* (AVT-59), which had replaced the smaller Pensacola-based World War II-era USS *Lexington* as the USN's training carrier for operations in the Gulf of Mexico during early 1992. With a 238 x 130 ft (72.5 x 39.5 m) flight deck, *Forrestal* represented a more representative simulation of

Carrying a target towing pod on the centreline, a Malaysian Hawk Mk 208 poses for the camera. This aircraft wears the Golden Eagle and red lightning flashes insignia of No. 9 Squadron. The new wing dressing applied to the Hawk 100 and Hawk 200 is clearly evident, with the inboard mini-fences, outboard single mini-fence and sixteen vortex generators.

Still in primer finish, and wearing a British military serial in order to allow the carriage of live weapons, the first Malaysian Hawk Mk 208 refuels from an RAF VC10 tanker, to prove the newly designed detachable inflight refuelling probe.

British Aerospace Hawk

operational carriers, and provided more space for a larger number of T-45s undertaking carrier qualification training. Clearance followed extensive operations from *Forrestal*, including night launches and landings. One problem which emerged during catapult trials was an engine compressor surge from steam ingestion during a simulated degraded (i.e. slow) launch. This was cured by increasing the high-pressure bleed during the initial take-off run. This results in a brief 10 per cent power loss until the extra HP bleed is automatically cancelled on catapult release.

Engine options explored

Further complications in the T-45 programme emerged in October 1991 when a Defense Acquisition Board review of the VTX programme directed officials to examine possible alternatives to the Goshawk's Adour engine. The T-45's thrust problems had been rectified by the 1989 selection of the uprated Adour Mk 871, but the engine was regarded as being primitive, and suffered the inherent disadvantage of being NIH (Not Invented Here). USN officials were, however, mystified at being directed to evaluate the relatively untried Garrett TFE1042 (F124-GA100) turbofan as a replacement engine. It was estimated the engine evaluation process would have added about $50 million to the already inflated programme costs, regardless of the eventual decision. There was, however, tremendous support for the proposal in Congress, since it was seen as partly fulfilling the long-standing attempts to increase US industry's share of the T-45 programme.

Garrett's TFE1042 engine was enthusiastically endorsed by an Arizona Congressional delegation, who quoted criticisms of the Adour made in an early USN Operation Evaluation (OPEVAL). Actually a product of the International Turbine Engine Corporation (ITEC), which combines Allied Signal's Garrett Engine Division and elements from Taiwan's Aero Industries Development Centre, the F124 is a non-afterburning version of the TFE1042-70 (F125-GA-100) turbofan produced for the Ching Kuo Indigenous Defensive Fighter. The F124 has a maximum take-off rating of almost 6,300 lb (28 kN) at ISA+3°C (37°F) for a weight of 1,367 lb (620 kg), as against 5,845 lb (26 kN) for the heavier 1,521 lb (690 kg) Adour 871. It also has claimed acceleration times from idling power to full thrust of 3.8 seconds, and from an approach setting to 95 per cent thrust of only 1.1 seconds.

On the other hand, total TF1042 test running, mostly with the afterburning version, stood at only 12,000 hours, while the first F124 test engine had completed only about 100 hours of operation at Garrett's Phoenix facilities, and was being prepared for altitude trials at the Naval Air Propulsion Center in New Jersey. In contrast, well over 2,000 Adours of several versions were then in world-wide service and had accumulated more than 3.6 million flying hours in a wide variety of environments.

Claiming that the F124 was cheaper to buy and to operate than the Adour, Garrett provided technical and cost data to the USN, which received allocations from Congress of $40 million in November 1991, plus $20 million in the following year, for the required evaluation. Garrett's confident early 1992 proposals were based on replacing the T-45's Adour powerplants with F124s from the 97th production Goshawk onwards. This would have involved making initial deliveries of the new production engine in mid-1996. All 286 aircraft then in the planned programme were to have eventually received the Garrett engine either on the line or by retrofit.

Development problems

The US Navy was apalled at the prospect of yet another potential T-45 development problem (since the new engine was largely untried) and at the prospect of having to set up a dual engine logistic support organisation. They steadfastly stonewalled action on the engine replacement proposal, and for three successive years failed to spend the annual appropriations voted for the evaluation by Congress. The Arizona senators and congressmen received a brief boost with President Clinton's inauguration, despite the USN's continued contention that this 'cost-saving' programme would require at least $100 million to implement, and would delay the T-45's service entry still further. In January 1994, the USN was finally allowed to drop the competitive engine evaluation process.

Some benefit did result to the US Navy and industry from this saga, in that it forced Rolls-Royce/Turboméca to transfer F405 Adour final assembly and support from Filton to the French company's Grand Prairie facility in Texas, close to the T-45's main operating base at Kingsville, TX. Hamilton Standard was also awarded a contract from Rolls-Royce in mid-1993 to provide a full-authority digital electronic control (FADEC) system for the Adour 871 (which became the 881) in the T-45 and BAe Hawks, while a durability upgrade was implemented for the Goshawk powerplant in early 1994.

The upgrade was available for all export Adour 871 engines, and aimed at doubling the times between overhauls for the combuster and turbine sections by the use of new materials. This would match the 2,000-hour compressor TBO, and was another part of the prolonged Rolls-Royce/Turboméca effort to combat Allied Signal's Congressional campaign to launch the F124 programme. The 85th aircraft was originally to have been the first with the new engine. Installation of the upgraded Adour is now understood to be planned from the 97th production T-45 (the 95th off the St Louis line), which will be the first Lot 8 FY 1997 aircraft.

Before Goshawks roll off the St.Louis line with the

The T-45 prototype as it was originally rolled-out. The aircaft retains the original Hawk wing, tailplane and short tailfin, but has a strengthened undercarriage, an arrestor hook and SMURFS. Poor low speed characteristics were to result in a plethora of changes to this baseline configuration.

upgraded engine, an even more significant modification will have been incorporated. A prototype Cockpit 21 installation was flown in the 37th production Goshawk (163635) in October 1994, and this is scheduled to become standard in all T-45As from the 73rd production aircraft (165093). During initial development of the VTX system it had been planned to install electronic flight instrumentation systems (EFIS) into the T-45, to match the advanced cockpits of new US Navy combat aircraft. Such plans were abandoned in the early 1980s due to financial constraints. Prospects for a more representative glass cockpit were revived in May 1992, when the USN signed a $73.5 million R&D contract with MDC for a cockpit upgrade.

Design of the new 'Cockpit 21' is now finalised. Two Elbit 5.1-in (13-cm) monochrome multi-function displays, linked by a 1553B digital databus, will replace the current electro-mechanical analog instruments in each of the T-45's twin cockpits. These will take inputs from a Litton LN100G ring-laser gyro INS (with embedded Collins GPS) and will be linked to a new Smiths Industries HUD in the front cockpit. Each of the MFDs will be able to show navigation, mapping, weapon aiming and release data, engine parameters and built-in test displays. Information presented on the HUD can also be displayed on either of the MFDs.

Earlier aircraft will be retrofitted with Cockpit 21 over a three-year period commencing in 1998. The original avionics includes Collins AN/ARN-182 UHF/VHF, plus AN/ARN-144 VOR/ILS, Sierra AN/ARN-136A TACAN, USN-2 standard attitude and heading reference system (SAHS), Bendix/King APX-100 IFF, Honeywell AN/APN-194 radio altimeter, Racal Acoustics stores management system, Teledyne caution/warning system, and Electrodynamics airborne data recorder. Most of this equipment will be retained in the upgraded aircraft.

Goshawk into service

Further delays in the T-45's long development programme resulted from the loss of the first prototype Goshawk in a landing accident at Edwards AFB, CA, on 4 June 1992. After a routine touch-down, the T-45 suddenly

Seen here in what amounts to production configuration, the first T-45A lands aboard USS John F. Kennedy. The taller, square-cut tailfin, leading edge slats, ventral fin and square-cut tailplane and wingtips are immediately apparent. A host of other changes cannot be discerned visually, but were as far-reaching and just as costly.

British Aerospace Hawk

The strengthened undercarriage units of the T-45A. The nose gear (right) is built by Cleveland Pneumatic, and features a Sterer dual gain nosewheel steering system and a standard US Navy catapult launch bar and hold back attachments. The main gear (far right) is made by AP Precision Hydraulics, and features a longer-stroke oleo (necessitating relocation further outboard). It is of levered suspension (trailing arm) configuration and is stressed to withstand the worst case carrier landings.

swung off the runway and struck the concrete foundations of an old building site. Lieutenant Owen P. Honors, of the NAWC's Strike Aircraft Test Directorate, made a successful zero-height low-speed ejection with his Martin-Baker Mk 14 NACES (Naval Aircraft Common Ejection-Seat) rocket-boosted seat, as the right landing gear, noseleg and half the right wing were torn off. The cause of the accident was traced to fouling of the left brake master cylinder, resulting in an uncommanded port brake application. A two-month grounded the remaining prototypes, pending investigation of the accident, and meant an effective loss of one third of the test fleet, a fourth test aircraft having already been handed over to the Navy. This resulted in the development programme slipping by another year, by preventing completion of carrier suitability and high Alpha handling trials. The start of the T-45's two-stage operational evaluation (Phase One OPEVAL), originally due in October 1992 at NAS Kingsville, TX, with four production Goshawks, two flight simulators and a computer-based training integration system, was effectively delayed until October 1993. Inauguration of USN student training was deferred until January 1994.

Carrier suitability trials advanced in early September 1993, when two T-45As completed a total of 112 catapult

The new fuselage mounted airbrake of the T-45A Goshawk is located just below the SMURF, in front of, and just below, the tailplane leading edge. It was necessary to reposition the airbrake of the basic Hawk in order to allow an arrestor hook to be installed. The airbrakes are perforated in order to reduce buffeting when they are actuated.

launchings and a similar number of arrested landings aboard the USS Saratoga. The second phase of operational evaluation was successfully completed after the conclusion of development flight testing. This included the advanced weapons, tactics and carrier-qualification stages of pilot training. Night clearance included coupled instrument approaches for the automatic ILS-type deck-landing system employed by USN fleet carriers.

Goshawk deliveries to the USN finally started in 1992, with 13 of the 19 T-45As produced by mid-1993 going to Advanced Training Squadron VT-21 'Red Hawks' at Kingsville for instructor conversion. Further delays in flight clearance deferred the start of the first 176-hour student pilot course until early 1994, some four or five years behind the original schedules.

Even after delivery from St Louis the first 24 production Goshawks had to undergo an additional 13 modifications by a 200-strong MDC team at Kingsville, prior to USN acceptance. These modifications have since been introduced on the production line and have mostly involved further reinforcement of the undercarriage legs and hook attachment area to cope with unexpected lateral and other loads, but have also include strengthened wing and fuselage attachment points, plus provision of a new tailhook bumper. The USN also plans to add small internal fuel tanks containing an extra 35 US gal (132 litre) between the intake ducts.

The T-45's long gestation period has been accompanied by considerable changes in USN pilot training requirements. There have been successive reductions in the required annual output of trained pilots from the original 530 graduates down to 300 or fewer at the present time. This has been reflected by cuts in the overall T-45 procurement programme to a current target total of 218, plus 16 operational flight simulators and eight instrument trainers, to be distributed between NAS Kingsville and Meridian. Over the same period, the overall T-45 training system cost has escalated from an estimated $5.5 billion in 1982 to $6.3 billion in 1993, including $700 million in R&D. Since total programme cost now covers only 218 aircraft instead of the originally planned 307 aircraft, unit price has risen dramatically. The fly-away unit cost of the T-45A, without its

associated ground training systems, was estimated at $14.5 million by late 1992. Programme totals of as few as 168 T-45s have been mentioned, and further cuts are by no means impossible.

Clearance for full-rate production of the T-45A and its ground-based training system was finally achieved in early 1995, following a successful Milestone III review on 17 January. This confirmed a continuing output of 12 aircraft per year, to supplement the 44 T-45As delivered to NAS Kingsville by early 1995. Some 174 Goshawks will be delivered by 2003.

While some observers (even including USN personnel) have queried whether all the changes demanded in the Hawk for the T-45 programme were essential or worthwhile, the result is arguably the best engineered and advanced trainer currently available, carrying the seal of approval of the US Navy, one of the world's most demanding customers for military aircraft. At the moment, some questions about the T-45 must remain unanswered. Pending lawsuits prompted McDonnell Douglas' lawyers to advise the PR department against answering some of our questions. This is particularly unfortunate, since the aircraft is picking up an excellent reputation from those who really count, the US Navy instructor pilots and engineers experiencing the aircraft at the sharp end. At one time, optimists hoped that the T-45A might be adopted for the US Air Force as well, but the long life remaining on that service's T-38s made any replacement programme impossible, although the T-45 would indisputably offer many advantages over the arguably more glamorous and rather faster Talon. MDC is, however, seeking to cash in on the US Navy's 'recommendation' by winning export sales for the aircraft.

Goshawk for export?

One of the earliest export hopes was the French Aéron-avale, which had a requirement for a carrier trainer to replace its ageing Fouga Magisters and Zéphyrs. Inevitably, a navalised version of the Dassault Alpha Jet was 'dusted off', but the small production run required put the McDonnell Douglas T-45A in a much stronger position. A Goshawk variant known as the T-45(AN), with Cockpit 21 and additional advanced avionics, including HOTAS and a laser rangefinder, was offered to the French navy in 1991-92. The French Navy's tiny requirement for aircrew, now standing at an annual class of 15 student fast jet pilots made procurement of a new trainer seem extremely expensive. In the end, perhaps not least due to the demands of national pride, it was not felt desirable to order a foreign aircraft type, and the decision was taken that Aéronavale pilots would instead be trained on the Goshawk in the USA.

McDonnell Douglas is also actively trying to market the T-45 to several overseas air forces, notably the RAAF, which has an increasingly urgent requirement for 30-40 lead-in fighter trainers. Here the T-45 is up against a number of rival aircraft types, including the 'original' BAe-built Hawk, in the shape of the Hawk 100. This raised the spectre of a British design (the Hawk) actually becoming most successful in the form of its US-built derivative, as has happened with the Harrier and AV-8B Harrier II.

Whatever the outcome of the trainer battle in Australia, it seems probable that the Hawk will continue to pour from its two assembly lines in rain-soaked Warton and in sun-kissed St Louis, providing useful work for two of the world's most successful aircraft companies, and providing new generations of pilots with one of the sweetest-handling jets military aviators have yet seen. And at the end of the day, while the Hawk's docile handling, reliability and economy are vitally important advantages, the fact that it is such sheer fun to fly may be what will win it the all-important tick from future evaluation pilots.

John Fricker

A production Goshawk on finals at NAS Kingsville, Texas. Despite development problems, the T-45A is now in productive service, graduating new naval aviators. It has proved to be a great success, and further improvements, including the new digital cockpit, are eagerly awaited.

Three T-45As in flight, with their arrestor hooks lowered. The acquisition of the Goshawk has given the US Navy a trainer which will be able to train pilots suitable for this latest generation of naval combat aircraft and the next.

Hawk Operators

United Kingdom

Royal Air Force

Following selection of the Hawk on 1 October 1971, the Royal Air Force issued a contract in May 1972 for 176 Hawk trainers, the first of which (XX154) was regarded as a pre-production machine. On 4 November 1976, the first two aircraft acquired by the service were officially handed over to the RAF on their delivery to Valley. These aircraft were those which BAe described as the second two production aircraft, XX162 and XX163. A follow-on order for 18 was "deferred indefinitely" in early 1981 by Minister of Defence John Nott. Build numbers and serials of the RAF production batch of 175 were as follows:

Build number	RAF serial		
02 to 052	XX156 to XX205	141 to 145	XX306 to 310
053 to 102	XX217 to XX266	147 to 150	XX311 to 314
103 to 106	XX278 to XX281	156	XX315
108 to 116	XX282 to 290	158 to 160	XX316 to 318
118/119	XX291/292	162 to 165	XX319 to 322
121/122	XX293/294	167 to 170	XX323 to 326
124/125	XX295/296	172	XX327
127	XX297	174	XX329
129	XX298	176 to 178	XX330 to XX332
131/132	XX299/300	180	XX333
134/135	XX301/302	182/183	XX334/335
137 to 139	XX303 to 305	185 to 199	XX336 to 350
		201 to 203	XX351 to XX353

The final serial batch should have been XX329 to XX363, but a clerical error resulted in them appearing as XX329 to XX353. This was never rectified. In addition to the 'real' aircraft, the RAF also bought two repilcas ('XX162' and 'XX262') for the Exhibition Flight, and BAe also used replicas for its sales work.

Initial deliveries all went to Valley, where 4 FTS began replacement of the Gnat T.Mk 1. The 100th Hawk was delivered to the RAF on 27 March 1979, and the last production aircraft was delivered to No. 151 Sqn on 9 February 1982, although this was followed by XX158 on 17 March, this aircraft having been held back. Losses to the RAF Hawk fleet by early 1995 included XX163 (1/7/93), XX166 (24/6/83), XX180 (7/11/84), XX182 (14/6/89), XX192 (19/9/89), XX197 (13/5/88), XX223 (7/7/86), XX229 (29/7/83), XX241 (16/11/87), XX243 (22/1/88), XX251 (21/3/84), XX257 (31/8/84), XX259 (16/11/87), XX262 (17/5/80), XX279 (30/1/85), XX291 (14/6/89), XX293 (17/4/85), XX297 (3/11/86), XX298 (25/10/84), XX300 (20/10/82), XX305 (28/7/82), XX333 (26/9/85), XX334 (30/9/92), XX336 (29/7/83), XX340 (26/9/85), XX344 (7/1/82), XX347 (9/5/90) and XX353 (29/7/83). At least four of these aircraft continued to serve after having been written off in a ground instructional function.

Through the 1980s the RAF training programme involved student pilots being selected for Group 1 (Fast Jet) training after 76 hours on the Jet Provost T.Mk 3A. They then underwent another 55-57 hours on the Jet Provost T.Mk 5A before transferring to No. 4 FTS for 75 hours (including 24 hours 35 minutes solo) in the Hawk to 'wings' standard. After achieving this milestone, the Valley graduates went to one of two Tactical Weapons Units. Hawks had arrived at these establishments from 1978 and had gradually replaced the venerable Hunter. The four-month TWU course involved learning and practising the tactical principles of fast jet operations in air defence and offensive support roles, including weapons instruction, for which the Hawks used rocket pods, practice bombs and the underfuselage cannon pod. Low-level and formation flying practice took on a distinctly tactical nature. From the TWU, successful students were posted to operational conversion units for conversion to the type of fast jet aircraft to be flown, and then to a front-line squadron.

This, then, was the RAF's fast-jet training hierarchy until 1992, when a considerable upheaval took place under the 'mirror flying training system'. Brawdy was closed, transferring its TWU commitments to Valley, while Chivenor took on the advanced training role in addition to TWU functions.

Thus, the RAF's flying training Hawk T.Mk 1s and T.Mk 1As, as well as its fast jet students, were then distributed between the two centres for 'all through' advanced training, although not without considerable criticism from the instructional establishment over the local incompatibilities of flying and weapons training in terms of airfield and firing range accessibility.

Continuing defence economies, however, coupled with reduced pilot training requirements, ensured that this state of affairs did not last for long, and in December 1993 the government announced that flying at Chivenor would cease on 1 October 1994, in preparation for its closure a year later, and all RAF Hawk training operations would be transferred to Valley. The disbandment of the Chivenor unit released a sizeable number of extra aircraft, which were dispersed to other units, including 4 FTS, while others went into storage at Shawbury. Further training base closures in 1995/96 will result in more aircraft being transferred to Valley, where all of the RAF's training Hawks, including the few CFS aircraft from Scampton and those from Finningley, will be concentrated.

Away from the training programme, the world-famous Red Arrows aerobatic display team took delivery of their all-red Hawks during 1979 to replace Gnat T.Mk 1s. These were pressed into service as eager ambassadors for the RAF and the United Kingdom, a role in which they continue today. In time of war, the Red Arrows would adopt a point defence tasking, and their aircraft were among the 89 Hawks modified to T.Mk 1A standard.

An MoD contract was placed on 31 January 1983 which modified the Hawks of the 'Reds' and the two Tactical Weapons Units to carry AIM-9L Sidewinder AAMs for the second-line defence of RAF installations. Aerodynamic trials with AIM-9s on the inner pylons were started on XX156 and XX160, followed by the first launches from the latter aircraft in 1980. After some queries concerning the effects of the missile smoke trail on the Hawk's Adour engine had been satisfactorily resolved, a useful Sidewinder firing envelope was approved in May 1983.

Work on the first of these T.Mk 1A conversions, each requiring 60-65 workings days, had started at Dunsfold in February 1983, and the last, in the form of XX256, was handed back to the RAF on 30 May 1986, 12 weeks ahead of schedule. Serial numbers of the T.Mk 1As were XX157, 158, 159, 186, 187, 188, 189, 190, 191, 192, 193, 194, 196, 197, 198, 199, 200, 201, 202, 203, 204, 205, 217, 218, 219, 220, 221, 222, 227, 230, 243, 246, 247, 248, 252, 253, 254, 255, 256, 258, 260, 261, 263, 264, 265, 266, 278, 279, 280, 281, 282, 284, 285, 286, 287, 289, 297, 301, 302, 303, 304, 306, 315, 316, 317, 318, 319, 320, 321, 322, 323, 324, 326, 329, 330, 331, 332, 333, 334, 335, 337, 339, 340, 345, 346, 348, 350, 351 and 352.

Some 72 of the Hawk T.Mk 1As were NATO-declared as part of the RAF's Mixed Fighter Force, usually operating in concert with the Tornado F.Mk 3, which could use its Foxhunter radar to vector Hawks for visual attacks. In the air defence role, the T.Mk 1As are flown by either Red Arrows team-members or TWU instructors. They still constitute a valuable low-level low-cost visual interceptor element for RAF airfield defence, and for emergency use against enemy transport aircraft and helicopters, although the declared fighter total dropped from 72 to 50 in 1993.

Hawks destined for the advanced training programme were initially delivered in a scheme of red lower fuselage with white upper fuselage, the wings being light grey with red wingtips. In 1986 two CFS aircraft received an eye-catching scheme for the display season which added dark blue along the top of the aircraft and on the fin, which also featured a Union Jack. Slightly modified for the 1987 season, this scheme (minus Union Jack) was subsequently adopted as standard for 4 FTS aircraft. Those for the TWUs were delivered in

In late 1992 the RAF conducted the Longview 2 trials at Chivenor, to investigate new colour schemes for the Hawk fleet. Trial schemes included a two-tone tactical camouflage, dark grey and matt black. In the event, gloss black was chosen. Note the red scheme showing through under the temporary paint.

Left: This formation depicts the four standard RAF colour schemes which graced Hawks during the early part of their career. Advanced trainers were delivered to Valley in a high-conspicuity red and white scheme with grey wings, while the TWU aircraft had a wraparound dark green/dark grey tactical scheme as befitted their weapons training role. This was subsequently changed to light grey for their secondary air defence role. Finally the Red Arrows aircraft had their patriotic scheme applied in high-gloss paint.

Right: This dark grey scheme, similar to that applied to Lightnings, was tried on the Hawk before adoption of the lighter grey scheme. Note the false canopy painted underneath.

green/grey tactical camouflage, but in late 1983 gained a light grey air defence scheme. Four aircraft (XX194, XX202, XX221 and XX304) received a scheme of dark grey upper sides and light grey lower surfaces, but a lighter scheme was adopted for the fleet. The Hawk paintshop was transferred from St Athan to Brawdy in March 1984. In the early 1990s both schemes were replaced by all-over gloss black, which offered good conspicuity against a wide range of backgrounds. The black scheme is slowly being applied to the fleet as aircraft undergo overhaul, and was first noted on a No. 63 Sqn aircraft in September 1991. In December 1992 the Longview 2 trials pitched a matt black aircraft against a two-tone

camouflaged example and one wearing dark grey. None of these alternatives was adopted. Most aircraft originally wore the three digits of their serial as identifying marks on the fin, although those originally assigned to the TWU had a three-digit running sequentially from '100'. Now that the majority of Hawks are assigned to a Reserve Squadron, aircraft commonly wear two-letter squadron codes.

Ongoing overhauls and disparate flying hours from airframe to airframe have resulted in a constant state of flux regarding unit allocations of individual aircraft. Aircraft held in storage are periodically retrieved to replace high-time aircraft in the active fleet.

Central Flying School (No. 19(R) Sqn), RAF Valley

Headquartered at RAF Scampton, the Central Flying School provides instructor training and devises training programmes. Its aircraft are usually detached away from Scampton, to bases where the same type of aircraft is the primary type. Not surprisingly, the first six Hawks to go to 4 FTS at Valley were actually assigned to the school's No. 1 Squadron, which also constituted the CFS detachment. The CFS has maintained Hawks at the Anglesey base ever since, although a handful also flew from the HQ at Scampton. The aircraft usually wear the CFS badge on the fin or intake sides.

On 1 October 1994, the CFS Valley detachment assumed the identity of No. 19 (Reserve) Squadron, taking the numberplate from the disbanding 7 FTS unit at Chivenor, as well as some extra aircraft released by the deactivation. In early 1995 19 aircraft were on charge, mostly coded in the 'Px' range as befits their new-found squadron status. Scampton is due to close in 1996, with any Hawks there being permanently based at Valley, while other CFS types are being dispersed to other Personnel and Training Command bases. Aircraft are adopting the gloss black scheme as they go through overhaul.

Above: Originating with the CFS display aircraft, this scheme was introduced in 1987, with two-letter codes adopted later. This aircraft was lost on the Valley runway in July 1993.

Left: The pennant of the Central Flying School was worn on the fin or intake sides.

Below: Grey CFS aircraft introduced the two-letter code in the 'Px' range.

Above: For the 1986 display season, this smart scheme was applied to two CFS aircraft. It was refined for the next year's show circuit.

Below: The CFS detachment at Valley now operates as No. 19(R) Sqn, and wears the dolphin badge of the famous fighter unit.

Hawk Operators

No. 4 Flying Training School (Nos 74(R)/208(R)/234(R) Sqns), RAF Valley

The red and white Hawks of 4 FTS were a familiar sight in North Wales throughout the late 1970s and 1980s, before different schemes were adopted. Hunters and Gnats wore the same scheme before them.

Above: Until 'shadow' squadrons were adopted, 4 FTS aircraft wore the unit's Egyptian badge on the fin, with the last three of the serial for individual aircraft identification purposes.

As noted previously, Hawks arrived at Valley to replace the Gnat T.Mk 1s of No. 4 FTS in late 1976, although these were assigned to the CFS detachment (No. 1 Squadron). The school's advanced training units, Nos 2 and 3 Training Squadrons, began to operate the Hawk in early 1977. The unit built up rapidly to an establishment of over 60 aircraft.

Valley's operations remained largely unchanged through the 1980s, but in August 1992 1 TWU at Brawdy was closed, and its tactical training taskings transferred to Valley under the 'mirror' training scheme. On 1 October that year No. 3 Squadron was officially assigned the numberplate of the UK's last Phantom fighter squadron to become No. 74 (Reserve) Squadron. One month later, on 1 November, No. 2 Squadron became No. 234 (Reserve) Squadron, this number having come from one of Brawdy's Hawk squadrons.

Further change came on 31 March 1994, when No. 234(R) became No. 208(R) Sqn. This switch was made to keep alive the traditions of the RAF's most famous ex-RNAS squadron, which ceased Buccaneer operations on the same day.

Having carried the famous 4 FTS badge of a palm tree and pyramid (signifying the unit's establishment at Abu Sueir in Egypt) for many years, the newly-organised squadrons began applying their traditional markings. No. 74 adopted the tiger stripe and a tiger's head on the fin, while No. 208 applied its blue and yellow pennant and the single winged eye on the tail. Earlier No. 234 had carried its winged dragon over as a tail marking. Two-letter codes in the range 'Tx' were applied to No. 74 aircraft, while No. 208 wears 'Dx' codes. The legends '2 Sqn' and '3 Sqn' appeared on the tails of some aircraft, and various display schemes were applied. In early 1995 each squadron was operating 22 aircraft, having gained some extra airframes from the disbandment of 7 FTS.

Within two days of the deactivation of 7

Left: The proximity of Snowdonia gives 4 FTS students an introduction to mountain flying. The Relief Landing Ground at nearby Mona was heavily used to reduce congestion in Valley's circuit.

No. 208(R) Sqn is one of two current 4 FTS squadrons. The Welsh legend on this aircraft was applied for one day only in July 1994 to mark Valley's association with a local school, which has 'adopted' one of the Hawks.

Prior to becoming No. 208(R) Sqn, one of the two advanced training squadrons at Valley carried the dragon badge of No. 234(R) Sqn on the fin. This unit had been the first of the TWU 'shadow' squadrons.

Above: One of the RAF's best-known fighter squadrons, No. 74, is now an advanced training unit at Valley. Naturally the tiger traditions are kept to the fore.

FTS, Valley Hawks arrived on 3 October 1994 for the first weapons training detachment to Chivenor, in order to use the Pembrey ranges in South Wales previously used by the Brawdy TWU. 4 FTS maintained a Hawk Support Flight at Chivenor to support aircraft while on detachment. On 17 March 1995 the final two Hawks left Chivenor, and the training detachment moved to St Athan.

A standard grey No. 74(R) Hawk partners the Valley display aircraft during a training sortie in 1994.

No. 6 Flying Training School, RAF Finningley

No. 6 FTS is the RAF's multi-engine and navigator training unit, providing courses on Jetstreams for the former and Dominies and Tucanos for the latter. Six Hawk T.Mk 1s were allocated to No. 6 FTS to provide fast-jet navigator students with high-speed low-level training after initial Tucano experience, this number having since risen to 12. The first (XX173 and XX295) arrived on 10 September 1992 to replace Jet Provost T.Mk 5s in this role, the Hawk proving infinitely better as its tandem seating, performance and manoeuvrability are far closer to operational jets. On 14 August 1993 Hawks joined Jet Provosts for a 'dying swan' formation to mark the Jet Provost's retirement. Two of the Hawks, XX168 and XX169, have also been used at No. 6 FTS by the RAF's Joint Forward Air Control Training and Standards Unit, and carry the JFACSTU badge on the fin. The training of forward air controllers had previously been undertaken at Brawdy, using Hawks, and earlier Jet Provost T.Mk 4s. With the pending closure of No. 6 FTS, all Finningley's Hawks are expected to transfer to Valley.

Most 6 FTS aircraft wear the unit's crest on the intake (above), but two are adorned with the JFACSTU badge on the fin for forward air controller training. This badge, consisting of an eagle over an anchor and rifle, highlights the joint-service nature of the unit's work. 6 FTS is due to deactivate, with the Hawks moving to Valley.

Hawk Operators

No. 7 Flying Training School (Nos 19(R)/63(R)/92(R)/151(R) Sqns), RAF Chivenor

On 1 April 1992, No. 2 TWU was redesignated as No. 7 FTS, previously a Jet Provost/Tucano basic training unit at Church Fenton. This came about under the 'mirror flying training system', with the deletion of the specialised tactical training units in favour of a joint advanced/tactical syllabus. The Chivenor Hawk unit took 50 per cent of Valley's advanced training roles and added these to its tactical training functions.

After No. 2 TWU became No. 7 FTS, the two shadow squadrons (Nos 63 and 151) assumed the identities of the two disbanding RAF Germany Phantom squadrons, Nos 19 and 92, which had ceased F-4 flying in January 1992 and July 1991 respectively. This did not occur officially until 1 September 1992, although both No. 19 and No. 92 aircraft were seen the previous month alongside those of Nos 63 and 151. The activation date was highly significant to both new squadrons, who held a memorable beer-call to mark the date 1/9/92 1992. Aircraft were repainted in the light blue/white check and dolphin badge of No. 19(R) Sqn, or the red/yellow check and cobra badge of No. 92(R) Sqn. No. 19's aircraft carried the 'last three' on the fin while the sister squadron had single-letter codes.

Between 1 April and 1 September 1992, Nos 63 and 151 Sqns continued their role as Chivenor's 'shadow' units. This machine, wearing No. 63's logo on the fin, was the display mount for the 1992 season.

Ongoing defence cuts, and their effect on pilot training requirements, resulted in the December 1993 government announcement that flying at Chivenor would cease on 1 October 1994, in preparation for its closure a year later. All further training would be accomplished at Valley. The disbandment parade involved a 10-ship airfield attack by Hawks and a diamond-nine flypast.

No. 92(R) Sqn disbanded at Chivenor on 30 September 1994, although most of its Hawks went on to Valley. The numberplate of 19 fared better, being assigned to the CFS detachment at Valley (4 FTS No. 1 Squadron). Hawk activity did not cease from Chivenor for, after the deactivation of 7 FTS, Valley immediately began sending weapon training detachments, and a sizeable ground force remained. These detachments ended in March 1995.

Two of the smartest Hawk schemes were those applied specially to a No. 19 Sqn aircraft (above) and one from No. 92 (left) during 1994. The two squadrons had been paired since 1961, moving to Germany in 1965 to fly Lightnings from Gutersloh. Fighter operations ceased at RAF Wildenrath in 1992, after operating the Phantom FGR.Mk 2 on air defence duty for 2 ATAF over northern Germany since 1976 (No. 19) and 1977 (No. 92).

Below: Upon taking up the new squadron markings, 2 TWU aircraft continued to be marked with the 'last-three' for one squadron and single-letter codes for the other. No. 19's dolphin badge commemorates the unit being the first to operate the Sopwith Dolphin, while No. 92's maple leaf and cobra signify that it was a Canadian squadron during World War I, and was one of the East India 'gift' squadrons in World War II.

No. 1 Tactical Weapons Unit (Nos 79(R)/234(R) Sqns), RAF Brawdy

When the first two Hawks (XX187 and XX190) arrived at RAF Brawdy on 2 December 1977, the resident unit was known as the Tactical Weapons Unit. It operated Hunter F.Mk 6/FGA.Mk 9/T.Mk 7s in the tactical training role, and had a few Jet Provost T.Mk 4s for the training of forward air controllers. The unit was assigned three 'shadow' squadron identities, Nos 63 and 234 for the regular tactical training units, and No. 79, which trained weapons instructors and provided short refresher courses for officers returning to flying status from desk jobs.

During the first half of 1978, the Hawks were used for familiarisation, standards formulisation and instructor training duties. No. 234 Sqn was chosen as the first to convert to the Hawk to begin training, and its diagonally-aligned red/black checkerboard appeared on Hawks from May 1978. The TWU was redesignated as No. 1 TWU on 31 July 1978, in preparation for the creation of a new unit, No. 2 TWU, at Lossiemouth. Thirty Hunters were dispatched from Brawdy to the Scottish base in September to form the equipment of 2 TWU, creating space at Brawdy for the steadily arriving Hawks, the number of which rose to over 40 of which about 30 were 'on line' at any one time. All were delivered in a green/grey tactical camouflage scheme and individual aircraft were painted with the 'last three' on the fin.

In 1980 the Lossiemouth Hunters returned to Brawdy and 2 TWU moved to Chivenor to begin its conversion to the Hawk. The Hunters were consolidated within Brawdy's second 'shadow' squadron, No. 79, and were used on short refresher courses until finally retired in 1985. No. 79 also operated the Jet Provosts, and its famous white bar with red arrows marking was finally applied to a Hawk in October 1981. This unit began using the Hawk for tactical training soon after, and the type slowly assumed the roles of the Hunter and Jet Provost, although the latter type was still on charge as late as 1988.

In addition to their tactical training tasks, the Brawdy Hawks were also given a point defence war role, to be flown by instructors, and most of the aircraft underwent the T.Mk 1A conversion which enabled them to carry AIM-9L Sidewinders. Under this scheme the Hawks would have deployed to other RAF airfields to provide short-range visual defence for those bases. In line with their war role, the Hawks changed from tactical camouflage to air defence grey. Different markings began to be seen, the squadrons adding their badges to the fin (a salamander leaping from flames for No. 79 and a rampant, winged, fire-breathing dragon for No. 234). For the 1987 display season a 1 TWU Hawk was painted with a yellow stripe running from the nose, along the fuselage and then sweeping up the tail. A dragon in low-visibility paint later appeared on the fins of the aircraft representing the Brawdy station badge.

Below: When the original TWU badge of a crossed sword and torch was taken back by 229 OCU for use on it Tornados, 1 TWU adopted the Brawdy station badge, which was worn on the fin and nose.

Above: When delivered to Brawdy, the first Hawks were adorned with the badge of the Tactical Weapons Unit.

Above: TWU aircraft initially carried a three-digit code in the '100' range. This aircraft is fitted with early AIM-9s on trial launcher rails.

Below: No. 234 Sqn was the first TWU 'shadow' to form. In the early days it acted as the Standards squadron for the TWU.

Right: The 1987 display season was handled by 1 TWU, this No. 79 Sqn aircraft receiving a yellow stripe along the fuselage and a yellow diagonal 'V' under the wings.

In the remorseless economies imposed on the RAF since the early 1990s, RAF Brawdy was closed in August 1992, and its tactical and weapons training commitments, along with several aircraft, were transferred to 4 FTS at Valley. A 16-ship formation flew over various Welsh sites on 26 August, and it was left to XX348 to perform the final 1 TWU sortie the following day. XX302 was the last aircraft out of Brawdy, not leaving until 23 November.

When the MoD was faced with closing either Brawdy or Chivenor, the Welsh base was the obvious candidate as it had always suffered from weather problems, notably fog.

Below: Flown by instructors, TWU Hawks were tasked with an air defence mission, working in concert with the Tornado F.Mk 3.

Hawk Operators

No. 2 Tactical Weapons Unit (Nos 63(R)/151(R) Sqns), RAF Chivenor

As noted in the 1 TWU heading, 2 TWU was formed by the transferral of 30 Hunters from Brawdy to Lossiemouth in 1978. This incarnation was short-lived, for the unit moved south to RAF Chivenor to begin conversion to the Hawk. The Devon base had been the subject of a major 1970s rebuilding programme to prepare it for the Hawk's arrival. No. 63 Sqn flew its last Hunter course from May 1979, and was chosen to be Chivenor's first Hawk squadron. The first six aircraft were XX219, 246, 247, 256, 282 and 286, and the unit commenced Hawk operations on 7 August 1980, although 2 TWU did not officially convert to the Hawk until 1 April 1981. Some two months before, the first Hawk had been noted wearing the marks of Chivenor's second 'shadow' squadron, No. 151. No. 63 Sqn applied its black/yellow checkerboard either side of the fuselage roundel, and painted the 'last three' on the fin. No.151 applied its traditional Cross of St Andrew markings, while issuing single-letter codes as individual identifiers. The unit officially formed in September, by which time Chivenor had 47 Hawks on strength. During the year Hawk XX278 was used for target-towing duties. On 20 October 1982, 2 TWU suffered its most unusual aircraft loss when XX300 of No.151 Sqn lost power on final approach to Chivenor. The pilot ejected, but the aircraft managed to land itself on the runway, although it was damaged beyond repair during the ensuing overrun.

Chivenor received the first and second 'Barley Grey' aircraft, although the first, XX282, had a much darker upper surface than the second, XX200, which arrived on 21 November 1983. The lighter scheme was adopted fleetwide. As with 1 TWU, the change from tactical camouflage to 'Barley Grey' was followed by a variation in markings. Toward the end of the 2 TWU careers, Hawks picked up black fins upon which was superimposed the squadron badge – No. 63 featured a hand holding a battleaxe, while No. 151 applied an owl landing on a seax. In late 1991 these markings were carried over to the all-black scheme, which appeared on No. 63 Sqn Hawk XX255 in December.

As part of the changes introduced by the 'mirror' scheme, No. 2 TWU took on half of Valley's advanced training tasking on 1 April 1992, becoming 7 FTS in the process. At the same time the parent organisation changed from Strike Command to Support Command (now restyled as Personnel and Training Command).

Right: No. 2 TWU applied black fins to its aircraft in the late 1980s, with squadron badges. No. 63's axe signifies leading into battle, in line with the unit's motto of 'Follow us to find the enemy'. No. 151's owl represents night-fighting and the seax the county of Essex, where the squadron was initially formed.

Above: An early formation of No. 63 Sqn aircraft. This unit had formerly flown Hunters at RAF Lossiemouth as part of 2 TWU prior to the move to Chivenor.

Above: Before inheriting the traditions of No. 151 Sqn, the unit was known as 1 Sqn/2 TWU, its aircraft carrying no marks apart from the huge single-letter code. In early 1981 the St Andrew's cross of No. 151 began to appear on 1 Sqn aircraft.

Right: During 1987 this T.Mk 1 was on loan to 2 TWU. While it retained the standard 4 FTS colour scheme, full No. 151 Sqn markings were applied. It carries a centreline cannon pod, not normally fitted to the T.Mk 1s employed on advanced training tasks.

Above: XX255 was the RAF's first all-black Hawk, finished in matt in late 1991 with No. 63 Sqn marks.

Left: At least twice in their career No. 151 Sqn staged a formation with the tailcodes spelling CHIVENOR, the first featuring camouflaged aircraft. These grey examples are seen over Lundy Island in April 1992.

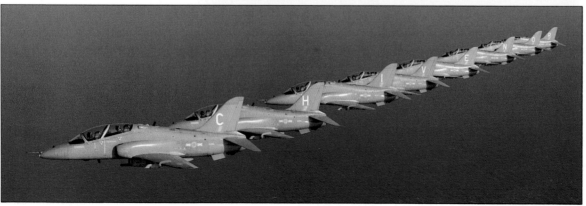

No. 100 Squadron, RAF Wyton/RAF Finningley

Role diversification for the RAF Hawk came on 6 September 1991, when six Mk 1s and six Mk 1As (starting with Mk 1A XX195 from No. 2 TWU and XX247 from No. 1 TWU) began replacing chaff-dispensing Canberra PR.Mk 7s and a radar calibration E.Mk 15 of No. 100 Sqn at Wyton for target towing and facilities tasks. The squadron's last Canberra sortie was mounted on 20 December 1991. No. 100 Sqn was transferred in 1993 to Finningley, and in early 1995 had seven T.Mk 1s and nine T.Mk 1As, coded in the 'Cx' range. These often carry a Luneberg lens to enhance their radar cross-section when acting as intercept targets. Markings consist of variations on the No. 100 Sqn badge of a skull and cross bones, and the unit's traditional blue/yellow check pennant. Its most celebrated squadron member was Flt Lt Rory Underwood, England's Rugby Union winger. With the impending closure of Finningley, No. 100 Sqn is due to move to RAF Leeming.

Above: The origins of the skull and crossbones badge of No. 100 Sqn remain obscure, but the use of the insignia dates back to World War I, when the unit was established with FE.2s as the RAF's first night bombing squadron.

A surfeit of Hawks caused by the reduction in pilot training requirements allowed No. 100 Sqn to adopt the type for target facilities work, replacing Canberras (above). Most wear the grey scheme, but in 1993 one wore its old Valley scheme (left) while two received colours for the 1993 75th anniversary of the RAF (below).

Hawk Operators

Red Arrows, RAF Scampton

The Red Arrows national aerobatic display team, then based at RAF Kemble in Gloucestershire, and led by Squadron Leader Brian Hoskins, received the first of their nine initial Hawks, comprising XX251, 252, 253, 257, 259, 260, 262, 264 and 266, on 17 August 1979. XX251 came from Boscombe Down where the Red Arrows modifications had been certificated. Prior to their delivery, the Red Arrows borrowed XX175, XX233 and XX244 from 4 FTS for familiarisation from April 1979. Red Arrows aircraft were converted for display use at BAe's Bitteswell factory, from which XX266 was the last delivered on 15 November 1979. Two more followed later as reserves. The 'Reds' flew their last Gnat display on 16 September 1979, appropriately at Valley, the Hawks being ready for the 1980 display season. XX262 became the first RAF Hawk loss on 17 May 1980 in a low-flying accident at Brighton, when the aircraft struck the mast of a yacht during a seafront display.

Apart from their special high-gloss red and white colour scheme, the 'Red Arrows' aircraft carry a ventral fuselage tank filled with diesel oil and red and blue dyes, ducted to three outlets above the jet-pipe for injection into the exhaust efflux when required for coloured smoke trail generation. The 'Red Arrow' aircraft were also fitted with Adour 151X engines with a fuel accelerator system for improved throttle response during formation aerobatics, and were later modified to Mk 1A standards to operate with AIM-9H/L Sidewinder AAMs for war emergency roles.

In addition to their heavy commitments on the UK air display schedule, the Red Arrows also undertook several high-profile tours, including two to the United States (1983 and 1993), the Middle East (1985), Far East (1986) and the former Soviet Union (1990). The latter trip involved routing out through Sweden and displays in both Russia and the Ukraine, before returning through Hungary and Germany.

Having operated from RAF Scampton for several years, the 'Red Arrows' were expected to move to Marham following an MoD announcement in late 1994 of the planned closure of the former base. In early 1995, the team was operating seven T.Mk 1As and five T.Mk 1s, including one on long-term loan from the CFS.

Above: During pre-season work-up the 'Reds' often borrow aircraft from the CFS. This black example (with grey rudder) carries the red-coloured dye tank under the belly.

Below: Little publicised is the war role of the Red Arrows. Several of the team's aircraft are T.Mk 1As, and can be rapidly fitted with cannon and Sidewinders.

Below: The 'Synchro Pair' is one of the highlights of any Red Arrows display. Routines vary from year to year to keep the crowds entertained.

St Athan Station Flight, RAF St Athan

As the RAF's main fast-jet maintenance facility, St Athan performs overhaul work on Harrier, Hawk, Jaguar and Tornado. Some aircraft are also stored at the facility. In order to ferry St Athan pilots to/from front-line bases to collect or deliver aircraft for overhaul, the Station Flight operates a pair of Hawks (XX172 and XX184). One of these is painted with a large Welsh dragon along the fuselage and up the fin.

Flagship of the Welsh air force, this St Athan 'hack' is a regular sight around the country, ferrying pilots from the maintenance unit.

One of two Hawks assigned to the St Athan Station Flight, XX184 briefly wore a Welsh dragon on the fin.

Royal Navy

Fleet Requirements and Direction Unit, RNAS Yeovilton

In May 1994, seven ex-RAF Hawks formerly operated by No. 4 FTS at Valley began replacing the Royal Navy's last single-seat Hunter GA.Mk 11s and two-seat T.Mk 8C/Ms operating with the Fleet Requirements and Aircraft Direction Unit at RNAS Yeovilton. FRADU is a civilian-operated unit, managed since 1983 by Flight Refuelling Aviation (now part of Cobham PLC) Aircraft Operating Division. The role of the unit is to provide target facilities to the Royal Navy surface fleet, including the simulation of sea-skimming anti-ship missiles. Delivered in their standard red, white and blue RAF training finish, the FRADU Hawk T.Mk 1s comprised XX175 (to be coded 861), XX242/Y (865), XX245 (866), XX311 (867), XX183 (868), XX165 (869) and XX234/DV

(872). FRADU's first T.Mk 1As (XX322 and XX337) arrived on 17 October 1994, both ex-No. 92 Sqn machines. Like the RAF's Hawks, the FRADU machines were scheduled for repainting in an overall gloss-black scheme and in 1995 began to pick up 'Royal Navy' titles. They were also expected to be modified to have additional wing stations to carry mission pods for electronic warfare training as well as external fuel tanks for increased low-level operating range in the target-facilities role. The unit is expected to move to Culdrose.

Photographed from a Cobham Group Falcon 20, this ex-Valley Hawk is now assigned to FRADU. Aircraft are expected to gain codes.

Ministry of Defence (Director-General Test & Evaluation)

Aeroplane and Armament Evaluation Establishment, A&AEE Boscombe Down

As the UK's principal aircraft test establishment, the A&AEE got its hands on the Hawk at an early stage. XX157, XX159 and XX160 operated from Boscombe in the early trials. After initial testing was completed, the A&AEE retained one aircraft (XX156) for ongoing trials work, including two months of cold weather trials at CFB Cold Lake in early 1978. This aircraft became something of a 'Cinderella', with regular transferrals between the A&AEE, RAE and manufacturer. In 1986 it was at

Dunsfold and then RAE Llanbedr. It returned to Boscombe for a while, before going back to Dunsfold to test the wing of the T-45. Another spell with the A&AEE ended in 1993 when it was transferred to the DRA at Bedford.

Seen during a sales tour with BAe, XX156 was regularly used by the A&AEE, wearing this two-tone TWU-style camouflage.

Defence Research Agency – Aerospace Division, A&AEE Boscombe Down

Previously known as the Royal Aerospace Establishment, and Royal Aircraft Establishment before that, the DRA operated from several bases on defence-related research tasks. XX344 was assigned to RAE Bedford but was written off on 7 January 1982 while landing on the Bedford runway. The airframe survived to be used for ground instruction, initially with the Battle Damage Repair Flight at Abingdon, and then with the DRA/IAM at Farnborough. The test fleet 'Cinderella' Hawk T.Mk 1 (XX156) was transferred from the A&AEE to then-RAE Bedford in 1993 for trials. On 25 March 1994, all DRA flying work was concentrated alongside the A&AEE at Boscombe, the Hawk returning to its former home from Bedford on the same day. The newly-concentrated DRA was organised into three units: fast-jet, rotary-wing and flying laboratory, with the Hawk naturally part of the former.

Resplendent in the 'raspberry ripple' scheme, Bedford's first Hawk was XX344, the last in a batch of four for test purposes. It crashed in 1982, but has since provided service as a ground test airframe.

Test and Evaluation Establishment, TEE Llanbedr

Seen carrying the badge of the RAE, this Hawk is now assigned to the TEE at Llanbedr. The marks on the fin are for photo-calibration.

Two ex-Valley Hawk T.Mk 1s (XX154 and XX160) are assigned to the Test and Evaluation Establishment (formerly part of the DRA organisation), and based at TEE Llanbedr on the Welsh coast. Hawk XX170 was also temporarily used by the unit, and during the mid-1980s the ubiquitous XX156 also operated from the Welsh base, then under the jurisdiction of the RAE. This facility is concerned primarily with air-to-air weaponry, and consequently operates drones and other unmanned targets. The two Hawks operate at present on chase duties during missile tests, but reports suggest that at least one may be converted to radio-controlled drone status in the future, albeit retaining manned-flight capability.

Hawk Operators

Empire Test Pilots School, A&AEE Boscombe Down

Hawks have operated for over a decade with the Empire Test Pilots' School at A&AEE Boscombe Down, under the control of the Defence Ministry Procurement Executive (now DGT&E). The first of three Hawk T.Mk 1s (XX341, 342 and 343) was received by ETPS in mid-1981, and these were fitted with special test instrumentation, including a modular data acquisition system (MODAS) for recording various performance and handling parameters from test exercises flown during the 10-month course. The first aircraft was converted at Cranfield to become the T.1 ASTRA, with variable-stability flight control software to enable it to simulate the handling of a wide range of aircraft types. The aircraft retains a standard Hawk control system (in the rear cockpit), which can be re-engaged by the safety pilot/instructor.

XX341 was converted by the Cranfield Institute of Technology to ASTRA standard, with variable-stability.

The ETPS trains test pilots using a variety of aircraft. Two of its three Hawks (XX342 and XX343) are used for general fast-jet handling training.

Institute of Aviation Medicine, A&AEE Boscombe Down

Following the retirement of Hunter T.Mk 8s and the single Hunter T.Mk 12, the Institute of Aviation Medicine was provided with Hawk XX327. This was used for the investigation of the physiological and psychological effects on aircrew of all aspects of flight, and other related subjects such as cockpit design. An early production Hawk (XX162) was later assigned to the unit, together with a Jaguar T.Mk 2 (ZB615). Long based at RAE/DRA Farnborough, the unit subsequently took up residence at Boscombe Down in 1994 following the closure of the DRA facilities at Farnborough.

Much of the IAM's work is concerned with the effects of high-speed, high-g flight on aircrew. Two Hawks are assigned as low-cost vehicles for providing the kind of flying experienced daily by operational crews.

British Aerospace

The manufacturer has retained several Hawks for its own use, with the twin aims of sales demonstration and product development. The seventh Hawk from the production line was retained as the company's first demonstrator, registered ZA101 for weapons trials and G-HAWK for demonstration purposes. Designated as a T.Mk 50, it undertook many export sales tours, including two to the United States in 1981 and 1983, the latter in a major flag-waving exercise in conjunction with the Red Arrows and Tornado GR.Mk 1s. It was subsequently modified to Hawk Mk 100 standard, in which it first flew on 21 October 1987. Trials aircraft XX156 also had two spells with British Aerospace. In the second, in 1988, it was fitted with BAe's own version of the T-45 wing, with vastly increased lift coefficient.

Company-funded single-seat development culminated in the first flight of Hawk Mk 200 prototype ZG200 on 19 May 1986. This aircraft was lost in tragic circumstances on 23 July after just 28 hours of flight. It was replaced by ZH200.

When the production line was at Dunsfold the BAe aircraft operated from there, but have since moved with the line to Warton. In early 1995 BAe had five aircraft for test work. The ever-faithful G-HAWK (ZA101) is still on charge in Mk 100 configuration, partnered by ZJ100, a Mk 102. Single-seat aircraft comprise ZH200 and ZJ201, the latter designated Mk 201RDA and in use as a radar development aircraft for the APG-66H. Finally T.Mk 1A XX204 arrived from Chivenor in late 1994 to swell the BAe fleet.

Above: Known as a Hawk Mk 102D, ZJ100 is one of two Mk 100 trials aircraft.

Left: Much Hawk development work has been accomplished with ZA101, seen in company with ZH200.

Right: ZJ201 is the Hawk 200 radar development aircraft.

Overseas customers

A combination of good handling, excellent performance and solid product support has made the Hawk one of Britain's great export successes of recent times. Finland was the first to order the type, but it was Kenya which took first delivery. By 1995 the following nations had signed up for the Hawk, arranged in order of contract signature:

Customer	First ordered	First delivery	Variants
Finland	December 1977	December 1980	Mk 51, Mk 51A
Kenya	February 1978	April 1980	Mk 52
Indonesia	April 1978	September 1980	Mk 53. Mk 109, Mk 209
Zimbabwe	January 1981	July 1982	Mk 60, Mk 60A
Dubai	June 1981	March 1983	Mk 61
Abu Dhabi	January 1983	October 1984	Mk 63, Mk 63A, Mk 63C
Kuwait	October 1983	November 1985	Mk 64
Saudi Arabia	February 1986	October 1987	Mk 65, Mk 65A
Switzerland	October 1987	November 1989	Mk 66
United States	January 1988	December 1992	T-45A
Oman	July 1990	December 1993	Mk 103, Mk 203
Malaysia	December 1990	January 1994	Mk 108, Mk 208
Korea (South)	July 1991	June 1993	Mk 67

In addition to their build numbers and locally applied serials, many of the export Hawks also carried MoD and B-class serials, which are listed under the relevant entries. By law any aircraft engaged in the live-firing of weapons in the United Kingdom has to carry an MoD serial, which accounted for several further Hawk identities. Since the production line moved to Warton, all Hawks have carried MoD serials. The application of construction and build numbers is the subject of some confusion. On some aircraft after 241 the build number of the centre or rear fuselage component differed from that of the front section, while the construction number sequence was also part-critical rather than completed airframe-critical. The normally-accepted numbers are quoted here. Subsequently, a simplified build number was adopted, prefixed by a two-letter code indicating the customer and type.

Additional interest for the Hawk came from Australia and Egypt early in the programme. The Mk 62 designator was assigned to Venezuela, which ordered 24 but was forced to cancel on cost grounds. Other nations identified with the type include Sweden (Mk 100s), Singapore Mk 100/200s) and the Philippines, which was looking for 12 Mk 100/200s in the early 1990s. An order by Iraq for Mk 100/200s was embargoed by the UK government. Brunei signed a Memorandum of Understanding for 16 Hawk Mk 100s in 1990, but this sale

For the 1994 Farnborough show, BAe borrowed 12 Hawks from the RAF to join two of its own development aircraft (Mks 100 and 200) in being applied with the flags of the customer nations.

has not been finalised. Announcements of an assembly line in Malaysia, and a joint training effort between the two nations would suggest that Brunei's aircraft will eventually be from the IPTN line. For the future BAe is looking closely at India, Israel and Australia. In the latter pair of potential customers the British industry will most likely face stiff competiton from McDonnell Douglas offering their own version of the T-45 Goshawk. If Australia selects the Hawk, it will be assembled by ASTA under a 1991 agreement with BAe.

Abu Dhabi
Abu Dhabi Air Force

Flying Training School, Maqatra

In the late 1970s, the United Arab Emirates issued a requirement for up to 30 advanced trainers, for which 24 Dassault/Dornier Alpha Jets were originally favoured. The Abu Dhabi air force, also known as Western Air Command of the UAEAF, followed Dubai's (Central Air Command) lead in ordering 16 Adour 861-powered Hawk Mk 63s. The order was placed on 2 January 1983, priced at about $180 million, including spares and technical support. Delivery of this first batch of aircraft took place between 5 October 1984 and May 1985.

Initial build number	ADAF serial
270	1001
271	1002
274	1003
276	1004
278	1005
281	1006
282	1007
283	1008
242	1009
243	1010
268	1011
256	1012
269	1013
273	1014
291	1015
295	1016

ADAF 1005 briefly wore the MoD serial ZE471 and 1014 wore ZE472 for weapons trials in the UK prior to delivery. The Hawks are operated on advanced instruction and weapons training at the ADAF Flying Training School, which was established at Maqatra in April 1982 with initial deliveries of 24 Pilatus PC-7 basic turboprop trainers.

Successful Hawk operation in desert conditions led to a further order in early 1989 for another 18 from British Aerospace, although this time for the new Adour 871-engined 100 series version in combat configuration. These were to feature wingtip AIM-9 Sidewinder air-to-air missile rails, radar warning receivers and revised wing aerodynamics for improved performance and agility. The ADAF's Hawk

Mk 102s were purchased for both lead-in fighter training and close-support roles, and their £100 million plus procurement contract was accompanied by an order for BAe to upgrade the ADAF's remaining 15 Hawk T.Mk 63s with some Series 100 features.

These included the new 'combat wing', with leading-edge droop, four stores stations and tip-mounted missile rails, plus uprated Adour Mk 871 engines. Lacking the Srs 100's advanced nav/attack systems, these hybrid T.Mk 63As are nevertheless highly capable, especially in the weapons training role. BAe had completed the first two ADAF Hawk Mk 63A conversions at Brough and Warton by October 1991, after which the company supervised the installation of component kits on the remaining Hawk Mk 63s at Al Dhafra.

From early 1993 the Abu Dhabi's second Hawk batch began to fly from Warton, and were delivered by the end of 1994. Details of these Mk 102s is presented below.

Build number	Temporary MoD serial	ADAF serial
364/AT001	ZH621	1051
365/AT002	ZH622	1052
372/AT003	ZH623	1053
373/AT004	ZH624	1054
375/AT005	ZH625	1055
376/AT006	ZH626	1056
379/AT007	ZH627	1057
380/AT008	ZH628	1058
384/AT009	ZH629	1059
385/AT010	ZH634	1060
389/AT011	ZH635	1061
390/AT012	ZH636	1062
394/AT013	ZH637	1063
396/AT014	ZH638	1064
401/AT015	ZH639	1065
404/AT016	ZH640	1066
406/AT017	ZH641	1067
407/AT018	ZH642	1068

Four further trainer aircraft were subsequently acquired from BAe under the designation Mk 63C. These are similar to the Mk 63A, with combat wing and leading-edge droop. These were delivered in 1995.

Build number	Temporary MoD serial	ADAF serial
3C001	ZH817	1017
3C002	ZH818	1018
3C003	ZH819	1019
3C004	ZH820	1020

Below: Abu Dhabi's first batch of Hawks comprised 16 Mk 63s, powered by the uprated Adour 861 engine.

Above: This aircraft is one of the four unannounced Mk 63Cs which were delivered from Warton in early 1995.

Below: Equipped with RWR and AAM rails (here seen faired over), Abu Dhabi's Mk 102s were delivered in 1994.

Dubai
Dubai Air Wing
Combat Wing, Mindhat

The UAE's early 1980s decision to standardise on the BAe Hawk for advanced training, light attack and reconnaissance was implemented on 30 June 1981 by a £40 million Dubai Air Wing order for eight Mk 61s, powered by the Adour 861 turbofan. For the reconnaissance portion of their taskings they were supplied with Vinten centreline camera pods.

Build number	DAW serial
232	501
233	502
234	503
240	504
248	505
250	506
251	507
252	508

The first of the eight Dubai Hawks flew at Dunsfold on 11 November 1982 with the B-class UK civilian serial G-9-502. On 29 March 1983 it left the UK via Malta for the DAW's main base at Mindhat wearing its new DAW serial 501. The remaining seven had made the journey by September 1983.

In DAW service the Hawk Mk 61s

combined advanced and weapons training roles with the DAW's main combat capabilities in its sole fighter squadron at Mindhat. Hawk 508 was damaged in early 1986, and on 4 April that year 505 crashed. A replacement aircraft – 335/509 – was delivered in 1988. Another DAW Hawk – 506 – was also lost in December 1991.

In addition to their training tasks, Dubai's Hawks also have a reconnaissance commitment using Vinten pods.

Finland
Suomen Ilmavoimat – Finnish Air Force

Ha'vLLv 11, Rovaniemi
Ha'vLLv 21, Tampere/ Pirrkala
Ha'vLLv 31, Kuopio/ Rissala
Tiedustelulentolaivue, Tikkakoski
Koulutuslentolaivue, Kauhava
KoeLtue, Kuorevesi/Halli

After a rigorous evaluation in competition with the Aero L-39 Albatros, Aermacchi MB.339, Dassault/Breguet Alpha Jet and Saab 105As, the Hawk gained its first export customer in the shape of the Finnish air force (Ilmavoimat). The Hawk was selected in 1976 for its advanced training requirement, with the express goal of replacing by 1987 the Fouga Magister light jet trainers then in service. Finland's choice was stated to be because of the Hawk's low operating costs, reliability, ease of

When first delivered, Finnish Hawks wore large national markings and serials.

The Hawk bridges the gap between the Valmet Vinka basic trainer and the operational types. Note the small presentation of the serial and national insignia on the nose.

maintenance, low manpower demands, good fatigue life and climatic tolerance. The Ilmavoimat also concluded that a reliable single-engined trainer suffered no significant disadvantages in attrition or instructional capability over a twin-jet type, while offering better economy.

Another major factor in Finland's Hawk selection, however, was the UK industry's first industrial and commercial agreement, to return 100 per cent of the overall contract value of FMk965 million (approximately £128 million) in offset trade. This agreement was made between British Aerospace, Rolls-Royce and other Hawk contractors and various Finnish companies. Contract signature was made on 30 December 1977 with BAe, covering 50 Hawks. In the tradition of BAe and its predecessors, the first of an export series was numbered above 50, so the Finnish aircraft were designated Mk 51s. Under the terms of the industrial offset agreement, all but the first four of these aircraft were to be part-manufactured (including the fins,

tailplane, airbrakes and flaps), assembled and test-flown in Finland by Valmet OY at Halli.

BAe handed over the first of its four completed Hawk 51s (c/n 312198 to 312201) on 16 December 1980 at Dunsfold. HW-302 and HW-303 left for Pori by air on 19 December, HW-305 and HW-306

following later. HW-305 had earlier worn the MoD serial ZD226 for weapons firing. Prior to the air deliveries, BAe had shipped fuselage and wing sets to Valmet for assembly by road and sea.

Finnish Hawks joined the Saab J 35 Draken interceptors of Ha'vLLv (Fighter Squadron) 11 in the Lapland Wing (Lappin Lennosto) at Rovaniemi, in the Arctic Circle. The rest (312202 to 312247) followed from the Valmet assembly line between 20 February 1981 and 1 September 1985. BAe supplied systems-equipped fuselage and wing units to Valmet, which then assembled them and added locally-produced components.

Build number	Ilmavoimat serial
133	HW-301
153	HW-302
173	HW-303
181	HW-304
184	HW-305
200	HW-306
204	HW-307
205	HW-308
206	HW-309
207	HW-310
208	HW-311
214	HW-312
215	HW-313
216	HW-314
217	HW-315
218	HW-316

and weapons training roles. For a short period in mid-1986, Hawks actually comprised the first-line equipment of Ha'vLLv 21, previously at Pori, with responsibility for the defence of south-west Finland, until more Drakens could enter Ilmavoimat service.

For these, and their planned close-support roles, the Hawk T.Mk 51s were the first to have four underwing as well as the ventral fuselage stations, the latter to accommodate the standard gun pod. In Finland, however, this was fitted with an indigenous 0.5-in (12.7-mm) VKT machine-gun instead of the RAF's ADEN cannon, in conjunction with a Saab RGS-2 lead-computing weapons sight. Provision was also made for carrying Sidewinder or similar IR-homing AAMs, bombs, MATRA rocket pods, other offensive stores, or Vinten 18/300 reconnaissance pods with optical and IR linescan sensors. These pods were specific to four Hawks operating alongside three similarly-equipped MiG-21bis in the Tiedustelulentolaivue (or Special Development Unit) at Tikkakoski, for recce roles.

The Ilmavoimat combat wings, in fact, received their Hawks well in advance of the Koulutuslentolaivue (KoulLLv/Training Squadron) of the Ilmasotakoulu (Air Academy) at Kauhava. This did not begin replacing its Magisters with 16-20 Hawks until 1983, the last Fouga-trained student finally graduating in early 1986. Pilot training was then reorganised so that new students flew an increased total of 110 hours on the

piston-engined Valmet 70 Vinka, followed by 105 hours to 'wings' standard on the Hawk. A further 100 hours was then flown on the Hawk weapons trainers in each combat wing before operational conversion to the Sk 35C Draken, MiG-21UM and now the MDC F/A-18D Hornet at the same unit.

In December 1990, a £210 million follow-up order was placed by the Finnish government with BAe for seven more British-built Hawks, to restore attrition losses and meet the demands of Ilmavoimat's hard-worked fleet. While retaining the Adour 851 of the original Mk 50s (for which 75 engines had been included in the initial contract), the new aircraft incorporated some of the structural improvements in Hawk wing design and the latest modification standards, resulting in their redesignation as Hawk T.Mk 51As.

Finland discarded its attractive three-tone camouflage to join the growing ranks of air arms with flat grey aircraft. This aircraft is from the follow-on batch of Mk 51As.

264	HW-334
265	HW-335
266	HW-336
267	HW-337
272	HW-338
275	HW-339
277	HW-340
286	HW-341
288	HW-342
290	HW-343
294	HW-346
297	HW-347
300	HW-348
301	HW-349
302	HW-350

224	HW-317
225	HW-318
229	HW-319
230	HW-320
231	HW-321
235	HW-322
236	HW-323
237	HW-324
238	HW-325
239	HW-326
241	HW-327
247	HW-344
253	HW-328
254	HW-329
257	HW-345
260	HW-330
261	HW-331
262	HW-332
263	HW-333

HW-302 led a very short life in Finnish service, hitting trees during an aerobatic routine on 17 March 1981. After Ha'vLLv 11, each of the remaining squadrons in the other two combat wings, Ha'vLLv 21 of Satakunnan Lennosto (Satakunta Wing) at Tampere/Pirkkala, and Ha'vLLv 31 of the Karjalan Lennosto (Karelian Wing) at Kuopio/Rissala, replaced their Magisters in turn with four or five Hawks for operational

Build number	Temporary MoD serial	Ilmavoimat serial
400/5F001	ZH675	HW-351
408/5F002	ZH699	HW-352
411/5F003	ZH700	HW-353
412/5F004	ZH701	HW-354
413/5F005	ZH702	HW-355
414/5F006	ZH703	HW-356
416/5F007	ZH704	HW-357

These were initially delivered to Ha'vLLv 21, from late 1993 to July 1994. In addition to the units mentioned above, three Hawks are also usually to be found with the KoeLtue (Test Squadron) at Kuorevesi/Halli.

Indonesia
Tentara Nasional Indonesia-Angkatan Udara – Indonesian Armed Forces-Air Force

Skwadron Latih Lanjut 103, Iswahyudi/Madiun Skwadron Udara 15, Iswahyudi/Madiun

In the mid-1970s Indonesia sought to procure an advanced trainer with weapons capability. After abandoning plans for the licence-production of 60 Aermacchi MB.326s, including single-seat attack versions, the Indonesian air force (TNI-AU) became the third export customer for the Hawk with an initial order for eight T.Mk 53s on 4 April 1978, to be used for advanced training and weapons instruction at a cost of some £23 million.

Build number	B-class serial	TNI-AU serial
126	G-9-466	LL-5301
152	G-9-467	LL-5302
155	G-9-468	LL-5303
161	G-9-469	LL-5304
166	G-9-470	LL-5305
171	G-9-471	LL-5306
175	G-9-472	LL-5307
179	G-9-473	LL-5308

Hawks assigned to weapons training received tactical camouflage.

LL-5301 also wore MoD serial ZB618 for firing trials. The first two (LL-5303 and LL-5304) left Dunsfold on 17 September 1980 for the trip to Indonesia, routing via Malta. These were delivered from 1 September 1980 to Adisutjipto, Jogjakarta, to equip No. 10 Sqn of No. 1 Training Wing, Indonesian aircrew having earlier recived training with the RAF. This first TNI-AU Hawk unit was later renamed Skwadron Latih Lanjut 103 (103 Advanced Flying Squadron), and was detached to Iswahyudi (Madiun) to reduce congestion at Adisutjipto.

A second TNI-AU contract on 18 May 1981 added five more Hawk Mk 53s, as well as eight sets of smoke-generating equipment for team display purposes and braking parachutes for all 13 aircraft at a cost of £18 million. Three of the original eight Indonesian Hawks were lost in their first year of operation, including LL-5307 and LL-5308 in a mid-air collision on 17 June 1981, but follow-up orders were placed for three more on 30 October 1981, and another four on 30 November 1982, increasing the overall TNI-AU total to 20.

Build number	TNI-AU serial
222	LL-5309
223	LL-5310
226	LL-5311
227	LL-5312
228	LL-5313

244	LL-5314
245	LL-5315
246	LL-5316
249	LL-5317
255	LL-5320
258	LL-5318
259	LL-5319

These were delivered between August 1982 and March 1984, and more than restored the operating strength of Training Squadron 103. This since appears to have evolved into an operational conversion/ground attack unit (Skwadron Udara 15) alongside the TNI-AU's Northrop F-5E/F-equipped 14th Air (Defence) Sqn at the same base.

This Mk 53 is from Indonesia's final batch of the trainer version. The RAF-style scheme is for aircraft used for advanced training.

New TNI-AU units are planned to operate the eight Adour 871-powered Hawk Mk 109s and 16 single-seat Mk 209s with Westinghouse APG-66 radar ordered in June 1993 through a £500 million contract from the Indonesian government. This followed a co-production agreement signed between BAe and IPTN at the 1991 Paris air show, and included options for another 16-20 unspecified variants. At the time of contract signature, IPTN chairman Dr Habibie said that Indonesia had an eventual requirement for up to 96 Hawks with combat capabilities, although he gave no indication of the likely timescale. Confirmation for this requirement came at the same time from Indonesia's military chief of staff, General Feisal Tanjung, who said that up to 100 new fighters would be required by the TNI-AU during the next 25 years, and $676 million has already been allocated in planned FY96/97 funding for 20 of these. Other Indonesian officials have indicated that Maverick-armed Hawk 200s are being considered as possible long-term replacements for the TNI-AU's two dozen ageing McDonnell Douglas A-4E/TA-4E Skyhawks equipping 11 and 12 Sqns at Ujung Padang and Pekanbaru. Delivery of the TNI-AU's Hawk 109s and 209s is expected to begin in 1996. Build numbers in the range IT001/IT008 have been assigned to the Mk 109s, and IS001/IS016 for the Mk 209s.

Kenya
Kenya Air Force

Having previously acquired BAe Strikemaster Mk 87s (replaced by Shorts Tucano Mk 51s from 1990), the Kenyan air force supplemented its advanced training and light ground attack strength with a 9 February 1978 order for 12 Hawk Mk 52s costing some $40 million. This was only the second Hawk order, and on 11 April 1980 the KAF actually became the first export recipient when arrived at Nanyuki in Kenya to become s/n 1001. The remaining KAF Hawks followed by early 1981, the last batch leaving Dunsfold on 6 February.

Build number	B-class serial	KAF serial
107	G-9-454/ZB609	1001
117	G-9-455	1002
120	G-9-456	1003
123	G-9-457	1004
128	G-9-458	1005
130	G-9-459	1006
136	G-9-460	1007
140	G-9-461	1008
146	G-9-462	1009
151	G-9-463	1010
154	G-9-464	1011
157	G-9-465	1012

These were the first Hawks to be equipped with a tail braking parachute, initially of 7-ft (2.13-m) diameter. 1001 wore the MoD serial ZB609 for weapons release tests prior to delivery.

Three of Kenya's Mk 52s 'patrol' the Surrey countryside prior to delivery from Dunsfold.

Korea (South)
Hankook Kong Goon – Republic of Korea Air Force

First mentioned as a Hawk customer in January 1990, a $260 million contract for the purchase of 20 Hawk Mk 67s was officially confirmed in July 1991. The aircraft were required to replace 35 RoKAF Lockheed T-33s, with possible follow-on orders for up to 100 to re-equip Cessna T-37 and A-37 basic trainer and light ground-attack units. While retaining the Adour 671 turbofan of the standard export Hawk Mk 60, the RoKAF's Mk 67s are unique in being fitted for tactical training and light ground-attack operations, with the extended nose of the Srs 100 version containing extra avionics rather than a radar or laser rangefinder. They also incorporate steerable nosewheels, among other additional options, together with wing pylons. Some mainplane parts are produced by Daewoo Heavy Industry for the RoK's military trainer offset programme. BAe also offered an advanced version of the Hawk as a joint $1 billion development project for the RoKAF's planned KTX-II supersonic trainer/light combat aircraft requirement, for which Samsung Aerospace Industries is prime contractor for an indigenous design.

Although basically Mk 60-series aircraft, those of the RoKAF are something of a hybrid, featuring the extended nose and other options of the Mk 100. Designated Mk 67, the type is used for the advanced and weapons training roles, with a secondary light attack tasking.

Build number	Temporary MoD serial	RoKAF serial
366/6K001	ZH593	67-496
367/6K002	ZH594	67-497
368/6K003	ZH595	67-498
369/6K004	ZH596	67-499
370/6K005	ZH597	67-500
371/6K006	ZH598	67-501
374/6K007	ZH599	67-502
377/6K008	ZH603	67-503
378/6K009	ZH604	67-504
381/6K010	ZH605	67-505
382/6K011	ZH606	67-506
386/6K012	ZH607	67-507
387/6K013	ZH608	67-508
388/6K014	ZH609	67-509
391/6K015	ZH610	67-510
392/6K016	ZH611	67-511
393/6K017	ZH612	67-512
397/6K018	ZH613	67-513
398/6K019	ZH614	67-514
399/6K020	ZH615	67-515

The first batch of seven Hawk Mk 67s was completed at Warton from September 1992, and entered service with the RoKAF in June 1993. Delivery was completed by November 1993 of the remaining 13 Hawk Mk 67s. The first RoKAF Hawk, 67-496, crashed on take-off on 2 June 1994, both crew ejecting safely.

Kuwait
Al Quwwat al Jawwiya al Kuwaitiya – Kuwait Air Force

No. 12 Squadron, Ahmed al Jaber

As part of its planned expansion in the early 1980s, the Kuwaiti air force chose the BAe Hawk in preference to Egyptian-assembled Alpha Jets for advanced training and close support roles, with an order for 12 Mk 64s on 31 October 1983.

Build number	KAF serial
279	140
292	141
280	142
284	143
287	144
289	145
296	146
299	147
303	148
304	149
306	150
285	151

First flight of 141 was on 4 September 1985, with deliveries to No. 12 Sqn at Ahmed al Jaber ensuing between November of that year and mid-1986. Before delivery, 140 and 142 wore the MoD serials ZF107 and ZF108 for weapons trials. The Hawks provided advanced instruction and weapons training for about 150 KuAF

Kuwaiti Hawks serve in both the advanced training and light attack roles. They flew a few sorties against the Iraqis in August 1990.

student pilots after they had completed basic flying courses in the US. That changed with the Iraqi invasion of Kuwait in August 1990. After limited contact with Iraqi forces, six of the Kuwaiti Hawks found refuge in Bahrain, where 142 was damaged on arrival, and they continued restricted training and support operations in Saudi Arabia. When Kuwait International Airport was reopened, they returned in July 1991.

In early 1992, they were joined by four of the original KuAF Hawks, which were among Kuwaiti military equipment finally released under pressure from Iraqi custody. Hawk 142 had also been repaired, restoring the KuAF fleet to a total of 10, which eventually returned to Ahmed al Jaber. The base was the subject of post-Gulf War reconstruction, together with the forward base of Ali al Salem, at a joint cost of some $105 million. Kuwait now requires more Hawks to meet its training requirements, and is a prime candidate for Hawk 100/200 procurement for lead-in fighter instruction for its 40 F/A-18C/Ds, and light strike/interception roles. This will have to wait, however, until the necessary funding can be found after settlement of the $70 billion post-war reconstruction budget deficit.

Four of Kuwait's Hawks were captured by Iraq, but it is not thought they were used.

Malaysia
Tentara Udara Diraja Malaysia – Royal Malaysian Air Force

No. 9 Jehat Skuadron, Kuantan
No. 3 Flying Training Centre, Butterworth

Malaysian interest in the Hawk was reported as early as 1980, but did not reach fruition until a decade later. As with Oman, this interest came after the nation had earlier seriously examined the Tornado, switching to the Hawk on cost grounds. In early December 1990 an order was placed for 10 two-seat Mk 108s and 18 single-seat Mk 208s. The order was worth Rgt2 billion ($738 million), and included large-scale offset contract commitments, among which was the establishment of a regional Hawk service centre with Airod in Malaysia, worth an estimated $156 million over 20 years. The RMAF Hawk contract also included the supply of Pathfinder 2000 advanced mission planning aids from GEC Avionics, in collaboration with Hunting Engineering.

RMAF Hawks incorporate several customer-specified modifications, including the addition of nosewheel steering. The Mk 208s are being fitted with a fixed inflight-refuelling probe level with the starboard windscreen, plus the associated plumbing. A trial mock-up probe installation was flown in 1991 on the first pre-production Hawk 200 (ZH200), and a similar air-refuelling capability was also planned by Oman for its Hawk Mk 203s. Malaysia does not at present have any tanker capacity, but will presumably modify some C-130s for the task.

The first Mk 108 was formally handed over at Warton on 19 January 1994 to the C-in-C of the RMAF, Lieutenant General Dato Ghani, who said that the new aircraft would allow trainee pilots to graduate from flying training school directly into tactical fighter training, as a lead-in to more advanced aircraft such as the eight MDC F/A-18Ds and 18 MiG-29s. He said that combat pilots on these types would require at least 1,000 hours of flying and operational training, which could be done economically on the Hawk. All of the Mk 108s were delivered to Malaysia by August 1994.

Seen wearing a 3 FTC badge, the Hawk 208 is intended primarily as an A-4PTM Skyhawk replacement. Note the bolt-on refuelling probe.

Build number	Temporary MoD serial	RMAF serial
415/MT001	ZH735	M40-01
418/MT002	ZH738	M40-02
420/MT003	ZH745	M40-03
421/MT004	ZH746	M40-04
423/MT005	ZH747	M40-05
425/MT006	ZH748	M40-06
426/MT007	ZH752	M40-07
428/MT008	ZH753	M40-08
429/MT009	ZH754	M40-09
431/MT010	ZH757	M40-10

The Hawk 108s went into service alongside Pilatus PC-7s and Aermacchi MB.339s at No. 3 Flying Training Centre, at Kuantan. This unit has since moved to Butterworth.

The RMAF's first Hawk Mk 208 first flew at Warton on 4 April 1994. It was then transferred to Boscombe Down while still in its factory primer finish for clearance of its air refuelling probe and systems, in trials with the RAF's VC10 K.Mk 3 tanker, ZA149/'H'. These included air refuelling contacts while carrying full loads of external stores, extending to 1,000 lb (453 kg) of bombs, drop tanks and wingtip Sidewinders. This aircraft left Warton on 25 July 1994 for delivery to Malaysia, delivery of the remainder being completed by mid-1995. The Mk 208 batch comprised:

Build number	Temporary MoD serial	RMAF serial
424/MS001	ZH778	M40-21
440/MS002	ZH779	M40-22
441/MS003	ZH780	M40-23
442/MS004	ZH781	M40-24
443/MS005	ZH782	M40-25
444/MS006	ZH783	M40-26
445/MS007	ZH784	M40-27
446/MS008	ZH785	M40-28
447/MS009	ZH786	M40-29
448/MS010	ZH787	M40-30
449/MS011	ZH788	M40-31
450/MS012	ZH789	M40-32
451/MS013	ZH790	M40-33
452/MS014	ZH791	M40-34
453/MS015	ZH792	M40-35
454/MS016	ZH793	M40-36
455/MS017	ZH794	M40-37
456/MS018	ZH795	M40-38

Mk 208s replaced the McDonnell Douglas A/TA-4PTMs which served with No.9 'Civet' Skuadron at Kuantan. In late 1994, the RMAF was evaluating pod-mounted radar jammers for these aircraft, from submissions by Elettronica, Ericsson-Rodale (A.100), GEC-Marconi Defence Systems (Apollo), Thomson-CSF (BAREM), and Westinghouse (ALQ-131).

Below: Malaysia acquired the Hawk Mk 108 for advanced training with No. 3 Flying Training Centre. Students progress to the Hawk from the PC-7 and MB.339.

Oman
Al Quwwat al Jawwiya al Oman – Royal Air Force of Oman

No. 6 Squadron, Masirah

In the late 1980s Oman placed a somewhat ambitious order for eight Tornado ADVs. This was cancelled in 1989, the Tornados joining the RAF instead. Oman's willingness to buy British was kept alive and switched to the more affordable and practical Hawk, and was satisfied on 30 July 1990 by an order estimated at £150 million from British Aerospace. This covered 12 single-seat APG-66 radar-equipped Hawk Mk 203 attack/interceptors and four two-seat Mk 103 lead-in fighter trainers for the Royal Air Force of Oman. Thus Oman became the launch customer for the Hawk 200, specifying installation of BAe's low-cost LINS 300 laser gyro INS, designed and produced by the group's Systems and Equipment Division at Plymouth for the nav/attack systems. The GEC-Marconi Defence Systems' Sky Guardian lightweight E-J band radar warning receiver was also selected for installation in both single- and two-seat Hawks.

· Equipped with FLIR and laser ranger/marking target seekers, the first of the RAFO's four Hawk Mk 103s made its initial flight at Warton in July 1993. It was followed in October by the first Mk 203, which was also the first production Hawk 200. Hawk 103 deliveries started with ZH669/101 on 8 December 1993, comprising:

Build number	Temporary MoD serial	RAFO serial
OT001	ZH669	101
OT002	ZH670	102
OT003	ZH671	103
OT004	ZH672	104

The first Omani Mk 203 was still at Warton in November 1994 pending completion of systems and weapons trials with BAe's Hawk 200 radar development aircraft, ZJ201. Deliveries got underway during late 1994/early 1995, the total batch consisting of:

Build number	Temporary MoD serial	RAFO serial
405/OS001	ZH710	121
422/OS002	ZH711	122
427/OS003	ZH712	123
430/OS004	ZH713	124
432/OS005	ZH714	125
433/OS006	ZH719	126
434/OS007	ZH720	127
435/OS008	ZH721	128
436/OS009	ZH722	129
437/OS010	ZH729	130
438/OS011	ZH730	131
439/OS012	ZH731	132

Both Omani Hawk variants were initially expected to replace the five surviving Hunter F.Mk 73A/Bs, single FR.Mk 10 and three two-seat T.Mk 66B/67s operating until November 1993 with No. 6 Sqn at Masirah.

Top: Resplendent in desert two-tone camouflage, the four Mk 103s for Oman provide lead-in training for the Hawk 200 fleet, fitted with Sidewinder launch rails on the wingtips. The Hawks have replaced Hunters which previously operated in the air defence role.

Left: Oman's purchase of a dozen Mk 203s has dramatically improved the effectiveness of the RAFO. Both variants have Sky Guardian RWR housed in the fin-top fairing and in antennas on the brake chute housing.

Saudi Arabia
Al Quwwat al Jawwiya as Sa'udiya – Royal Saudi Air Force

No. 11 Squadron, Riyadh
No. 21 Squadron, Riyadh
No. 37 Squadron, Dhahran/Al Kharj

On 17 February 1986 Saudi Arabia signed the Memorandum of Understanding for the original Al Yamamah arms contract with British Aerospace. This massive arms buy was worth some £5 billion over three years, and virtually amounted to the purchase of a complete air force. In addition to Hawks, Al Yamamah included 48 Tornado IDS, 24 Tornado ADV, 30 BAe-built Pilatus PC-9 turboprop basic trainers and two specially-equipped Jetstream 31s for weapons system operator training. Thirty Hawk Mk 65s were included among the 134 aircraft that made up the complete order.

Al Yamamah provided for a straight-through training programme from basic to advanced to operational type. Students graduating on the PC-9 from the King Faisal Air Academy at Riyadh moved to the Hawk for advanced follow-on training with the Academy's No. 21 Squadron. Consequently, the RSAF Hawks were not planned for any secondary ground-attack roles, apart from weapons training.

Formal delivery of the first two RSAF Hawks was made on 11 August 1987 at Dunsfold to the UK MoD's Director-General of the Saudi Arabian Project, Air Vice Marshal R. Stuart-Paul, as handling contractor. Their delivery started in October 1987 and the first 12 were delivered by the end of January 1988.

Build number	RSAF serial
298/SA1	2110
305/SA2	2111
307/SA3	2112
308/SA4	2113
309/SA5	2114
310/SA6	2115
311/SA7	2116
312/SA8	2117
313/SA9	2118
314/SA10	2119
315/SA11	2120
316/SA12	2121
317/SA13	3751
318/SA14	3752
318/SA15	3753
320/SA16	3754
321/SA17	3755
322/SA18	3756
323/SA19	3757
324/SA20	3758
325/SA21	3759
326/SA22	3760
327/SA23	3761
328/SA24	3762
329/SA25	3763
330/SA26	3764
331/SA27	3765
332/SA28	3766
333/SA29	3767
334/SA30	3768

The first Al Yamamah contract covered provision of a complete training package, including BAe-built PC-9s for basic training and a pair of Jetstream 31s for radar training. Both these and the Hawks initially went to No. 21 Sqn.

The initial batch of Saudi Mk 65s was intended to be followed by a mix of 100s and 200s, but in the event Al Yamamah II included only upgraded Mk 65As. Combat-capable aircraft may follow in the future.

As the first two digits of their serials indicated, the first dozen were destined for No. 21 Sqn of the RSAF's Riyadh Air Academy, and were followed from February 1988 by the remaining 18, ostensibly for No. 37 Sqn at Dhahran/Al Kharj. Some Hawks were also reportedly delivered to No. 11 Sqn at Riyadh, to complete replacement of the BAe Strikemasters formerly operated by the Air Academy.

A letter of intent for the follow-on Al Yamamah II contract was signed in July 1988. This arms procurement package was initially much larger than the first, valued at some £10 billion. This would have funded another 36 Tornado ADVs, 12 Tornado IDS, and 60 more Hawks. Further inclusions in AY II were BAe 125 and 146 transports, more Jetstreams, and 88 Westland WS-70 helicopters. Full AY II implementation was deferred because of falling oil revenues, but in January 1993 agreement was finally reached with the UK on funding arrangements for the revised procurement of 48 Tornado IDS versions costing £3 billion, for delivery in 1996-97.

On 8 September 1994, the UK MoD also confirmed similar delivery dates for another 20 Hawks for the RSAF. In the original AY II deal the 60 Hawks would have included

significant numbers of Mk 100s and Mk 200s, but the revised agreement is now apparently confined to more Mk 65s for advanced training. The new Hawks will incorporate product improvements made to the aircraft since the original Al Yamamah

buy, and are designated Mk 65A accordingly. Build numbers have been assigned as 6Y001 to 6Y020.

The new Hawk order was accompanied by a similar follow-up contract for another 20 PC-9s, both types being required to train

additional RSAF aircrew to man the new Tornado and 72 McDonnell Douglas F-15S Eagle strike/air defence aircraft now on order. The originally planned Srs 100s or 200s do remain as a longer-term requirement.

Switzerland
(Kommando der Flieger- und Fliegerabwehrtruppen – Swiss Air Force and Anti-Aircraft Command)

Fliegerschule 1, Emmen

With a desperate need to replace its 39-strong fleet of de Havilland Vampire T.Mk 55s, which averaged 36 years in age, Switzerland held a competition for a new trainer in the mid-1980s. A competitive evlauation was staged between the Aermacchi MB.339, British Aerospace Hawk, Dassault/Dornier Alpha Jet and the CASA C.101. The field was narrowed to two with the rejection of the MB.339 and CASA Aviojet, and the trials culminated in a six-week fly-off. Two Hawks were involved, T.Mk 1 XX345 and a loaned Kuwaiti Mk 64 with the temporary British military serial ZF627. The evaluation was held against the Franco-German trainer at Emmen and Sion, and resulted in the Swiss Military Department recommending the purchase of the BAe Hawk on 14 January 1987. Parliamentary approval was followed by a £160 million SAFAAC contract, for which BAe undertook 100 per cent offset compensation. This was signed in Berne on 20 October 1987 for the supply of 20 Hawk Mk 66 advanced trainers, together with a logistic and training package which included a Rediffusion SP-X 500HT flight simulator.

With the temporary British serial ZG974 required for live armament trials, the first SAFAAC Hawk made its initial flight in the hands of Paul Hopkins at Dunsfold on 7 April 1989. SAFAAC took delivery of this aircraft from BAe in November 1989, the remaining 19 being co-produced, assembled and flight-tested at the Federal Aircraft Factory (F+W) at Emmen, initially to Fliegerschule 1 at the same airfield, from 1990. With detail changes to meet SAFAAC requirements, the Swiss Hawks' Mk 861A-3 turbofans were also assembled in Switzerland by Sulzer Brothers.

Build number	SAFAAC serial
336	U-1251
337	U-1252
338	U-1253
339	U-1254
340	U-1255
341	U-1256
342	U-1257
343	U-1258
344	U-1259
345	U-1260
346	U-1261
347	U-1262
348	U-1263
349	U-1264
350	U-1265
351	U-1266
352	U-1267
353	U-1268
354	U-1269
355	U-1270

Completed on schedule in October 1991, the overall Swiss Hawk programme was quoted as worth SwFr395 million. However, BAe's aircraft element was valued at only SwFr198 million, reflecting cautious Swiss policies of including large stocks of spares to ensure maximum independence from manufacturers for up to 20 years. This was based on a planned utilisation of about 200 hours for each

aircraft per year. SAFAAC jet students now fly about 115 hours in Phase 2 training on 15 Hawk Mk 66s of Fliegerschule 1 at Emmen, plus 25 hours in the simulator, after 100 hours basic flying on the turboprop Pilatus PC-7. Tactical conversion is accomplished on the Northrop F-5E/F at the same base. Another three Hawks were operating from Sion during 1994 on unspecified tasks.

Below: Cavorting around the Matterhorn, this Hawk demonstrates how the Swiss adapted the standard RAF trainer scheme for their aircraft. Unit marks are not worn, and the emergency triangles are much larger than on other Hawks to accommodate three languages.

United States

United States Navy

On 26 January 1988, the US Navy announced the go-ahead for the T-45 programme. The initial contract for $429.4 million was awarded to McDonnell Douglas for the first 12 aircraft, and also included a Rediffusion (now Hughes Simulation System) SP-X 500HT flight simulator like that selected by the Swiss for its Hawks. Two prototypes (BuAer 162787 and 162788), plus the first two production aircraft (163599 and 163600), were used in the protracted development programme undertaken primarily at the Naval Air Test Center at Patuxent River. The USN received its first Goshawk (163600/ 200) at NAS Kingsville, TX, in December 1992, and subsequent deliveries were initially aimed at replacing the TA-4J Skyhawk. An initial batch of 60 was funded in four Lots:

Lot 1	163599 to 163610	(12)
Lot 2	163611 to 163634	(24)
Lot 3	163635 to 163646	(12)
Lot 4	163647 to 163658	(12)

Funding for a second batch of 36 aircraft was allocated in 1992, in three Lots:

Lot 5	165057 to 165068	(12)
Lot 6	165069 to 165080	(12)
Lot 7	165081 to 165092	(12)

With the delivery of the second batch of aircraft the US Navy will begin replacement of its 85 Rockwell T-2C Buckeyes, currently used in the intermediate strike training role. Under current planning these will be replaced early in the next century, with production running at about one per month. The T-45A buy was originally stated at 300 aircraft, plus the two pre-production machines, but is now set at 268 and is likely to drop further with more budget cutbacks. After instructor conversion and mission qualification, plus service clearances, USN students began training on the T-45A with VT-21 at Kingsville on 4 January 1994. After 60-70 hours of basic flying training in the Beech T-34C, the intermediate and advanced training syllabus covers 132 flights in the T-45A totalling 176 hours, of which about 30 per cent is solo. This includes 10 solo deck take-offs and landings. Also in the course are 98 hours in flight simulators, 115 hours of flight briefings, and 81 hours of classroom

Below: T-45s on approach to Kingsville display the radically modified undercarriage, necessary for carrier training.

instruction in 203 working days, or 40.4 weeks in all. Two T-45As – 163629/229 and 163639/239 – of VT-21 were lost during the first course when two of the Goshawks collided during a four-aircraft solo formation exercise near Kingsville on 17 August 1994. One of the pilots ejected safely, but the other was killed in the ensuing crash.

Training Wing 1 (VT-7 'Eagles', VT-19 'Fighting Frogs'), NAS Meridian, MS

Following conversion of TRAWING 2 at Kingsville, the USN's sole remaining TA-4J unit was VT-7, operating 76 two-seat Skyhawks at NAS Meridian, MS. A smaller number of T-45As are due to replace these by October 1997. The Meridian-based Rockwell T-2C Buckeyes of VT-19 are due

Above and below: Training Wing 2 at Kingsville was the first service recipient of the Hawk. The wing has VT-21 and VT-22 with the T-45A.

Left: 'Ship One' on a test flight displays the revised rear end of the T-45 with single dorsal fin, side-mounted airbrakes and arrester hook. Only two pre-production aircraft were funded, although they were joined in trials by the first production machines.

for replacement early in the next century. Meridian has, however, been identified as a base due for closure in the near future.

Training Wing 2 (VT-21 'Red Hawks'/VT-22 'King Eagles', VT-23 'Professionals'), NAS Kingsville, TX

The first US Navy Goshawk squadron, VT-21, became operational on 27 June 1992 to begin instructor training. However, the crash of the first T-45 during trials at Edwards AFB halted deliveries for some time. After receiving its first aircraft, a four-ship operational evlauation lasted for a month from 18 October 1993 to allow training to begin after the new year. By September 1994, some 45 T-45As (163600/200 to 163644/244), bearing the unit identification 'B' on their red-painted fins, had completely replaced the McDonnell Douglas TA-4Js in the Advanced Training Squadrons VT-21 'Red Hawks' and VT-22 'King Eagles' of Training Wing 2. VT-21 has an additional task of training pilots for the Aéronavale. The T-2 squadron, VT-23, will convert at a later date.

Training Wing 6 (VT-4 'Rubber Ducks', VT-86 'Sabre Hawks'), NAS Pensacola, FL

Twenty T-2Cs used at Pensacola are due for replacement by the T-45 after 2000.

VT-4 currently undertakes NFO (naval flight officer) training, providing rudimentary flying instruction for non-pilot aircrew such as F-14 radar intercept officers, A-6 bombardier/navigators, EA-6 electronic warfare officers and P-3 navigators. The squadron also provides a specialised course for pilots destined for the C-2 Greyhound and E-2 Hawkeye. VT-86 is the navigator

The graceful curves of the Hawk's wings and tailplanes have been totally lost in the Goshawk redesign.

training unit, and currently employs the T-2C to provide low-level fast-jet navigation training. TRAWING 6 aircraft have the letter 'F' on the fin.

Zimbabwe
Air Force of Zimbabwe

No. 2 Squadron, Gwelo

To replace its elderly Vampire FB.Mk 9s and T.Mk 11s, the Air Force of Zimbabwe ordered eight Hawk 60s. In so doing, the AFZ became the first customer for this uprated version, through a $70 million contract signed on 9 January 1981. Zimbabwe's Hawks were also the first to have the larger (8.5-ft/2.59-m) tail braking parachute, and to have provision for Vinten 18/300 recce pods. The initial delivery batch comprised:

Build number	B-class serial	AFZ serial
209	G-9-486	600
210	G-9-487	601
211	G-9-488	602
212	G-9-489	603
213	G-9-490	604
219	G-9-491	605
220	G-9-492	606
221	G-9-493	607

The first four AFZ Hawks were delivered to No. 2 Squadron at the former Thornhill airfield, later known as Gwelo or Gweru, on 13 July 1982, having flown via Malta. Only 12 days later, however, the AFZ saw its brand-new Hawk fleet effectively demolished by sabotage in the early hours of 25 July. An attack by dissident AFZ personnel destroyed one Hawk (602), three Hunters and a Reims-Cessna FTB.337 Lynx. The explosive charges also damaged the remaining three Hawks and five Hunters. One of the damaged Hawks (601) proved to be locally repairable, with BAe help, but 600 and 603 had to be returned to the UK for an extensive rebuild.

The second batch of four Hawk T.Mk 60s arrived in Zimbabwe on 5 October 1982, being joined in October 1984 by the return from BAe Kingston of their two rebuilt counterparts.

In 1990, a follow-up order was placed for a further five Hawk T.Mk 60As to the later export build standard, and these were delivered in two batches from Dunsfold from 1 to 6 September 1992.

Build number	Temporary MoD serial	AFZ serial
360/6Z001	ZH570	608
361/6Z002	ZH571	609
357/6Z003	ZH572	610
362/6Z004	ZH573	611
363/6Z005	ZH574	612

First to arrive were 610 to 612, followed 16 days later by 608 and 609. At least one AFZ Hawk has since been lost in an accident.

Above: Zimbabwe was the launch customer for the Mk 60. One of the these first four aircraft (602) was lost in a terrorist attack shortly after they had been delivered.

Below: This pair of Zimbabwe Hawks is depicted while demonstrating the type's multi-role versatility, with dummy bombs and Sidewinders.

Lockheed F-16 Variant Briefing

Part 2: F-16XL and F-16C/D derivatives

F-16XL (F-16E/F)

The F-16XL is configured with a 'cranked arrow', or modified delta wing developed in co-operation with NASA (National Aeronautics and Space Administration) based on studies to minimise drag in the transonic and supersonic regimes. This wing spans 32 ft 5 in (10.03 m) (without AIM-9 launch rails at the wingtips) and gives 663 sq ft (62 m2) of area. The fuselage was extended with the insertion of two plugs; one immediately in front of the F-16A forward fuel cell (lengthening the fuselage but not the inlet beneath) and a second plug slightly aft of the mainwheel well rear bulkhead. The plugs are 2 ft 6 in (0.77 m) and 2 ft 2 in (0.67 m) long, fore and aft, respectively. The plugs lengthened the fuselage to 54 ft 1.86 in (16.51 m) and the 'cranked-arrow' wing incorporated carbon composite materials to save weight.

The ventral fins of the standard F-16 have been deleted, the longer aft fuselage increasing the vertical tail movement arm to maintain directional stability. The absence of ventrals and the canting of the aft fuselage 3° allow greater angles of attack on landing, hence decreased approach speeds, with sufficient exhaust nozzle clearance.

The drag chute assembly common to Norwegian, Belgian and Venezuelan F-16s was included in the F-16XL design for reduced landing distances when necessary. An early proposal included an F-16 horizontal tail surface as an all-flying vertical tail atop the braking chute housing but was rejected in favour of the standard F-16 fin. The much-changed delta wing shape was proposed by GD in February 1980 and, after NASA joined the effort, caused the aircraft

to become known as SCAMP (Supersonic Cruise and Maneuvering Prototype). The F-16XL has also been dubbed the 'Wedge' and the 'Cranked Falcon'.

The F-16XL has 17 hardpoints with 29 stations for external stores. The centreline and two inlet stations are common to the F-16C/D. Four AIM-120 AMRAAM stations are partially submerged in the wingroots. Four hardpoints with 10 stations are beneath each inboard wing panel and AIM-9/AIM-120 missile launch rails can be

accommodated on each wingtip.

Initially funded by the manufacturer, the F-16XL programme called for modification of two FSD F-16As. The first of these, formerly the fifth FSD F-16A, with single seat and standard P&W F100 engine, made its first flight at Fort Worth on 15 July 1982 with pilot Jim McKinney at the controls.

The second F-16XL, originally the third FSD F-16A which had been damaged in a landing mishap and was converted to two-seat configuration, was retrofitted with the GE F110 (formerly the F101 Derivative Fighter Engine and also flown on the F-16/101). This ship is dubbed the F-16XL-2. It joined flight operations with the F-16E Combined Test Force (CTF) of the 6510th Test Wing at Edwards AFB, California in October 1982, soon after the first ship. For a brief period in 1983, it was painted in a Heatley-Ferris disruptive camouflage scheme.

With the F-16XL already a reality, the USAF was studying possible ETF (Enhanced Tactical Fighter) concepts to

The two-seat F-16XL would have been known as the F-16F if it had entered service. The aircraft was re-engined with the General Electric F110 engine.

replace the F-111 'Aardvark' in the low-level, night and bad-weather interdiction role. Although the F-111 has proven more difficult to replace than was once suspected, these examinations led to a fly-off contest between the proposed F-15E Strike Eagle and the F-16XL, known in its ETF context as the F-16E (F-16F, in two-seat configuration). The F-15E was chosen in 1984, not because of any flaw on the part of the 'cranked arrow'-winged Falcon but on the basis of cost projections.

Both F-16XLs returned from Edwards to Fort Worth during the summer of 1985 for storage, having made 437 (XL-1) and 361 (XL-2) flights for a total of 940 hours. In January 1989 NASA signed a leasing deal with GD to operate the two aircraft on

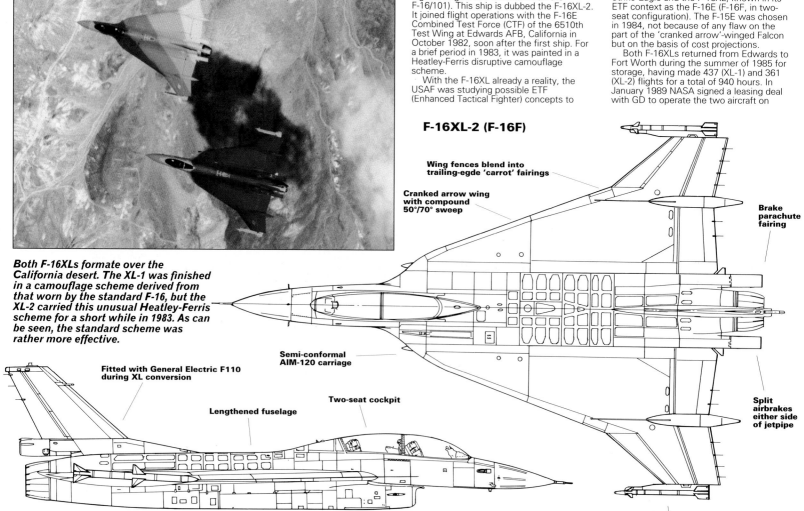

Both F-16XLs formate over the California desert. The XL-1 was finished in a camouflage scheme derived from that worn by the standard F-16, but the XL-2 carried this unusual Heatley-Ferris scheme for a short while in 1983. As can be seen, the standard scheme was rather more effective.

F-16XL-2 (F-16F)

Wing fences blend into trailing-egde 'carrot' fairings

Cranked arrow wing with compound 50°/70° sweep

Brake parachute fairing

Semi-conformal AIM-120 carriage

Split airbrakes either side of jetpipe

Fitted with General Electric F110 during XL conversion

Lengthened fuselage

Two-seat cockpit

Wingtip rails for AIM-9 or AIM-120 missiles

Ventral fins deleted

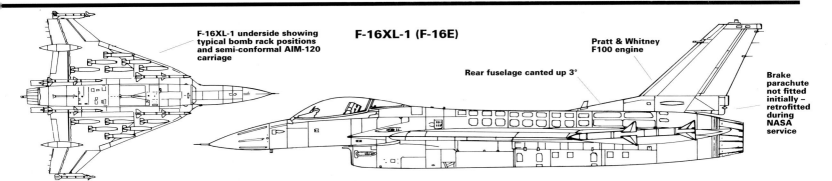

F-16XL-1 underside showing typical bomb rack positions and semi-conformal AIM-120 carriage

F-16XL-1 (F-16E)

Rear fuselage canted up 3°

Pratt & Whitney F100 engine

Brake parachute not fitted initially – retrofitted during NASA service

Right: Cruising across Rogers Dry Lake, the F-16XL-1 displays the new port wing section which was fitted by NASA Dryden for supersonic laminar flow control work. The wing section had millions of holes through which the sluggish boundary layer was sucked.

aerodynamic trials to evaluate concepts designed to improve airflow during sustained supersonic flight. The single-seat XL-1 was returned to Edwards (NASA Dryden) on 10 April 1989 and was subsequently modified for laminar flow studies with an experimental titanium section on its left wing with active suction to siphon off a portion of the layer of turbulent surface air with millions of tiny laser-cut holes – thereby producing data to validate computer codes to aid in the design of future aircraft. Pilot Steve Ishmael made the first flight with the new wing on 3 May 1990. Assigned NASA number 849, the single-seat F-16XL was briefly assigned to the NASA/Langley facility at Langley AFB, Virginia from April to November 1994, to evaluate take-off performance, engine noise, and other techniques to make airports quieter as part of NASA's High-Lift Project aimed at evaluating the putative configuration of a future High-Speed Civil Transport.

Once the notional F-16E/F was denied a production contract, the two-seat F-16XL-2 reverted to NASA/Dryden at Edwards, waiting to resume flying in tests with high-lift devices such as vortex flaps. The aircraft has worn NASA numbers 846 (briefly) and 848. The two-seater carried on with laminar-flow studies begun by the single-seater. The single-seat aircraft became NASA 849.

1995 flight tests with an F-16XL at the NASA-Dryden Flight Research Center at Edwards will test an advanced wing design

Right: In the second phase of SLFC trials NASA Dryden used the F-16XL-2, fitted with experimental passive (i.e. non-sucking) sections on its starboard wing.

as part of the Supersonic Laminar Flow Control programme being conducted in concert with the US air transport industry. The left wing of the aircraft is to be modified to test SLFC concepts.

F-16XL serials: 75-0747 (NASA 846, 848); 75-0749 (NASA 849)

Below: For a period in 1994 the F-16XL-1 was assigned to the NASA facility at Langley, and was repainted in this smart black scheme. The Langley flights were part of future airliner trials.

Lockheed F-16 Variants

F-16C/D Block 25

F-16C/D Block 25 fighters, also known as MSIP II aircraft, introduced some features common to all F-16C/D aircraft and distinguishing them from all F-16A/Bs. These include Westinghouse APG-68 radar in place of the -66, provisions for the AGM-65D Maverick, improvements in the cockpit and avionics areas, a wide-angle conventional HUD, or head-up display (the type of HUD varies by block, but no wide-angle HUDs were installed on A/B models), and increased capacity in the electrical and air-conditioning systems. The base of the vertical tail of all F-16C/Ds is enlarged to accommodate avionics associated with the ASPJ (Airborne Self-Protection Jammer) instead of the aircraft carrying an external ECM pod. All F-16C/D aircraft have a UHF (ultra high-frequency) radio blade antenna protruding at 35° sweepback on the forward base of the vertical fin; the same antenna on F-16A/B aircraft is internal, and is hidden beneath a dielectric panel.

First flight of an F-16C Block 25 (83-1118) was made at Fort Worth on 15 June 1984 by company test pilot Kevin Dwyer. First flight of an F-16D Block 25 (83-1174) was made 14 September 1984 by pilots John Fergione and Jim Smolka. F-16Ds in all blocks are two-seat versions which retain single-seat F-16C weight and dimensions and induce no added aerodynamic drag, but sacrifice 1,500 lb (580 kg) of fuel and, hence, endurance and range.

Block 25 Fighting Falcons were delivered with the F100-PW-200 engine, which has had teething problems. Among other things, the -200 engine lacks a DEEC, or digital electronic engine control, inevitably called a 'deek' by pilots. These aircraft have since been retrofitted at the local base level with either the F100-PW-220 engine (a 'new build' powerplant) or F100-PW-220E (modified from an existing -200). All engines from the -220 on have the DEEC which helps with stall-free performance, allows the engine to expand its envelope somewhat, and is more reliable, with a negligible loss of thrust. The F-16C/D Block 25 series also marks the last point at which P&W enjoyed a monopoly on producing engines for the Fighting Falcon.

The Block 25 series is the lightest of the F-16C/D series with an empty weight of 16,803 lb (7621 kg), which is 1,192 lb (543 kg) less than the Block 30. Although Block 25s have the fin-bottom shape for ASPJ once planned for F-16Cs (but not F-16Ds), it is empty: these aircraft do not have wiring, wave guides, ECS (environmental control systems) ducting and vents needed to accommodate ASPJ which, in any event, was cancelled by the USAF.

Block 25, 30/32, and 40/42 aircraft employ the ALR-69 radar warning receiver (RWR). Block 25 aircraft have two ALE-40 chaff/flare dispensers.

The US Air Force applies a 'G' prefix to non-flyable aircraft assigned to the Technical Training Center at Sheppard AFB, Texas for the purpose of training aircraft mechanics and crew chiefs. Of the 29 GF-16s assigned as of 30 September 1994, 24 were GF-16A/B models. However, Sheppard also has five GF-16C aircraft assigned, of which four are GF-16C Block 25s.

F-16C Block 25 serials: 83-1118/1124 (USAF)

F-16D Block 25 serials: 83-1174/1177 (USAF)

F-16C Block 25A serials: 83-1125/1140 (USAF)

F-16D Block 25A serials: 83-1178/1180 (USAF)

F-16C Block 25B serials: 83-1141/1165 (USAF)

A 301st FW Block 25 aircraft manoeuvres at low level. Originally powered by the F100-PW-200, all Block 25s now have -220 or -220E engines with digital control for more carefree manoeuvring.

Right: 83-1118 was the first F-16C, seen here on a test flight still wearing its GD construction number on the intake. The C model was readily distinguishable from the A by the lengthened dorsal fairing and small blade antenna, and by having a gold-tinted canopy, although this feature was later retrofitted to many As.

Right: The last active-duty user of the Block 25 aircraft was the 366th Wing at Mountain Home, although this switched to Block 52Ds in 1994. This aircraft is seen armed with an AIM-120 AMRAAM on the wingtip.

F-16D Block 25B serials: 83-1181/1185 (USAF)

F-16C Block 25C serials: 84-1212/1246 (USAF)

F-16D Block 25C serials: 84-1319/1323 (USAF)

F-16C Block 25D serials: 84-1247/1286 (USAF)

F-16D Block 25D serials: 84-1324/1327 (USAF)

F-16C Block 25E serials: 84-1287/1318, 84-1374/1388 (USAF)

F-16D Block 25E serials: 84-1328/1331 (USAF)

F-16C Block 25F serials: 84-1389/1395, 85-1399, 85-1401, 85-1403/1407, 85-1409, 85-1411, 85-1413, 85-1415/1421, 85-1423, 85-1425, 85-1427, 85-1429/1431, 85-1433, 85-1435, 85-1437, 85-1439, 85-1441, 85-1443, 85-1445, 85-1447, 85-1452 (USAF)

F-16D Block 25F serials: 84-1396/1397, 85-1506/1508, 85-1510, 85-1512, 85-1514/1516 (USAF)

Right: Block 25s now serve with reservist units, including the 457th FS, 301st FW at NAS Fort Worth, which recently celebrated its 30th birthday.

RF-16D/F-16 Recce

An F-16D Block 25E (84-1330) was tested in the mid-1980s at Edwards with a multi-purpose centreline reconnaissance pod. The aircraft was never designated RF-16, although this term has been used informally to refer to this proposed RF-4C Phantom replacement.

First flight of this aircraft was made on 13 June 1986 with company pilot John Fergione and flight test engineer James Sergeant aboard. Sergeant is believed to be the only non-pilot ever to have made a Fighting Falcon 'first flight'.

Marked on its tail as the 'F-16 RECCE,' this aircraft was the subject of a variety of sensor package evaluations, including the fitment of a LANTIRN-type system in addition to the reconnaissance pod. This Fighting Falcon made its last flight with the reconnaissance package on 19 August 1986. Further efforts to develop and field an RF-16 are not expected.

F-16 Recce trials aircraft

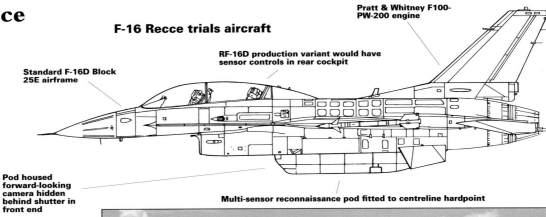

- Pratt & Whitney F100-PW-200 engine
- RF-16D production variant would have sensor controls in rear cockpit
- Standard F-16D Block 25E airframe
- Pod housed forward-looking camera hidden behind shutter in front end
- Multi-sensor reconnaissance pod fitted to centreline hardpoint

Left: During the F-16 Recce trials, the aircraft was also fitted with the targeting pod from the LANTIRN system.

Above: The reconnaissance pod fitted to the F-16 Recce was tight on ground clearance. The small slit was for a linescan system.

F-16ES

The F-16ES ('Extended Strategic') fighter is a manufacturer's concept for a longer-range Fighting Falcon. Under the concept, a standard F-16C/D would be configured with above-wing conformal fuel tanks for increased range. This began as a 1994 proposal for Israel, possibly inspired by the similarly-configured F-4ES Phantom, three of which were converted for Israel by General Dynamics-Fort Worth in the 1970s. Instead of the F-16ES, Israel chose the McDonnell Douglas F-15I Eagle and arranged to take delivery of 50 early model F-16s. The F-16ES remains on the table as a Lockheed-Fort Worth proposal for other potential customers.

The company tested the concept on the modified third F-16C aircraft (an F-16C Block 25 which itself had earlier become a testbed for the Block 30's GE F110-GE-100 engine and 'modular common inlet duct') leased from the Air Force and normally based at Edwards. This aircraft made its first flight in F-16ES configuration on 3 November 1994, flown by company test pilot Joe Sweeney. The aircraft was configured with shapes representing two

During flight trials the F-16ES demonstrator was tested in full load-out with underwing tanks and two 2,000-lb Paveway I LGBs in addition to the upper tanks.

24-ft (7.43-m) conformal fuel tanks attached to the upper wing and fuselage on each side of the aircraft. The conformal tanks hold about 3,200 lb (1451 kg) of fuel giving the F-16ES an unrefuelled combat radius of over 1,000 miles (1610 km) with ordnance. In 21 test flights, Sweeney and others completed stability, control, and high angle-of-attack testing to determine whether the external tanks would have any effect on the F-16's flight performance. Sweeney reported that the tanks "appear to have a negligible impact on the controllability of the aircraft." The aircraft was also flown with 600-US gal (2270-litre) underwing tanks, a shape representing an internal nose-mounted FLIR, and weapons loadings of two 2,000-lb (907-kg) bombs. The flight test effort was concluded in January 1995; the aircraft was demodified and returned to Edwards on 23 January 1995.

F-16ES testbed serial: 83-1120

F-16ES demonstrator

- General Electric F110-GE-100 engine
- Conformal fuel tanks on upper surface of wing/fuselage blend adding 6,400 lb (2903 kg) of fuel
- Representative FLIR turrets above and below nose

Trials with FLIR-type sensors began with just the upper sensor, and culminated in flights with one above and one under the nose.

F-16C/D Block 30

Beginning with Block 30, all F-16C/D aircraft come with a configured engine bay (often called 'common' engine bay although, as we shall see, like the F-16's 'common' air intake, it is nothing of the sort). This bay, in theory, accepts either the GE F100 or the P&W F100-PW engine. In reality, a change of engine type requires a modification kit which must be provided from depot. The bay has appropriate mountings but lacks actuator rods and cables to make engines interchangeable. In practice, the USAF does not use GE and P&W engines interchangeably but, rather, segregates them within squadrons or wings. With some exceptions, the USAF has stationed GE-powered aircraft overseas and PW-powered aircraft in the continental US.

Beginning with Block 30, all F-16Cs (but not F-16Ds) are fully wired and configured for ASPJ, including wiring, wave guides, ECS (environmental control systems) ducting and vents. Block 30 also introduces a flap-mounted RWR described in the entry for Block 32.

The F-16C/D Block 30 is the first 'Viper' to be powered by a General Electric engine, the F110-GE-100. The F110 is somewhat larger than the F100 and about 771 lb (350 kg) heavier, but claims better figures for engine reliability and fuel consumption. The sorely misnamed 'modular common inlet duct', which has no commonality with P&W-powered aircraft at all, is the 'big mouth' or larger air intake found on all GE-powered Vipers, meaning Blocks 30, 40, and 50, except for the first few Block 30A and 30B aircraft. The 'big mouth' intake allows air mass flow to increase from 254 to 270 lb/sec (115 to 122 kg/sec). On 'big mouth' aircraft, the ECS ram air inlet duct below the fuselage and above the engine air intake is canted slightly forward, a recognition feature making it possible to distinguish a 'big mouth' from a 'small mouth' when viewed from the side. The engine exhaust nozzle for GE-powered aircraft is slightly shorter and more round than that of P&W-powered fighters. Because P&W engines cannot accommodate the increase in air, P&W-powered 'Vipers' in Blocks 32, 42, and 42 retain the original, smaller inlet shape.

F-16C/D Block 30 fighters introduced expanded computer memory and AGM-45 Shrike anti-radar missile and the AIM-120 AMRAAM (Advanced Medium-Range Air-to-Air Missile) capability. These aircraft use the AN/ALE-40 radar warning receiver.

Block 30 aircraft, which have an empty weight of 17,995 lb (8162 kg), introduce the capability for ALE-47 chaff/flare dispensers in place of the ALE-40 on earlier aircraft. Aircraft with fiscal year 1987 serials onward (i.e. from Block 30F) added provisions for four, rather than two, chaff/flare dispensers, added on the left side of the aircraft (a small amount of fuel from the aft-fuselage fuel cell was deleted to make this accommodation); the change in number (though not in type of dispenser) applies to all subsequent USAF Fighting Falcons. Block 30s also introduce structural upgrades to strengthen the airframe.

First flight of an F-16C Block 30 (85-1398) was made on 12 June 1986 at Fort Worth by company pilot John Fergione. First flight of an F-16D Block 30 (85-1509) came on 30 July 1986 with the late Joe Bill Dryden and Dave Thigpen in the cockpit.

All F-16C/Ds from Block 30 on were delivered with adhesively sealed center and aft tanks. Incremental changes for Block 30 include: Block 30B with provision for AMRAAM; Block 30C with upgraded F100 engine; Block 30D with 'modular common inlet duct'.

Among 'G'-prefixed aircraft assigned to the Technical Training Center at Sheppard AFB, Texas as non-flying trainers, as of 30 September 1994 the USAF had one GF-16C Block 30 aircraft. This ship (89-1146) is the only GF-16 in inventory with a General Electric engine (F110).

In September 1983, Turkey announced plans to buy 160 F-16s. As it has evolved, the order includes 44 F-16C/D Block 30s (35 F-16C, 9 F-16D). Turkey and Greece have the only F-16C/D models with braking parachutes.

In the early 1990s, the US Air Force sought to acquire 300 Block 30/32 aircraft as F/A-16 CAS/BAI (close air support/battlefield interdiction) aircraft with a head-steered FLIR (forward-looking infra-red), Pave Penny laser ranger and 30-mm cannon pod. This proposed Block 30/32 upgrade was abandoned in January 1992 when the service decided to focus on later-model Vipers instead.

F-16C/D Block 30 aircraft have been delivered to Israel (under a programme codenamed Peace Marble), Greece (Peace Xenia), and Turkey (Peace Onyx). Greek F-16C/D Block 30s are the only Fighting Falcons equipped with an I.D. light (identification light) located on the right (starboard) side of the aircraft. Included in the F-16C Block 30B/C/D/E series are 22 F-16Ns, and in the F-16D Block 30E series four TF-16Ns, both adversary aircraft for the US Navy described in separate entries.

F-16C Block 30 serials: 85-1398; 85-1400; 85-1402; 85-1408; 85-1410; 85-1412; 85-1414; 85-1422; 85-1424; 85-1426; 85-1428; 85-1432; 85-1434; 85-1436; 85-1438; 85-1440 (USAF); 86-1598/1601 (Israel 301, 304, 305, 307)

F-16D Block 30 serials: 85-1509, 85-1511 (USAF)

F-16C Block 30A serials: 85-1442; 85-1444; 85-1446; 85-1448/1451; 85-1453/1485 (USAF); 86-1602/1612 (Israel 309, 310, 315, 317, 318, 321, 324, 326, 332, 333, 337); 87-1661/4 (Israel 340, 341, 344, 343)

F-16D Block 30A serials: 85-1513, 85-1517 (USAF); 87-1694 (Israel 020)

F-16C Block 30B serials: 85-1486/1505; 85-1544/1570 (USAF); 86-0066/0072, 87-0009/0018 (Turkey); 87-1665/1679 (Israel 348, 349, 350, 353, 355, 356, 360, 364, 367, 368, 371, 373, 374, 377, 378)

F-16D Block 30B serials: 85-1571/1573, 86-0191/0196 (Turkey)

F-16C Block 30C serials: 86-0207/0209; 86-0216, 86-0219, 86-0221/0235; 86-0237, 86-0242/0249; 86-0254/0255;

Left: Greece's Block 30 aircraft are fitted with an ID light in the side of the nose and a brake parachute housing.

Below: The 52nd FW received Block 30s because of their AGM-45 Shrike capability for the lethal SEAD role. This aircraft is seen in fighter configuration with AIM-120.

Ground crew manhandle an F110 engine from a Block 30 F-16. A trained eye can tell a GE engine by the curvature of the exhaust nozzle.

86-0258/0261 (USAF); 87-1680/1693 (Israel 381, 384, 386, 388, 389, 391, 393, 394, 392, 397, 399, 383, 385, 376); 88-1709/1710 (Israel 359, 313)

F-16D Block 30C serials: 86-0042/0043 (USAF)

F-16C Block 30D serials: 86-0262/0268; 86-0270, 86-0274/0278; 86-0282, 86-0284, 86-0286/0290, 86-0293/0295;

86-0297/0298; 86-0300/0316 (USAF); 88-1711 (Israel 329)

F-16D Block 30D serials: 86-0044/0047 (USAF); 87-1695/1698 (Israel)

F-16C Block 30E serials: 86-0317/0371 (USAF); 87-0019/0021, 88-0019/0032 (Turkey)

F-16D Block 30E serials: 86-0049/0053 (USAF); 87-1699/1708 (Israel 036, 022, 041, 045, 039, 046, 050, 057, 061, 055); 87-0002/0003, 88-0013 (Turkey)

F-16C Block 30F serials: 87-0217/0266; 87-0268 (USAF)

F-16D Block 30F serials: 87-0363/0368 (USAF); 88-1712/1720 (Israel 072, 063, 069, 077, 074, 079, 075, 088, 083)

F-16C Block 30H serials: 87-0270/0292; 87-0294, 87-0296, 87-0298, 87-0300, 87-0302, 87-0304, 87-0306, 87-0308, 87-0310, 87-0312, 87-0314 (USAF); 88-0110/0111 (Greece 110/111)

F-16D Block 30H serials: 87-0370/0380, 87-0382 (USAF); 88-0144/0147 (Greece 144/147)

F-16C Block 30J serials: 87-0316, 87-0318, 87-0320, 87-0322, 87-0324, 87-0326, 87-0328, 87-0330, 87-0332, 87-0334/0349

This Block 30 was used at Eglin to test the AGM-84 Harpoon anti-ship missile, later used by Korea.

(USAF); 88-0112/0123 (Greece 112/123)

F-16D Block 30J serials: 87-0383/0390 (USAF); 88-0148/0149 (Greece 148/149)

F-16C Block 30K serials: 88-0397/0411 (USAF); 88-0124/0139 (Greece 124/139)

F-16D Block 30K serials: 88-0150/0152 (USAF)

F-16C Block 30L serials: 88-0140/0143 (Greece 140/143)

F-16N

The F-16N is an F-16C Block 30B/C/D/E aircraft built as an adversary aircraft for the US Navy. These aircraft do not have the M61A1 Vulcan 20-mm cannon installed (to save weight) and are equipped with Westinghouse APG-66 radar (which is less capable than the -68 employed on other C

and D models) which was chosen because it is lighter. The F-16N is the most manoeuvrable Fighting Falcon ever built: the combination of the GE F110 engine and greatly reduced weight makes it the best dogfighter in the Fighting Falcon family. These characteristics apply to the two-seat TF-16Ns.

First flight of an F-16N (85-1369/BuNo. 163268) was made at Fort Worth on 24

March 1987 by company test pilot Dave Palmer. The F-16N equipped several aggressor squadrons, but the US Navy is expected to retire these aircraft soon, in part because the fleet is too small to be economical and bears the added cost of being maintained by a civil contractor.

F-16N Block 30B serials: 85-1369/1372 (BuNos 163268/163271)

F-16N Block 30C serials: 85-1373/1378 (BuNos 163272/163277); 86-1684/1685 (BuNos 163566/163567)

F-16N Block 30D serials: 86-1686/1693 (BuNos 163568/163575)

F-16N Block 30E serials: 86-1694/1695 (BuNos 163576/153577)

Above: Assigned to the Naval Fighter Weapons School, this F-16N is painted in a scheme to represent a Sukhoi Su-27 'Flanker'.

Left: The F-16N is the highest-performing and most manoeuvrable of the entire family. However, the constant rigours of high-g flight have caused some fatigue problems.

Below: The first F-16N was delivered in standard USAF camouflage. It wore the badges of the NFWS, VF-126 and VF-45 on the tail, with a US Navy 75th anniversary badge on the intake. In addition to the above three units, VF-43 joined the ranks of Navy F-16 users.

F-16N

Lighter and less capable APG-66 radar in place of APG-68

M61A1 cannon deleted to save weight

Wing pylons able to carry AIM-9 acquisition rounds and AIS instrumentation pods only

Strengthened airframe, including titanium lower wing fittings

General Electric F110-GE-100 engine

Radar reflectors on intake sides to enhance cross-section

Based on standard Block 30 airframe and delivered from USAF production blocks

TF-16N

The TF-16N is an F-16D Block 30E aircraft built for the US Navy. First flight of one of these two-seaters (86-1379/BuNo. 163278) was made on 25 March 1988 at Fort Worth by Joe Sweeney and Joe Bill Dryden. Apart from its second crew seat, the four TFs are identical to the F-16N. The TF-16N has served valiantly as an adversary aircraft but is to be retired from service.

TF-16N Block 30E serials: 85-1379/1382 (BuNos 163278/163281)

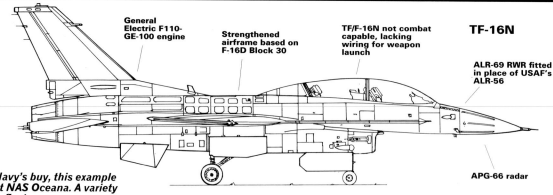

General Electric F110-GE-100 engine

Strengthened airframe based on F-16D Block 30

TF/F-16N not combat capable, lacking wiring for weapon launch

TF-16N

ALR-69 RWR fitted in place of USAF's ALR-56

APG-66 radar

Four two-seat TF-16Ns were included in the Navy's buy, this example being assigned to VF-43 'Challengers' based at NAS Oceana. A variety of colour schemes has been worn by the Navy fleet.

NF-16D VISTA

The USAF designation NF-16D, the 'N' prefix signifying a permanent change in configuration for test purposes, applies to a single F-16D Block 30D aircraft which served during 1992-1993 as the VISTA/F-16 (Variable-Stability In-Flight Simulator Test Aircraft), modified as a flying simulator to employ flight control computers to duplicate the dynamic motions and angles of other types of aircraft. This is possibly the only F-16 equipped with a centre

control stick in addition to the sidestick controller found on other Fighting Falcons. The NF-16D is configured so that the aircraft commander sits in the rear cockpit.

The VISTA/F-16 was funded by the USAF, US Navy and NASA for research related to new and modified aircraft designs. In this configuration, the aircraft made its first flight on 9 April 1992 at Fort Worth with Major Bob Wilson and Joe Sobczak on board. Wilson is believed to be the first US Air Force officer to have made a 'first flight' in a Fighting Falcon variant.

In 1993, the VISTA aircraft became the

F-16/MATV (separate entry). In January 1995, the aircraft reverted to its VISTA/F-16 identity and was taken over by Calspan Corp. at Wright-Patterson AFB, Ohio, replacing a long-serving Lockheed NT-33A Shooting Star as a variable stability flight demonstrator. The eventual goal is to make this aircraft available on a cost basis to any customers who want to use it for research or to train test pilots.

The USAF plans to install a Pratt & Whitney F100-PW-229 engine with multi-axis thrust vectoring in 1996, replacing this airframe's GE powerplant. This will require

modifying the engine air inlet to 'small mouth' configuration. 1996 will also be devoted to developing computer software for this aircraft which will then undergo a six-month test programme and will be ready for customers by 1998.

Pending uses of the VISTA/F-16 a.k.a. NF-16D include flight control development and evaluation flights for the Lockheed F-22 and the Indian Light Combat Aircraft (LCA).

NF-16D (VISTA/F-16) serial: 86-0048

Above: VISTA's cockpit is unique in having two control columns, a central unit and the standard F-16 sidestick. On the left-hand panel are controls for the software, including a button marked 'F-16 Engage'. This throws the software back from the VISTA settings to the standard F-16.

Left: After a spell as the MATV testbed, 86-0048 is now back in VISTA configuration. An F100-PW-229 IPE will now be fitted.

NF-16D MATV

The F-16/MATV (Multi-Axis Thrust Vectoring) test aircraft, which began its research duties as the VISTA/F-16 and returned to the latter designation, was a Block 30D aircraft powered during its first life as VISTA and its MATV incarnation by a GE F110-GE-129 engine.

The GE engine was equipped with an AVEN (Axisymmetric Vectoring Exhaust Nozzle) for a programme aimed at testing combinations of pitch and yaw thrust-vectoring, plus high angle of attack testing. The US Air Force initially balked at underwriting this costly but important exploration into high angle-of-attack manoeuvre, and the aircraft and engine manufacturers moved ahead with support from Israel, which was considering having AVEN nozzles retrofitted to its F-16 fleet. At one juncture, Israel was expected to provide an F-16D for the tests. In 1991, the Wright Laboratory became interested in MATV as a potential source of data for its much broader PACIR (Propulsion, Aerodynamic, Controls Integrated Research) programme. When Israel withdrew from MATV in 1992, it became a co-operative effort between the manufacturers and the USAF.

For the MATV programme, the proposed flight effort could have been conducted by any two-seat F-16 with a dorsal spine offering space for avionics. It was happenstance that the VISTA/F-16 was available. For the MATV programme, the VISTA's variable stability computers were removed to restore its weight to a figure

On display at Edwards AFB, the F-16/MATV is seen with the AVEN nozzle vectored downwards. The nozzle employs the simple concept of using a ring around the segments of the exhaust. By moving the ring away from the central position, the nozzle will conform to the new shape and deflect the thrust accordingly.

closely approximating that of a standard F-16.

The F-16/MATV made its first flight with its new appellation on 2 July 1993 at Fort Worth with company test pilot Joe Sweeney and Major Mike Gerzanics on board. From July 1993 to March 1994, pilots from the 422nd Test and Evaluation Squadron at Nellis AFB, Nevada, were called in to fly, and also to fly against, the F-16/MATV. 422nd pilots rotated between MATV and their own bandit, or aggressor, aircraft which were F-16C/D Block 32 fighters. In October and November 1994, the MATV airframe carried out ACTIVE (Advanced Control Technology for Integrated Vehicles) trials in a joint effort by the USAF and NASA at Edwards AFB, California.

The airframe has since been turned over to Calspan Corp. at Wright-Patterson AFB,

The NF-16D was fitted with thrust-vectoring for about 18 months, and flew both test and representative air combat missions. The aircraft achieved a stabilised angle of attack of 86°, and could reach 115° in a cobra manoeuvre. The AVEN nozzle could vector thrust up to 18° from the aircraft central axis.

Ohio, was to be re-engined with a P&W powerplant, and has reverted to its VISTA/F-16 designation, as from January 1995.

NF-16D (F-16/MATV) serial: 86-0048

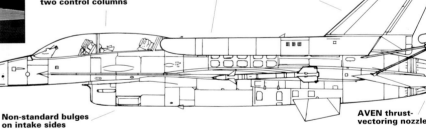

NF-16D VISTA/MATV

Missionised cockpits with two control columns

Swollen spine fairing housing additional avionics

Spin recovery parachute fitted for MATV trials

Instrumented extended nose boom

Non-standard bulges on intake sides

AVEN thrust-vectoring nozzle

F-16C/D Block 32

F-16C/D Block 32 Fighting Falcons are powered by the 23,770-lb (105.73-kN) thrust Pratt & Whitney F100-PW-220. In contrast to GE-powered Block 30s, P&W-propelled Blocks 25 and 32 are almost identical in external appearance except for the latter's ducts for ASPJ. Block 32 aircraft have an empty weight of 17,201 lb (7802 kg). One distinctive feature which began with this Block 30/32 aircraft but has been retrofitted to many F-16s is a radar warning receiver located in a knob-like fairing on the leading-edge flap on both sides, replacing an RWR previously located on the nose. The new location gives better hemispherical coverage in the forward quadrant of the aircraft.

First flight of an F-16C Block 32 (86-0210) was made at Fort Worth on 12 June 1986 by John Fergione. First flight of an F-16D Block 32 (86-0039) was made on the same day by Dave Thigpen and Joe Bill Dryden.

Block 32 aeroplanes went initially to the 422nd Test and Evaluation Squadron at

Nellis AFB, Nevada. The 302nd Fighter Squadron 'Sun Devils', 944th Fighter Group at Luke Air Force Base, Arizona, an Air Force Reserve unit, was activated in October 1987 as the first user of F-16C/D Block 32 aircraft. These were the first F-16C/Ds to go to reserve forces.

Aircraft flown by the USAF 'Thunderbirds' flight demonstration team (which formerly flew F-16A/B models) are Block 32s with no significant modifications apart from a system to feed oil into the exhaust to create coloured plumes for displays. The USAF requires that they be capable of being modified back to full combat status in 72 hours.

F-16C/D Block 32 aircraft have been exported to Egypt and Korea (Peace Bridge).

F-16C Block 32 serials: 84-1332 (Egypt 9501); 85-1574/1575 (Korea)

F-16D Block 32 serials: 84-1340/1343 (Egypt 9401/9404)

The Republic of Korea chose Pratt & Whitney power for all its F-16s, the first of which were Block 32s. These replaced Phantoms with the 161st and 162nd TFS, within the 11th Fighter Wing at Taegu.

F-16C Block 32A serials: 84-1333/1339, 85-1518/1523 (Egypt 9502/9509); 85-1576/1579 (Korea)

F-16D Block 32A serials: 84-1344/1345 (Egypt 9405/9406); 84-1370/1373 (Korea); 85-1584/1585 (Korea)

F-16C Block 32B serials: 85-1524/1543 (Egypt 9515/9534); 85-1580/1583 (Korea)

F-16C Block 32C serials: 86-0210/0215; 86-0217/0218; 86-0220, 86-0236, 86-0238/0241; 86-0250/0253; 86-0256/0257 (USAF); 86-1586/1589 (Korea)

F-16D Block 32C serials: 86-0039/0041 (USAF)

F-16C Block 32D serials: 86-0269, 86-0271/0273; 86-0279/0281; 86-0283, 86-0285, 86-0291/0292; 86-0296, 86-0299 (USAF); 86-1590/1593 (Korea)

F-16C Block 32E serials: 86-1594/1597 (Korea)

F-16C Block 32F serials: 87-0267, 87-0269 (USAF); 87-1653/1656 (Korea)

Considerable numbers of Block 32 aircraft are at Nellis AFB with the 57th Wing. The 414th TS (above) flies this variant on Adversary Tactics work, the aircraft often carrying centreline ECM pods to replicate foreign EW systems, while the Aerial Demonstration Squadron (right) has nine F-16Cs and two F-16Ds for formation display work.

F-16D Block 32F serial: 87-0369 (USAF)

F-16C Block 32H serials: 87-0293, 87-0295, 87-0297, 87-0299, 87-0301, 87-0303, 87-0305, 87-0307, 87-0309, 87-0311, 87-0313 (USAF); 87-1657/1660 (Korea)

F-16D Block 32H serial: 87-0381 (USAF)

F-16C Block 32J serials: 87-0315, 87-0317, 87-0319, 87-0321, 87-0323, 87-0325, 87-0327, 87-0329, 87-0331, 87-0333 (USAF)

F-16D Block 32Q serials: 90-0938/0941 (Korea)

Right: One minor modification applied to Block 32 Thunderbirds aircraft is the smoke-generating pipe scabbed to a 'turkey feather'.

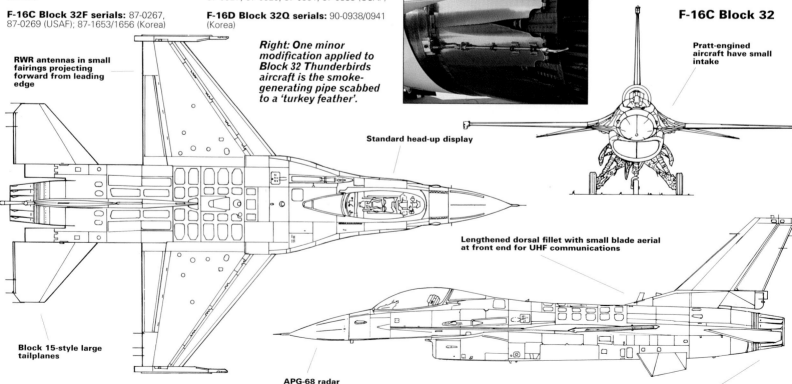

RWR antennas in small fairings projecting forward from leading edge

Block 15-style large tailplanes

APG-68 radar

Standard head-up display

Lengthened dorsal fillet with small blade aerial at front end for UHF communications

Pratt & Whitney F100-PW-220 engine with straight-profiled engine exhaust nozzle

F-16C Block 32

Pratt-engined aircraft have small intake

F-16C/D Block 40

F-16C/D Block 40 Night Falcon aircraft are powered by GE F110-GE-100 engines, and have an empty weight of 18,765 lb (8511 kg). Beginning with Block 40/42 and continuing with 50/52, Fighting Falcons have bigger wheels, struts, tyres, brakes, and bulged gear doors. Another identifying feature: prior to Block 40, F-16s had round landing gear lights located in the main landing gear well. Beginning with Block 40s and in all subsequent Fighting Falcons, these lights are rectangular and are in the nose gear landing door.

The HUD on Block 40/42 is different from that of any other F-16 variant. A diffractive optics and holographic, wide-angle HUD, it is broader in size than those on other Fighting Falcons, including the wide-angle HUDs of other C and D models.

Block 40/42 introduced the reliability-enhanced Westinghouse APG-68V radar, an improved fire control computer, a digital flight control system, automatic terrain following, GPS (global positioning system) provisions, and in particular the Martin Marietta LANTIRN (Low-Altitude, Navigation and Targeting, Infra-red for Night) system, which includes the AAQ-13 navigation pod and AAQ-14 targeting pod (right) and AAQ-13 navigation pod (left). LANTIRN also equips the McDonnell F-15E Eagle.

Block 40/42 aircraft introduced further structural upgrades related not merely to LANTIRN but to heavier load-carrying expectations for this block.

Beginning with Block 40 and continuing through Blocks 42, 50, and 52, the Fighting Falcon has a digital flight control system which among other things allows terrain following. Data goes straight from the LANTIRN pod into the flight control system and allows the pod to fly the aeroplane over any terrain.

The addition of LANTIRN allows the Block 40 to undertake precision attacks. These 23rd Wing aircraft are carrying Mavericks for night CAS.

First flight by an F-16C Block 40 (87-0350) was made at Fort Worth on 23 December 1988 by company test pilot Steve Barter. First flight of an F-16D Block 40 (87-0391) was made on 8 February 1989 by Keith Giles and Joe Sweeney. The first F-16C Block 40 was deployed to Luke AFB, Arizona in May 1989.

In September 1983, Turkey announced a Viper 'buy' of 160 F-16s which includes 116 F-16C/D Block 40s (101 F-16Cs, 15 F-16Ds). Eight aircraft in the order were manufactured in Fort Worth and final assembly of 152 aeroplanes is the responsibility of TUSAS Aerospace Industries (TAI) at Murted. Turkey is using 40 LANTIRN navigation pods, 20 targeting pods, and test and support equipment and declared LANTIRN operational for low-level night missions in August 1994.

F-16C/D Block 40 aircraft have been exported to Bahrain (using the programme name Peace Crown), Egypt (Peace Vector), and Israel (Peace Marble) in addition to Turkey (Peace Onyx).

F-16C Block 40 serials: 87-350/0351 (USAF)

F-16C Block 40A serials: 87-0352/0355, 87-0357, 87-0359 (USAF); 88-0033/0037, 89-0022/0033 (Turkey)

F-16D Block 40A serials: 87-0391/0393, (USAF), 88-0014/0015, 89-0042 (Turkey)

F-16C Block 40B serials: 88-0413, 88-0415/0416, 88-0418/0419, 88-0421/0422, 88-0424/0426, 88-0428/0433, 88-0435/0440 (USAF)

F-16C Block 40C serials: 88-0441, 88-0443/0444, 88-0446/0447, 88-0449/0450, 88-0452/0454, 88-0456/0457, 88-0459/88-0460, 88-0462/0463, 88-0465/0468, 88-0470/0471, 88-0473/0474, 88-0476/0477, 88-0479/0480, 88-0482/0483, 88-0485/0486, 88-0488/0489, 88-0491/0492, 88-0494/0495 (USAF)

Above: The first Block 40 was rolled out resplendent with 'Night Falcon' logo to highlight the type's new-found nocturnal capabilities.

Below: Bahrain purchased 12 Block 40 aircraft for its premier fighter squadron at Sheikh Isa air base. Four are two-seaters.

F-16D Block 40C serials: 88-0166, 88-0168, 88-0170 (USAF)

F-16C Block 40D serials: 88-0497/0498, 88-0500/0501, 88-0503/0504, 88-0506/0507, 88-0509/0510, 88-0512/0513, 88-0515/0516, 88-0518/0519, 88-0521/0523, 88-0525/0526, 88-0528/0529, 88-0531/0533, 88-0535/0538, 88-0540/0541, 88-0543/0544, 88-0546/0547, 88-0549/0550 (USAF); 90-0028/0029 (Bahrain 101, 103); 89-0034/0041, 90-0001/0009 (Turkey)

F-16D Block 40D serials: 88-0171/0174 (USAF), 90-0036/0039 (Bahrain 150, 152,

Lockheed F-16 Variants

F-16D Block 40J serials: 90-0791/0792; 90-0794/0796 (USAF); 90-0935/0936 (Egypt 9805/9806); 90-0879/0886 (Israel 612, 615, 619, 621, 624, 628, 630, 633); 91-0022/0024 (Turkey)

F-16C Block 40K serials: 90-0771/0776 (USAF), 90-0908/0922 (Egypt 9912/9926); 90-0863/0870 (Israel 528, 530, 531, 534, 535, 536, 538, 539)

F-16D Block 40K serials: 90-0797/0800 (USAF); 90-0937 (Egypt 9807); 90-0887/0894 (Israel 637, 638, 642, 647, 648, 651, 652, 656)

F-16C Block 40L serials: 90-0923/0930 (Egypt 9927/9934); 90-0871/0874 (Israel 542, 543, 546, 547), 91-0486/0489 (Israel 551, 554, 557, 558); 92-0001/0017 (Turkey)

F-16D Block 40L serials: 90-0895/0898 (Israel 660, 664, 666, 667), 91-0490/0495 (Israel 673, 676, 678, 682, 684, 687); 92-0022/0024 (Turkey)

F-16C Block 40M serial: 90-0953 (Egypt 9935)

F-16D Block 40M serial: 90-0954 (Egypt 9808)

F-16D Block 40N serials: 90-0955/0958 (Egypt 9809/8912), 93-0513/0516 (Egypt 9851/9854)

F-16C Block 40P serials: 92-0018/0021, 93-0001/0014 (Turkey)

F-16D Block 40P serials: 93-0517/0524 (Egypt 9855/9862)

F-16C Block 40Q serials: 93-0485/0487 (Egypt 9951/9953)

F-16C Block 40R serials: 93-0488/0512 (Egypt 9954/9978); 93-0525/0530 (Egypt 9979/9984)

(Plus 60 F-16C Block 40s for Israel; serials not yet assigned)

Turkey's large order for Block 40 aircraft was accompanied by smaller numbers of LANTIRN pods for night interdiction missions. All bar the first eight aircraft were assembled in Turkey by TUSAS from Fort Worth-supplied kits.

154, 156), 89-0043/0045 (Turkey)

F-16C Block 40E serials: 89-2000/2001, 89-2003, 89-2005/2006, 89-2008/2009, 89-2011, 89-2013/2016, 89-2018, 89-2020/2021, 89-2023/2024, 89-2026/2027, 89-2029/2030, 89-2032/2033, 89-2035/2036, 89-2038/2039, 89-2041/2044, 89-2046/2047, 89-2049/2050, 89-2052,

2131, 89-2133/2134, 89-2136/2137, 89-2139/2140, 89-2143 (USAF); 89-0278/0279 (Egypt 9901, 9902)

F-16D Block 40G serials: 89-2172/2174, 89-2176, 89-2178 (USAF)

F-16C Block 40H serials: 89-2144, 89-2146/2147, 89-2149/2150, 89-2152/2153, 90-0703, 90-0709/0711, 90-0714, 90-0717/0718, 90-0723/0725, 90-0733/0736 (USAF); 89-0277 (Israel 502); 90-0850/0854 (Israel 503, 506, 508, 511, 512); 90-0741/0768 (USAF); 90-0899/0907 (Egypt 9903/9911); 90-0855/0862 (Israel 514, 516, 519, 520, 522, 523, 525, 527); 91-0006/0021 (Turkey)

F-16D Block 40H serials: 90-0777, 90-0779/0780; 90-0782, 90-0784 (USAF); 90-0931/0934 (Egypt 9801/9804); 90-0875/0878 (Israel 601, 603, 606, 610)

F-16C Block 40J serials: 90-0742/0745; 90-0753, 90-0756, 90-0763

89-2054 (USAF); 90-0030/0035 (Bahrain 105, 107, 109, 111, 113, 115)

F-16C Block 40F serials: 89-2055, 89-2057/2058, 89-2060/2069, 89-2071/2072, 89-2074/2075, 89-2077/2078, 89-2080/2081, 89-2083/2084, 89-2086/2087, 89-2090, 89-2092/2093, 89-2095/2096, 89-2099, 89-2101/2102 (USAF), 90-0010/0021, 91-0001/0005 (Turkey)

F-16D Block 40F serials: 89-2166/2169, 89-2171 (USAF); 90-0022/0024 (Turkey)

F-16C Block 40G serials: 89-2103/2105, 89-2108, 89-2110/2111, 89-2113, 89-2115/2116, 89-2118/2119, 89-2121/2122, 89-2124/2125, 89-2127, 89-2130/

Egypt switched to General Electric power for its Block 40 aircraft after having acquired PW-engined aircraft from Blocks 15 and 32. Most of the Egyptian aircraft were completed at Fort Worth but the last few from Blocks 40N, P, Q and R are from the TUSAS final assembly line in Turkey.

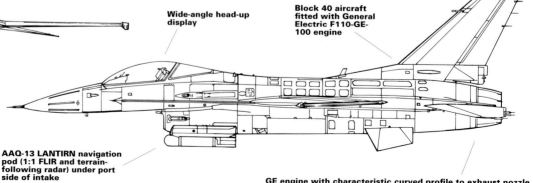

All but the first few F110-powered F-16s have the large 'big lips' intake

AAQ-14 LANTIRN targeting pod (zoom attack FLIR and boresighted laser designator) under starboard side of intake

Wide-angle head-up display

Block 40 aircraft fitted with General Electric F110-GE-100 engine

F-16C Block 40

AAQ-13 LANTIRN navigation pod (1:1 FLIR and terrain-following radar) under port side of intake

GE engine with characteristic curved profile to exhaust nozzle

F-16C/D Block 42 Night Falcon

F-16C/D Block 42 Night Falcon aircraft are virtually identical to Block 40s and are LANTIRN-capable, but were delivered with Pratt & Whitney F100-PW-220 engines. References to some of these aircraft being built with -200 engines or retrofitted with -220Es are in error. Block 42 aircraft have an empty weight of 18,007 lb (8167 kg).

First flight of an F-16C Block 42 (87-0356) was made at Fort Worth on 25 April 1989 by company test pilot Bland Smith. The initial trip aloft by an F-16D Block 42 (87-0394) was accomplished on 26 May 1989 by Joe Sweeney and Tim Eason. The first user of the Block 42 aircraft was the 58th Tactical Training Wing (today's 56th FW) at Luke AFB, Arizona.

F-16C Block 42A serials: 87-0356, 87-0358, 87-0360/0362, 88-0412

F-16D Block 42A serials: 87-0394/0396, 88-0153/0165

F-16C Block 42B serials: 88-0414, 88-0417, 88-0420, 88-0423, 88-0427, 88-0434 (USAF)

F-16C Block 42C serials: 88-0442, 88-0445, 88-8448, 88-0451, 88-0455, 88-0458, 88-0461, 88-0464, 88-0469, 88-0472, 88-0475, 88-0478, 88-0481, 88-0484, 88-0487, 88-0490, 88-0493, 88-0496

F-16D Block 42C serials: 88-0167, 88-0169 (USAF)

F-16C Block 42D serials: 88-0499, 88-0502, 88-0505. 88-0508, 88-0511, 88-0514, 88-0517, 88-0520, 88-0524, 88-0527, 88-0530, 88-0534, 88-0539, 88-0542, 88-0545, 88-0548 (USAF)

F-16D Block 42D serials: 88-0170, 88-0175 (USAF)

F-16C Block 42E serials: 89-2002, 89-2004, 89-2007, 89-2010, 89-2012, 89-2017, 89-2019, 89-2022, 89-2025, 89-2028, 89-2031, 89-2034, 89-2037, 89-2040, 89-2045, 89-2048, 89-2051, 89-2053 (USAF)

F-16D Block 42E serials: 89-2155/2159 (USAF)

F-16C Block 42F serials: 89-2056, 89-

Below: USAF F-16 training is undertaken by the 56th FW at Luke AFB. The furthest aircraft of these Block 42s was the first such variant.

Right: Block 42s serve with several Guard units, including the 112th FS, 180th FG of the Ohio ANG.

2059, 89-2070, 89-2073, 89-2076, 89-2079, 89-2082, 89-2085, 89-2088/2089, 89-2091, 89-2094, 89-2097/2098, 89-2100 (USAF)

F-16D Block 42F serials: 89-2160/2165 (USAF)

F-16C Block 42G serials: 89-2106/2107, 89-2109, 89-2112, 89-2114, 89-2117, 89-2120, 89-2123, 89-2126, 89-2128/2129, 89-2132, 89-2135, 89-2138, 89-2141/2142 (USAF)

F-16D Block 42G serials: 89-2170, 89-2175, 89-2177, 89-2179 (USAF)

F-16C Block 42H serials: 89-2145, 89-2148, 89-2151, 89-2154, 90-0700/0702, 90-0704/0708; 90-0712/0713; 90-0715/0716; 90-0719/90-0722; 90-0726/0732; 90-0737/0740 (USAF)

F-16D Block 42H serials: 90-0778, 90-0781, 90-0783, 90-0785/0787 (USAF)

F-16C Block 42J serials: 90-0741,

90-0746-0752; 90-0754/0755; 90-0757/0762; 90-0764/0768 (USAF)

F-16D Block 42J serials: 90-0788/0793

F-16C Block 42K serials: 90-0769/0770 (USAF)

Below: MiG-killer – this F-16D Block 42, 90-0778, wears a star to mark the MiG-25 the aircraft shot down over Iraq on 27 December 1992. This was the USAF's first F-16 victory, and the first for the AIM-120 missile.

Lockheed F-16 Variants

F-16C/D Block 50/50D

F-16C/D Block 50/52 fighters are not LANTIRN capable, and have the old-style Block 30 HUD (which is still a wide-angle HUD) but with digital instrumentation. These aircraft introduce significantly improved engines. In the case of Block 50, powerplant is a 29,000-lb (129-kN) maximum thrust General Electric F110-GE-129 IPE (Increased Performance Engine). The F-16C/D Block 50 employs Hughes APG-68(V5) radar with advanced signal processing capabilities, ALR-56M Advanced RWR in place of the ALR-69 on earlier aircraft, and improved ALE-47 Group A chaff/flare dispenser system. Block 50/52s have upgraded wheels and brakes which retain the larger size of those on Block

This aircraft was the first Block 50D machine, this variant introducing the capability to carry the ASQ-213 HARM Targeting System.

40/42s but have some improved features. Block 50 'Vipers' have an empty weight of 18,917 lb (8578 kg), making them the heaviest aircraft in the F-16 series.

Since both Blocks 40 and 50 have GE engines, they can be quickly distinguished only by the latter's almond-shaped (rather than triangular) holes in its wheels (which have slightly different brakes) and different HUD.

First flight of an F-16C Block 50 (90-0801)

was made at Fort Worth on 22 October 1991 by company test pilot Keith Giles. The initial flight by an F-16D Block 50 (90-0834)

happened on 1 April 1992 with Steve Barter and Bland Smith on board.

The USAF accepted delivery of its first

Lockheed F-16C Block 50/52

1 Pitot head/air data probe
2 Glass-fibre radome
3 Lightning conducting strips
4 Planar radar scanner
5 Radome hinge point, opens to starboard
6 Scanner tracking mechanism
7 ILS glideslope antenna
8 Radar mounting bulkhead
9 Incidence vane, port and starboard
10 IFF antenna
11 GBU-12B laser-guided bomb
12 AN/APG-68 digital pulse-Doppler, multi-mode radar equipment bay
13 Forward oblique radar warning antennas, port and starboard
14 Front pressure bulkhead
15 Static ports
16 Fuselage forebody strake fairing
17 Forward avionics equipment bay
18 Canopy jettison charge
19 Instrument panel shroud
20 Instrument panel, multi-function CRT head-down displays
21 Sidestick controller, fly-by-wire control system
22 Video recorder
23 GEC wide-angle head-up display
24 CBU-52/58/71 submunition dispenser
25 LAU-3A 19-round rocket launcher
26 2.75-in (68-mm) FFAR
27 CBU-87/89 Gator submunition dispenser
28 Starboard intake flank (No. 5R) stores pylon adaptor
29 LANTIRN (FLIR) targeting pod
30 One-piece frameless cockpit canopy
31 Ejection seat headrest
32 McDonnell-Douglas ACES II zero-zero ejection seat
33 Side console panel
34 Canopy frame fairing
35 Canopy external emergency release
36 Engine throttle lever incorporating HOTAS (hands-on throttle-and-stick) radar controls
37 Canopy jettison handle
38 Cockpit section frame structure
39 Boundary layer splitter plate
40 Fixed-geometry engine air intake
41 Nosewheel, aft retracting
42 LANTIRN (FLIR/TFR) navigation pod
43 Port intake flank (No. 5L) stores pylon adaptor

44 Port position light
45 Intake duct framing
46 Intake ducting
47 Gun gas suppression muzzle aperture
48 Aft avionics equipment bay
49 Cockpit rear pressure bulkhead
50 Canopy hinge point
51 Ejection seat launch rails
52 Canopy rotary actuator
53 Conditioned air delivery duct
54 Canopy sealing frame
55 Canopy aft glazing
56 600-US gal (500-Imp gal; 2271-litre) external fuel tank
57 Garrett hydrazine turbine emergency power unit (EPU)
58 Hydrazine fuel tank
59 Fuel tank bay access panel
60 Forward fuselage bag-type fuel tank, total internal capacity 6972 lb (3162 kg)
61 Fuselage upper longeron
62 Conditioned air ducting
63 Cannon barrels
64 Forebody frame construction
65 Air system ground connection
66 Ventral air conditioning system equipment bay
67 Centreline 300-US gal (250-Imp gal; 1136-litre) fuel tank
68 Mainwheel door hydraulic actuator
69 Mainwheel door
70 Hydraulic system ground connectors
71 Gun bay ventral gas vent
72 GE M61A1 Vulcan 20-mm rotary cannon
73 Ammunition feed chute
74 Hydraulic gun drive motor
75 Port hydraulic reservoir
76 Centre fuselage integral fuel tank
77 Leading-edge flap drive hydraulic motor
78 Ammunition drum with 511 rounds
79 Upper position light/refuelling floodlight
80 TACAN antenna
81 Hydraulic accumulator
82 Starboard hydraulic reservoir
83 Leading-edge flap drive shaft
84 Inboard, No. 6 stores station 4,500-lb (2041-kg) capacity
85 Pylon attachment hardpoint
86 Leading-edge flap drive shaft and rotary actuators
87 No. 7 stores hardpoint, capacity 3,500 lb (1588 kg)
88 Starboard forward radar warning antenna
89 Missile launch rails
90 AIM-120 AMRAAM medium-range AAMs

91 MXU-648 baggage pod, carriage of essential ground equipment and personal effects for off-base deployment
92 Starboard leading-edge manoeuvre flap, down position
93 Outboard, No. 8 stores station, capacity 700 lb (318 kg)
94 Wingtip, No. 9 stores station, capacity 425 lb (193 kg)
95 Wingtip AMRAAM
96 Starboard navigation light
97 Fixed portion of trailing edge
98 Static dischargers
99 Starboard flaperon
100 Starboard wing integral fuel tank
101 Fuel system piping
102 Fuel pump
103 Starboard wingroot attachment fishplates
104 Fuel tank access panels
105 Universal air refuelling receptacle (UARSSI), open
106 Engine intake centrebody fairing
107 Airframe mounted accessory equipment gearbox
108 Jet fuel starter
109 Machined wing attachment bulkheads
110 Engine fuel management equipment
111 Pressure refuelling receptacle ventral adaptor
112 Pratt & Whitney F100-PW-229 afterburning turbofan engine
113 VHF/IFF antenna
114 Starboard flaperon hydraulic actuator
115 Fuel tank tail fins
116 Sidebody fairing integral fuel tank
117 Position light
118 Cooling air ram air intake
119 Finroot fairing
120 Forward engine support link
121 Rear fuselage integral fuel tank
122 Thermally insulated tank inner skin
123 Tank access panels
124 Radar warning system power amplifier
125 Finroot attachment fittings
126 Flight control system hydraulic accumulators
127 Multi-spar fin torsion box structure
128 Starboard all-moving tailplane (tailplane panels interchangeable)
129 General Electric F110-GE-129 alternative powerplant

130 Fin leading-edge honeycomb core
131 Dynamic pressure probe
132 Carbon-fibre fin skin panelling
133 VHF comms antenna (AM/FM)
134 Fintip antenna fairing
135 Anti-collision light
136 Threat warning antennas
137 Static dischargers
138 Rudder honeycomb core structure
139 Rudder hydraulic actuator
140 ECM antenna fairing
141 Tail navigation light
142 Variable-area afterburner nozzle
143 Afterburner nozzle flaps
144 Nozzle sealing fairing
145 Afterburner nozzle fueldraulic actuators (5)
146 Port split trailing-edge airbrake panel, open, upper and lower surfaces
147 Airbrake actuating linkage
148 Port all-moving tailplane
149 Static dischargers
150 Graphite-epoxy tailplane skin panels
151 Leading-edge honeycomb construction
152 Corrugated aluminium sub-structure
153 Tailplane pivot mounting
154 Tailplane hydraulic actuator
155 Fuel jettison chamber, port and starboard
156 Afterburner ducting
157 Rear fuselage machined bulkheads

158 Port navigation light
159 AN/ALE-40(VO-4) chaff/flare launcher, port and starboard
160 Main engine thrust mounting, port and starboard
161 Sidebody fairing frame structure
162 Runway arrester hook
163 Composite ventral fin, port and starboard
164 Port flaperon hydraulic actuator
165 Flaperon hinges
166 Port flaperon, lowered
167 External fuel tank tail fairing
168 Flaperon honeycomb core structure
169 Fixed portion of trailing edge
170 Static dischargers
171 Port navigation light
172 Wingtip, No. 1 stores station, capacity 425 lb (193 kg)

173 Port wingtip AMRAAM
174 AGM-88 HARM (High-speed Anti-Radiation Missile)
175 Mk 84 low-drag 2,000-lb (907-kg) HE bomb
176 Mk 83 Snakeye retarded bomb
177 AIM-9L Sidewinder air-to-air missile
178 Missile launch rails
179 No. 2 stores station, capacity 700 lb (318 Kg)
180 No. 3 stores station, capacity 3,500 lb (1588 Kg)
181 Port forward radar warning antenna
182 Mk 82 500 lb (227 kg) HE bombs

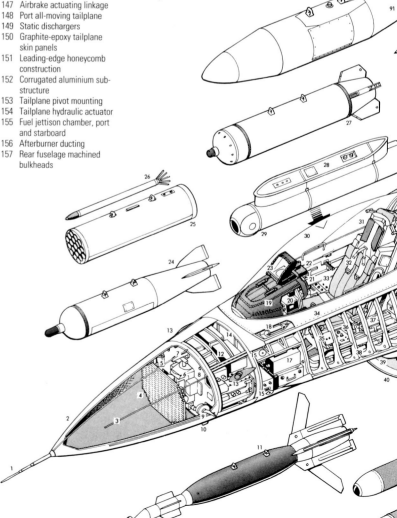

F-16C/D Block 50 aircraft in November 1991. The first user of Block 50 fighters was the 388th Fighter Wing at Hill AFB, Utah.

Block 50/52 were supposed to incorporate an on-board oxygen generating system identical to that on the F-14D Tomcat, as compared with earlier F-16s which have liquid oxygen tanks. It is understood that this system has been delayed.

The USAF has encountered problems with failures in low-time F110 powerplants, possibly caused by a turbine seal problem, which may have caused a loss of an F-16C Block 50 at Hill AFB, Utah on 25 October 1994 and is also being investigated in connection with the three other mishaps.

F-16C/D Block 50 aircraft were reported to be the only tactical aircraft capable of

carrying the Northrop AGM-137 TSSAM (Tri-Service Stand-off Attack Missile) which was under development until the Pentagon announced its cancellation in December 1994.

Incremental changes for Block 50 include the introduction of a Texas Instruments AN/ASQ-213 HARM Targeting System (HTS) which enables the Viper to operate in the SEAD (suppression of enemy air defences) mission independently of the F-4G Advanced Wild Weasel. The HTS-equipped aircraft is known in jargon as the 'mini-D.' The 85th Test Squadron at Eglin

Having been the very first F-16 user, the 388th FW at Hill also became the first to gain Block 50s. These are yellow-tails of the 4th FS.

183 Triple ejector rack
184 Intermediate wing pylon
185 Leading-edge manoeuvre flap honeycomb core structure
186 Flap drive shaft and rotary actuators
187 Multi-spar wing torsion box structure
188 Port wing integral fuel tankage

189 No. 4 stores station hardpoint, capacity 4,500 lb (2041 kg)
190 Wing panel root attachment fishplates
191 Undercarriage leg mounted landing light
192 Articulated retraction/drag link

193 Main undercarriage leg strut
194 Shock absorber strut
195 Port leading-edge manoeuvre flap, down position
196 Inboard wing pylon
197 Port mainwheel, forward retracting
198 Fuel filler caps
199 Port 370-US gal (308-Imp gal; 1400-litre) external tank

200 Centreline, No. 5 stores pylon, capacity 2,200 lb (998 kg)
201 AN/ALQ-184(V)-2 (short) ECM pod
202 AGM-65 Maverick air-to-surface missiles
203 LAU-88 triple missile carrier/launcher

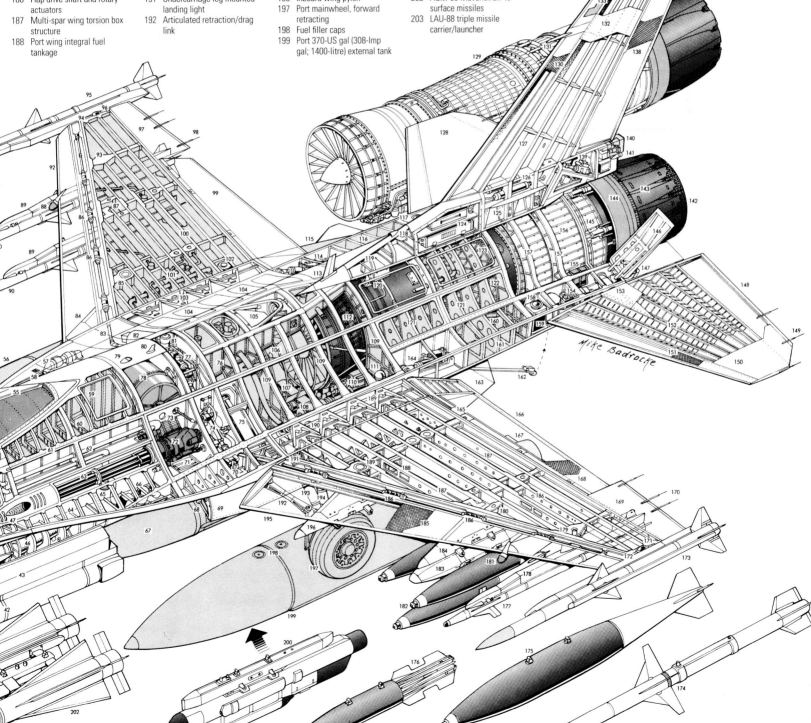

HARM-capable Block 50Ds have been issued to selected units to provide defence suppression. The aircraft are still tasked with conventional duties in addition to lethal SEAD.

AFB, Florida conducted tests with an HTS fitted on the starboard side of the air intake on an F-16D Block 50D (91-0469) early in 1994. These tests were completed in early 1994, enabling the Air Force to employ HTS on new-build Block 50Ds and retrofit it on Block 50Cs. The first Block 50Ds were delivered to the 79th Fighter Squadron, 20th Fighter Wing, at Shaw AFB, South Carolina in 1994 and were almost immediately deployed to the Middle East to support 'no fly' operations against Iraq.

The ASQ-213 pod has also been fitted to selected aircraft with the 23rd Fighter Squadron, 52nd Fighter Wing at Spangdahlem AB, Germany. These aircraft will retain their conventional bombing role while adding SEAD as a secondary duty. In mid-1994, HTS was used by F-16s to launch 12 HARMs in an evaluation programme deemed the key event for declaration of IOC (Initial Operating Capability).

258 F-16C Block 50 (92-0100/0218; 93-0315/0453) and 42 F-16D Block 50 (92-0219/0249; 93-0454/0464) aircraft were cancelled by the USAF.

F-16C Block 50 serials: 90-0801/0804 (USAF)

F-16C Block 50A serials: 90-0805/0808; 90-0810/0812 (USAF)

F-16D Block 50A serials: 90-0834/0838; 90-0840/0841 (USAF)

F-16C Block 50B serials: 90-0813/0833, 91-0336/0338 (USAF)

F-16D Block 50B serials: 90-0842/0849 (USAF)

F-16C Block 50C serials: 91-0339/0359 (USAF)

F-16D Block 50C serials: 91-0462/0465 (USAF)

F-16C Block 50D serials: 91-0360/0361, 91-0363/369; 91-0371/0373; 91-0375/0385; 91-0387/0391; 91-0394/0400; 91-0402/0403; 91-0405/0412; 91-0414/

In Europe the Block 50D flies with the 52nd FW at Spangdahlem, for many years entrusted with defence suppression missions in the theatre.

0423 (USAF) [91-0424/0461 (USAF) cancelled]

F-16D Block 50D serials: 91-0468/0469; 90-0471/0472; 90-0474, 90-0476/0477; 90-0480/0481 (USAF) [91-0482/0485 (USAF) cancelled]

F-16C Block 50P serials: 92-3883/3884; 92-3886/3887; 92-3891/3895; 92-3897; 92-3900/3901; 92-3904, 92-3906/3907; 92-3910, 92-3912/3913; 92-3915, 92-3918/3921; 92-3923 (USAF)

F-16C Block 50Q serials: 93-0532, 93-0534, 93-0536, 93-0538, 93-0540, 93-0542, 93-0544, 93-0546, 93-0548, 93-0550, 93-0552, 93-0554 (USAF)

(Plus 32 F-16C Block 50s and eight F-16D Block 50s for Greece, five F-16C Block 50s and six F-16D Block 50s for Singapore (Peace Carvin), 78 F-16C Block 50s and 12 F-16D Block 50s for Turkey; serials not yet assigned)

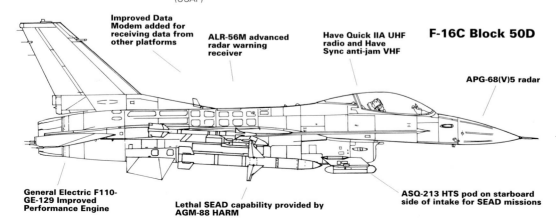

F-16C Block 50D

Improved Data Modem added for receiving data from other platforms

ALR-56M advanced radar warning receiver

Have Quick IIA UHF radio and Have Sync anti-jam VHF

APG-68(V)5 radar

General Electric F110-GE-129 Improved Performance Engine

Lethal SEAD capability provided by AGM-88 HARM

ASQ-213 HTS pod on starboard side of intake for SEAD missions

F-16C/D Block 52/52D

F-16C Block 52 fighters are virtually identical to Block 50s but are powered by the 29,000-lb (129-kN) maximum thrust Pratt & Whitney F100-PW-229 IPE (Increased Performance Engine). Some aircraft were temporarily retrofitted with earlier F100 engines in July 1991 while P&W resolved a problem in the IPE's fourth-stage compressor blade. Tactical Air Command (today's Air Combat Command) issued a TCTO (Time Compliance Technical Order) mandating the change, which was in effect until IPE blade problems were resolved in October 1991. Block 52 aircraft have an empty weight of 18,591 lb (8432 kg). One feature of Block 52 aircraft not found on any other Fighting Falcon variant is that the exhaust outlet's 'turkey feathers' are a glossy black petrochemical material.

First flight of an F-16C Block 52 (90-0809) was made at Fort Worth by Steve Barter on 22 October 1992. First flight of an F-16D Block 52 (90-0893) was made by Joe Sweeney and Barter on 24 November 1992.

The first of 120 F-16C/D Block 52s for South Korea was delivered in early December 1994. Korean F-16s will subsequently be armed with the AGM-84 Harpoon all-weather anti-ship missile.

F-16C Block 52A serial: 90-0809 (USAF)

F-16D Block 52A serial: 90-0839

F-16C Block 52D serials: 91-0362, 91-0370, 91-0374, 91-0386, 91-0392/0393, 91-0401, 91-0404, 91-0413 (USAF)

F-16D Block 52D serials: 91-0466/0467; 91-0470, 91-0473, 91-0475, 91-0478/0479

F-16C Block 52G serial: 92-4000 (Korea)

F-16D Block 52G serials: 92-4028/4031 (Korea)

F-16C Block 52H serial: 92-4001 (Korea)

Block 52D aircraft have recently been assigned to the 366th Wing at Mountain Home. Two of the wing's squadrons fly F-15s, so the choice of the Pratt-engined F-16 for the 389th FS was logical to ease maintenance and logistics problems.

F-16D Block 52H serials: 92-4032/4037 (Korea)

F-16C Block 52J serials: 92-4002/4003 (Korea)

F-16C Block 52K serials: 92-4004/4008 (Korea)

F-16D Block 52K serial: 92-4038 (Korea)

F-16C Block 52L serials: 92-4009/4013 (Korea)

F-16D Block 52L serial: 92-4039 (Korea)

F-16C Block 52M serials: 92-4014/4017 (Korea)

F-16D Block 52M serials: 92-4040/4041 (Korea)

F-16C Block 52N serials: 92-4018/4027 (Korea)

F-16D Block 52N serials: 92-4042/4047 (Korea)

F-16C Block 52P serials: 92-3880/3882; 92-3885, 92-3888/3890; 92-3896, 92-3898/3899; 92-3902/3903; 92-3905, 92-3908/3909; 92-3911, 92-3914, 92-3916/3917; 92-3922 (USAF)

F-16C Block 52P serials: 92-3924/3927 (USAF)

F-16C Block 52Q serials: 93-0531, 93-0533, 93-0535, 93-0537, 93-0539, 93-0541, 93-0543, 93-0545, 93-0547, 93-0549, 93-0551, 93-0553 (USAF)

(Plus 62 additional F-16C Block 52s and 20 additional F-16D Block 52s for Korea; serials not yet assigned)

Above: A Block 52D displays the defence suppression configuration with HTS pod. The Block 52 is notable for having a black covering to some of the exhaust nozzle, unique to the F100-PW-229 IPE.

Below: This F-16D Block 52D serves with the 57th Wing at Nellis, specifically the 422nd TES which evluates and devises new operational tactics. In addition to the HTS and AGM-88, the aircraft carries an AGM-65 Maverick missile, itself a useful SEAD tool.

F-16C/D Israel

Israel has the most diverse 'mix' of Fighting Falcons of any operator today, ranging from early F-16A Block 10 'small tail' aircraft (at least 50 of which were delivered recently, and others of which were originally Block 5s) to Block 40 aeroplanes. Israel has its own names for the aircraft: Netz (Hawk) for the F-16A/B, Barak (Lightning) for the F-16C, and Brakeet (Thunderbolt) for the F-16D

Among overseas users, Israel is unique in having applied the innovations of its own aerospace industry to its F-16 fighters. Most or all Israeli F-16s have major differences which set them apart from production Fighting Falcons employed by other air arms.

Like earlier F-16s, Israeli F-16Cs have been fitted with a number of locally specified equipment items including Elta EL/L-8240 ECM to replace Loral Rapport III and AN/ALE-40 chaff/flare dispensers (or an indigenous equipment) in lieu of newer AN/ALE-47s found on C models elsewhere, scabbed to the fins of some aircraft. The local BVR company's rangeless ACM debriefing system can also be fitted to Israeli Defence Force/Air Force (IDF/AF) F-16s. Packaged into an inert AIM-9 airframe, this uses a differential GPS to record the exact tracks of aircraft for replay during debriefings. Israeli F-16s may have extensive modifications, with different avionics and higher gross weight, requiring changes in the landing gear and new wheels. One source gives a maximum all-up weight of 48,000 lb (21772 kg) for an Israeli F-16C as compared with 42,300 lb (19186 kg) for a standard USAF F-16C Block 40.

Some Israeli F-16s may use an indigenous radar such as the Elta 2021B or 2032 in lieu of the APG-68. A prominent feature of all Israeli F-16Ds is a 'hump' fillet on the dorsal spine of the aircraft carrying Israeli-made avionics, possibly the Elisra SPS 300 ECM jamming system, for anti-SAM operations. Other speculation is that the 'hump' on some of these aircraft is for a nuclear delivery capability. The 'hump' is fitted at the Fort Worth factory during construction.

Above: Vapour boils from the leading-edge root extensions of an Israeli F-16D Block 40L. Quite apart from the bulged spine and brake parachute, an obvious Israeli modification is the ECM antenna fairing on the intake side, with navigation light mounted on the end.

Below: Carrying Rafael Python 3 missiles, this F-16C Block 30 is testing the Rafael Litening pod. This has a stabilised FLIR and laser designator, similar to the LANTIRN targeting pod, and is used for the delivery of laser-guided weapons.

Above: A Block 40 aircraft takes off on a test flight from Fort Worth. An addition to the Israeli Block 40s is an antenna fairing under the intake.

Below: Carrying an unidentified pod, this F-16D carries an out-of-sequence serial, and may be undertaking tests at Fort Worth.

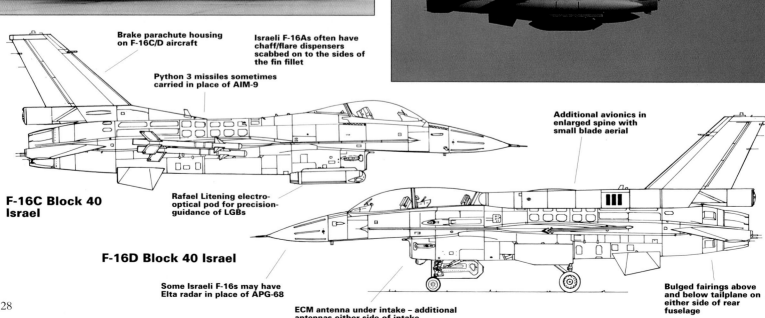

Brake parachute housing on F-16C/D aircraft

Israeli F-16As often have chaff/flare dispensers scabbed on to the sides of the fin fillet

Python 3 missiles sometimes carried in place of AIM-9

Additional avionics in enlarged spine with small blade aerial

F-16C Block 40 Israel

Rafael Litening electro-optical pod for precision-guidance of LGBs

F-16D Block 40 Israel

Some Israeli F-16s may have Elta radar in place of APG-68

ECM antenna under intake – additional antennas either side of intake

Bulged fairings above and below tailplane on either side of rear fuselage

Mitsubishi FS-X/TFS-X

The FS-X assembled by Mitsubishi is Japan's fighter project based upon the F-16C and powered by the General Electric F110-GE-129. Production examples of the GE engine will be manufactured under licence in Japan by Ishikawajima-Harima Heavy Industries.

The FS-X closely resembles the F-16C but has a 25 per cent larger wing, a stretched fuselage with a longer nose, and a drag chute. Its canopy is reinforced with a bow frame in front because of mission requirements for low-level flight and the risk of bird strikes. The FS-X makes extensive use of co-cured composite technology throughout the wing to cut weight by about one-third and to reduce radar signature. The FS-X's maximum take-off weight is about 49,000 lb (22226 kg) as compared to 42,300 lb (19186 kg) for a standard USAF F-16C Block 40. The FS-X has a wing span of 36 ft (11.14 m) as compared with 32 ft 9 ¾ in (10.14 m) for an F-16C. Fuselage length is 50 ft 1 in (15.27 m), contrasted with the American fighter's 49 ft 6 in (15.03 m). The FS-X has larger horizontal tail surfaces than the F-16C but has dispensed with canards which were part of the original design.

The FS-X will employ a phased array radar using an electronically steered antenna and developed by Mitsubishi Electric. The Japanese fighter has two more stores stations on the wings than an F-16. In addition to familiar weaponry such as the AIM-9L Sidewinder, the FS-X will carry two or four Mitsubishi ASM-2 anti-submarine missiles.

Japan's Defence Agency has ordered two single-seat and two dual-seat TFS-X prototypes, plus two ground test articles. The official requirement is for 130 fighters for the JASDF (Japan Air Self-Defence Force) although the figure is expected to drop, perhaps as low as three squadrons of 18 fighters each plus attrition aircraft and trainers.

Japan announced in October 1987 that the F-16 had been selected as the basis for its FS-X programme. Critics have charged that the US is giving away technology under this co-development arrangement.

Above right: The full-scale mock-up of the FS-X shows the revised canopy arrangement with a stiffening bow to meet JASDF birdstrike requirements.

Right: The first prototype FS-X (63-0001) is seen at its public roll-out, wearing the markings of the TRDI, the central trials establishment.

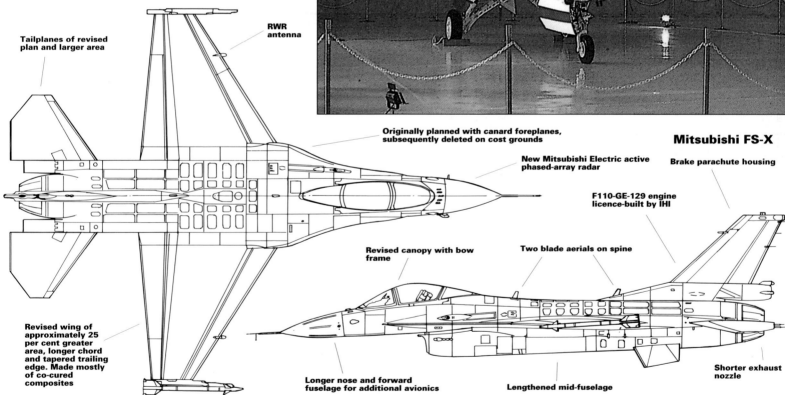

Tailplanes of revised plan and larger area

RWR antenna

Originally planned with canard foreplanes, subsequently deleted on cost grounds

New Mitsubishi Electric active phased-array radar

Mitsubishi FS-X

Brake parachute housing

F110-GE-129 engine licence-built by IHI

Two blade aerials on spine

Revised canopy with bow frame

Revised wing of approximately 25 per cent greater area, longer chord and tapered trailing edge. Made mostly of co-cured composites

Longer nose and forward fuselage for additional avionics

Lengthened mid-fuselage

Shorter exhaust nozzle

F-16C/D Block 60/62

The proposed F-16C/D Block 60 aircraft would have an internal targeting and navigation system similar to LANTIRN with only the sensor heads outside the aircraft and an auxiliary power unit, and would be powered by the GE IPE engine. The Block 62 would be similar but feature the Pratt & Whitney F100-PW-229 IPE. Internal fuel capacity would be increased by using a dorsal spine similar in shape to that of Israel's F-16Ds. Lockheed's sales effort is currently focused on the Block 50/52 series, and the manufacturer appears not to be soliciting interest in Block 60/62.

The designation F/A-16C/D has also been mentioned in connerction with the Block 60/62, highlighting the attack potential of this proposed variant.

F-16X and F-16U

The designations F-16X and F-16U refer to the same proposal, resulting from the family of designs which started with the F-16XL (separate entry) and included the Falcon 2000.

Lockheed proposed in 1993 to develop an F-16X version of the Fighting Falcon with no horizontal tail and with a modified version of the wing found on the F-22 fighter. The F-16X would go into production in time to replace the bulk of the F-16C/D fleet, from 2010. The F-16X requires a 'go ahead' from the Pentagon, not seen as likely in today's environment; this would be followed by construction of an F-16X demonstrator at the company's Skunk Works in Palmdale, California.

Using the F-16X concept, Lockheed proposed the F-16U in 1994 for the United Arab Emirates (UAE) which has been seeking to underwrite development of its own version of advanced US fighters. The UAE has also been looking at a McDonnell F-15U+ (F-15U Plus). The F-16U proposed by Lockheed will feature a larger delta wing derived from the F-16XL programme.

At one point, the F-16X was the basis for Lockheed's proposal for US Air Force multi-role fighter (MRF), itself a concept developed as an F-16 replacement. The MRF project was cancelled in early planning stages.

Robert F. Dorr

Spanish
Guardians
From the cockpit of José Terol
(with additional photography by Hans Nijhuis)

As an EF-18 pilot with Escuadrón 121, José Terol owns the most sought-after place in the Spanish air force. With him, **World Air Power Journal** looks at life in the Spanish Hornet community.

Top: The 1994 decision to contribute to Operation Deny Flight has taken the Ejercito del Aire's F/A-18s into a new realm of operations. Extensive systems upgrades and effective pilot training means the Spanish Hornets and their crews are among the most capable aircraft at NATO's disposal.

Above left: Spain bucked the European trend towards the F-16 with its 1983 order for 72 Hornets (down from a projected 84, with 69 surviving). Two units operate the type, Ala de Caza 12 (Torrejon) and Grupo 15 (Zaragoza) – the latter's badge is seen here. Each unit has two operational Escuadrónes (121/122 and 151/152). Ala 12 maintains a third notional squadron, as the Hornet OCU. In 1996 Grupo 21 will equip with 24 ex-USN F/A-18s.

Right: Spain's 12 two-seat Hornets are fully combat-capable and suffer only from a reduced fuel load (down by six per cent) as compared to the single-seat aircraft.

Left: The Hornet was major leap for the pilots that had spent the previous years with F-4Cs. José Terol flew Phantoms from 1989 until 1991, when Escuadrón 121 ('Poker Sqn') transitioned to the EF-18A.

Left and above: Eight Hornets were deployed for Red Flag 94-4. Tanker support came in the form of six KC-130Hs and two Boeing 707TTs. The Hercules also provided SAR coverage with air-droppable survival gear, while the 707s carried most of the required personnel for the three-week deployment and supervised the oceanic crossing. Ala 45 has two Sargent-Fletcher refuelling pod-equipped 707s, along with a third VIP aircraft.

Above: Prior to their first Red Flag deployment, Spanish Hornets had exercised over the British Aerospace-operated North Sea Air Combat Range. Frequent adversaries were French air force Mirage 2000s, which the Spanish pilots credited as qualified BVR opponents. Upon their visit to Red Flag 94-4, the Spanish pilots were faced with a much more tactically challenging environment, where they could also practise their air-to-ground skills.

Right: C-130Hs and KC-130Hs are also based at Zaragoza, with Ala 31, of which Grupo 15 is now a subordinate. KC-130s supported the F/A-18 deployment to Red Flag, before engaging in combat assault, C-SAR and air-drop training over the Nellis ranges.

Above: Spanish Hornets are designated EF-18s (España – Spain). Three two-seat EF-18Bs were deployed to Red Flag to give newly-qualified pilots some experience of combat training. The EF-18Bs are now spread 'six and six' between the two Hornet bases of Torrejon and Zaragoza.

Below: Between 1992 and 1995 the EF-18A/B fleet was upgraded to EF-18A+/B+ standard, incorporating new avionics and EW systems and adding AIM-120 capability. This makes Spain's Lots 17- to 31-standard Hornets equivalent to US Navy F/A-18C/Ds.

Right: Escuadrón 152 is specifically tasked with the SEAD mission, using AGM-88 HARM and LGBs (GBU-10 and GBU-16). Its sister unit, Esc 151, is primarily an all-weather interceptor unit (offensive/defensive counter-air), with a secondary fighter-bomber role.

Right: During Red Flag 94-4, Spanish Hornets undertook 118 missions – 52 interdiction, 34 CAS, 14 SEAD and a number of familiarisation and work-up sorties. With the decision made to support Operation Deny Flight, or Operación Icaro in Spanish terms, rapid last-minute changes were made to the EF-18 contingent to include HARM-qualified aircrew and ground crew.

Below: Despite the availability of LGBs and AN/AAS-38A NITE Hawk targeting pods (visible on this aircraft), the weapon of choice for EF-18 CAS and interdiction sorties was the Mk 82 bomb. Live weapons were always used.

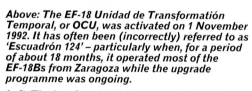

Above: The EF-18 Unidad de Transformatión Temporal, or OCU, was activated on 1 November 1992. It has often been (incorrectly) referred to as 'Escuadrón 124' – particularly when, for a period of about 18 months, it operated most of the EF-18Bs from Zaragoza while the upgrade programme was ongoing.

Left: The last Spanish F-5s are a mix of F-5As, RF-5As and F-5Bs which serve with Ala 23, the air force fast-jet training school. The F-5Bs have been upgraded by Bristol Aerospace and have a secondary CAS role using a laser designator operated by the backseater. Some students are 'fast tracked' on USAF T-38s, and complete only a short jet course with Ala 23.

Bottom left: After nine months of ground instruction, simulator time and 61 sorties, a new pilot is declared Limited Combat Ready and moves to operational training with a specific squadron.

Above: A full load of three tanks proves a necessity for the EF-18B. Even the single-seat aircraft have a mission duration of only 90 minutes with this much extra fuel. Another Red Flag essential was GPS, borrowed from the USAF.

Right: Zaragoza, in north-eastern Spain, is a busy base which accommodates two Hornet Escuadrónes, two Hercules Escuadrónes and a Do 27 unit. Mando Aérea de Levante, or Eastern Air Command, is headquartered there also.

Below: Spain's Hornets will remain in use until 2010 at least, and are scheduled for an MLU between 1999 and 2002.

South African Air Force
Suid-Afrikaanse Lugmag

The democratisation of South Africa and the end of the old apartheid regime has brought an end to the state of virtual war which existed between the country and its immediate neighbours. This in turn has led to a dramatic reduction in the military threat facing South Africa, and its armed forces have been forced to scale down and redeploy in the light of the changed situation. While the emergence of a new democratic government has had many advantages, including an end to sanctions, the armed forces have also faced new problems. The SAAF has been starved of funding and has had to integrate new members drawn from the military wing of the old enemy, and the race is on to replace the old leadership. As it celebrates its Diamond Jubilee in 1995, the South African Air Force can look forward to the future with a degree of confidence. With democracy established, South Africa can take its place as a member of the world community, and the SAAF, smaller and leaner than before, will act as guarantor of the new nation's security, building on proud traditions resulting from participation in World War II. Even the years of isolation have left a valuable legacy, forcing the establishment of an indigenous armaments industry which became a world leader in many fields.

On 2 February 1990 State President Frederik de Klerk announced that South Africa would break with its past, setting a course which would lead to democracy. This was finally achieved on 10 May 1994 when a new Government of National Unity, led by Nelson Mandela, assumed office, ending some 300 years of European and colonial rule, which began with the Dutch occupation of the Cape of Good Hope in 1652. Following was a period of British influence, during which South Africa was a full Dominion within the British Empire, a position reinforced by the establishment of the Union of South Africa in 1910. White rule culminated in a four-decade period where the domestic policies of the government of the day thrust the country into isolation.

A beginning

South African military aviation dates back to 1914, when five South African pilots were attached to the British Royal Flying Corps. These officers were quickly recalled to form the basis of the South African Aviation Corps, whose Farman F27s operated alongside a pair of detached British RNAS BE.2cs in operations against German forces in South West Africa. When the Germans surrendered in July 1915, the Corps was disbanded. Several of its members volunteered for further service, however, and returned to England to form No. 26 (South African) Squadron, which was subsequently sent to Kenya, where South African and British troops were fighting German forces. Apart from these purely South African squadrons, some 3,000 South Africans flew with the RFC, RNAS and RAF during the World War I, these including several aces, a future Marshal of the Royal Air Force, Sir Hugh Saunders, and a VC winner, Andrew Weatherby Beauchamp-Proctor, who scored 41 victories.

It was on 1 February 1920 – just one year and 11 months after the Royal Air Force came into being – that the South African Air Force was formally founded as an independent entity. It possessed 113 aircraft comprising Avro 504Ks, SE.5As, DH.4s and DH.9s and BE.2es. The majority of these (some 100 aircraft) were an Imperial Gift from Britain. RAF influence was strong in the newly formed air arm, since most of its pilots had flown with the RFC and RAF during the war. Many RAF traditions remain to this day.

The SAAF saw action when it was asked to participate in the quelling of the 1922 miners' strike. Two DH.9s were written off and one crashed during this operation, the only time the SAAF ever operated against its own people within the borders of South Africa. During the 1920s the SAAF did not expand, and it was only in 1930 that 20 Avro Avians were acquired to replace the Avro 504s. In 1931 the first of 27 locally-built Westland Wapitis was delivered. A Gloster AS.31 survey aircraft was acquired in 1933, followed by three DH.66 Hercules transports in 1934. Seven Hawker Furies were acquired to replace obsolete SE.5As in the fighter role (although the ancient World War I scouts remained in service for some time thereafter). Modern monoplanes, in the form of seven Airspeed Envoys, arrived in 1936. These deliveries were followed by 65 locally-built Hawker Hartbees (in addition to four imported examples), and by 52 Avro Tutors, with 100 ex-RAF Hawker Harts following for use in the advanced training role.

At war again

With war clouds looming in Europe, the first truly modern aircraft arrived in 1939. These comprised six Hawker Hurricane Mk Is, along with single examples of the Fairey Battle and Bristol Blenheim Mk I light bombers. The outbreak of war in 1939 thus caught the SAAF unprepared for large-scale operational deployment. When the South African Parliament voted against neutrality, effectively committing South Africa to World War II, the SAAF had 221 aircraft, but most of these were the survivors of the types delivered during the early 1930s. The situation was improved, at least on the transport front, when the country's entire population of civil aircraft, including South African Airways' fleet of Junkers Ju 52/3ms and Ju 86s, was impressed into the military. Despite this, the SAAF entered the war with only about 100 front-line aircraft, most of which were obsolete. As SAAF participation in the war progressed, expansion and modernisation became phenomenal. Apart from safeguarding the South African coast, the SAAF was deployed further afield, to the theatres of East Africa, North Africa, Madagascar, the Mediterranean, the Balkans, Italy and Europe. Perhaps the most important part played by the SAAF was its participation in the drive through North Africa, Italy and the Balkans, during which SAAF fighter, fighter-bomber and bomber squadrons played a vital part, equipped with a range of aircraft types, including Gauntlets, Gladiators, Hurricanes, Kitty-hawks, Mustangs, Spitfires, Ansons, Beauforts, Wellingtons, Baltimores, Marylands, Bostons, Marauders, Venturas, Beaufighters, Catalinas and Liberators. Full details of the SAAF war effort would be impossible to relate in this analysis, yet it is worthy of note that the SAAF itself flew a total of 82,401 wartime missions, in which 2,227 SAAF members lost their lives. Besides this, many South Africans served with RAF units, some as attached members of the SAAF, others having joined the RAF itself before the war. Such men included Group Captain Adolph 'Sailor' Malan, arguably the RAF's greatest fighter leader, and Captain Edwin Swales, SAAF, who won a posthumous Victoria Cross while serving as a Master Bomber marking targets with No. 8 Pathfinder Group. Another South African VC winner was Squadron Leader John Nettleton, RAF, another Lancaster pilot.

At home, South Africa made an offer to Britain to establish flying training facilities. This resulted in the Joint Air Training Scheme, probably the largest single operation every undertaken by the SAAF, although it was undertaken in partnership with the RAF. As part of the Commonwealth's Empire Air Training Scheme, 33,347 aircrew were trained for the RAF, SAAF and Allied air forces at 38 South African Flying Training Schools. As the the war widened, a shuttle air service between South Africa and northern Africa was established in 1941. After the war, Venturas, Sunderlands and Dakotas operating on this service flew home thousands of South African servicemen. Remarkably, many of the participating Dakotas still survive in SAAF service to this day.

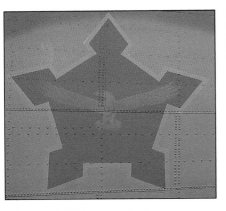

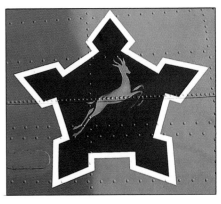

Above and right: The insignia of the new South African Air Force has an eagle superimposed on the stylised fort. The new national flag integrates the colours of the new and old South Africas.

Above: The old springbok insignia is fast disappearing in South Africa, since it is felt to represent the old order. High-visibility markings are also disappearing, except on second-line types.

Above: The Mirage F1AZs of No. 1 Squadron are the SAAF's only dedicated fighter-bombers.

Below: A couple of Mirage F1CZs remain airworthy, one serving as a glass cockpit testbed, for a proposed Mirage F1AZ upgrade.

Above: A Mirage F1AZ of No. 1 Squadron wears an unusual brown and green camouflage, in place of the original sand/green.

Below: Most Mirage F1AZs now wear an overall toned-down grey colour scheme, with only the upper surfaces camouflaged.

The immediate post-war period saw the inevitable scaling down of SAAF activities. A large-scale disposal of aircraft took place, many being returned to the USA under the terms of lend-lease agreements, with many others being sold for scrap. Some lend-lease aircraft were, however, retained by the SAAF. These included a sizeable number of Harvards, and some 80 Dakotas. In 1946, in a vastly reduced SAAF, flying training was performed using Tiger Moths, Harvards and B-34 Venturas at the Central Flying School at Dunnottar. Harvards were also used for training at operational squadron level. The type served in large numbers with the Bombing, Gunnery and Air Navigation School at Langebaanweg, serving beside Ansons, and B-34 and PV-1 Venturas. The Dakota was the SAAF's standard transport aircraft, but Ansons, Venturas and Rapides were also used together with a single VIP-configured Avro York, all of these serving with 28 Squadron at Zwartkop. Maritime patrols were performed by the 15 Short Sunderland GR.Mk Vs of No. 35 Squadron (replacing Catalinas) at Congella Durban, aided by the PV-1 Venturas of Nos 17 and 22 Squadrons at Brooklyn Air Station (later known as Ysterplaat). B-34 Venturas were also used to augment the Mosquitos of No. 60 Squadron as the standard bomber. Photographic reconnaissance and surveys were performed by DH Mosquitoes and by a small number of modified Ansons. At Potchefstroom Air Station, Harvards performed tactical reconnaissance sorties, with AOP duties being flown by No. 42 AOP Flight's Auster Mk Vs at the same base. A few Avro Ansons were fitted out for aerial spraying to combat the tstetse fly menace in Zululand. The surviving Hurricanes were no longer an economically viable proposition to maintain, so a number of Spitfire Mk IXs were ordered. The first, of an eventual total of 137, was delivered in April 1947, equipping Nos 1 and 2 Squadrons and part of No. 60 Squadron. Nos 1 and 2 Squadrons formed the SAAF's mobile fighter attack force, and were nominally based at Waterkloof. RAF Spitfires, 'on loan', had been used by several squadrons during the war, but these new deliveries were the first to wear SAAF serials.

Importance of the Reserves

The small core of full-time active squadrons were augmented by the reserve units of the Active Citizen Force (equivalent to the British Royal Auxiliary Air Force) and by the pupil pilot scheme (equivalent to the RAF's Reserve Flying Schools). The Citizens Force scheme continued into the late 1980s, and relied on taking military-trained pilots (from the RAF, Rhodesian or South African Air Forces) and using them as required, paying them only for the duty time they actually put in, and not having to provide social infrastructure like housing. Several squadrons had Citizens Force elements (including Nos 27, 41 and 44) and there were separate Citizens Force Squadrons (including Nos 4, 5, 6, 7, 8 and 40), which had only a small regular core, and which flew Harvards and later Impalas. As the SAAF down-sized, the Citizen Force elements were wound down and disbanded, or reformed as active squadrons.

International operations by the SAAF were not uncommon. During 1946 and 1947 Avro Ansons were sent to Tanganyika to spray a plague of red locusts, for example. The following year

the SAAF was called upon to contribute aircrews for the Anglo-American Berlin Airlift. SAAF crews flew no fewer than 2,500 missions in RAF Dakotas, mainly operating from Lubeck. By the time the blockade was lifted, South African crews had lifted 8,333 tons of supplies into West Berlin.

The remainder of the late 1940s produced little more than the delivery of the first of three Sikorsky S-51s to No. 12 Squadron in 1948. These S-51s were the first helicopters in South Africa, and were fitted out as tsetse fly sprayers to replace Ansons which had proved only marginally suitable. The other notable event at that time was the allocation of the first jet, even though this aircraft was only on loan. A single RAF Gloster Meteor Mk III was evaluated for a 30-month period, flying some 185 hours. By the time the Meteor was repatriated to the UK in August 1948, the SAAF had made up its mind as to which type would become the force's first jet interceptor, and the replacement for the Spitfire. It was not to be the Meteor, however. In October 1948, the single-engined de Havilland Vampire FB.Mk 5 was chosen to usher the SAAF into the jet age, when 10 aircraft were ordered.

War in Korea

Before the Vampire could become operational, the Korean War broke out as Communist North Korea invaded the South on 25 June 1950. South Africa offered the services of No. 2 (Cheetah) Squadron, and in September the first group of pilots and ground crew left South Africa to join the USAF's 18th Fighter-Bomber Wing, flying F-51D Mustangs. Later, in March 1953, No. 2 Squadron converted to F-86F Sabres. By the time the South Africans returned, the SAAF had flown a total of 12,067 sorties for the loss of 34 pilots. Seventy-four out of 94 Mustangs and four out of 22 Sabres had been lost. The surviving aircraft were returned to their owner, the US Air Force. None went to South Africa.

Pilots destined for Korea continued to be trained on Spitfires at the BG & ANS, Langebaanweg, but these were eventually phased out in 1954. The re-equipment programme of the 1950s had commenced with the introduction of the first 10 Vampire FB.Mk 5s in February 1950, as the standard front-line interceptor. These were augmented by an additional 10 FB.Mk 52s during the second half of 1951, followed by six T.Mk 11 operational trainers just a year later. Vampire deliveries continued with the first of a batch of 30 FB.Mk 52s in June 1953, and then by the first of 21 T.Mk 55 trainers, these arriving a year later. The Vampire's time as a front-line aircraft of Nos 1 and 2 Squadrons was rather limited, however. The SAAF had gained a very favourable impression of the Sabre in Korea, and consequently selected the type to replace the Vampire, preferring the improved Orenda-powered Canadair CL-13B to the American-built F-86E or F-86F. In September 1956, the first Sabre was taken on charge, and 34 were eventually delivered to re-equip Nos 1 and 2 Squadrons.

While the fighter force modernised, other communities continued to operate less modern aircraft types. The antiquated Sunderlands, as well as the last PV-1 Venturas, were still soldiering on in the maritime patrol role for example. This situation was soon to change. Eight Avro Shackleton MR.Mk 3s were ordered to replace the Sunderlands, and the first of the big Avros arrived in

1957. Venturas continued in the close inshore patrol role with No. 35 Squadron, alongside the new Shackletons, and for navigation training with the Air Navigation School. They were finally replaced by Dakotas in both roles during 1960.

The Dakota continues

The venerable Dakota continued as the SAAF's only transport aircraft and fulfilled a variety of tasks, even operating long-distance VIP flights to Britain. A single Viscount 781D was acquired for No. 28 Squadron in 1958 as a more suitable long-range aircraft. Earlier, in 1955, two Herons were bought for No. 28 Squadron's VIP flight to augment the nine DH Devons procured during 1949. In the AOP role, the few war-time Auster Mk 5s were supplemented by five Auster AOP.Mk 6s and two AOP.Mk 9s between 1953 and 1957. No. 17 Squadron operated the single surviving Sikorsky S-51 and three S-55Cs (delivered from 1956 onwards), initially on air-sea rescue duties, but later in a wider variety of roles.

The 1960s saw the SAAF embarking on a massive modernisation programme, prompted by overseas opposition to the South African government's internal policies. Attempts to isolate South Africa were frequent, and the perceived threat to the country's sovereignty was such that rearmament became necessary. Many of the older types in service (such as the Harvard, Dakota, Vampire and Sabre) were to remain on strength, however, the notable casualty in 1960 being the withdrawal of the last PV-1 Venturas. The early Vampire FB.Mk 5s were by then all in storage, while the Devons, Herons, Austers and Sikorsky helicopters were sold on the civil market during the early 1960s. It was the SAAF's helicopter component which first benefitted from the modernisation programme when the first of eight Alouette II trainers was delivered (to No. 17 Squadron) in December 1960. This was followed, in February 1962, by the first Sud SE 3160 Alouette IIIs. By 1980, 120 had been delivered. Many of these aircraft, together with most surviving Vampires, were clandestinely passed to Rhodesia from 1972-73, during that country's long 'Bush war'.

South African involvement in the war in Rhodesia really lies outside the scope of this analysis, although insurgency into Rhodesia was seen as being potentially threatening to stability within South Africa itself. This justified a high degree of support to Rhodesian security forces by the South African Police and by the South African armed forces. SAAF Alouettes and their crews were seconded to the Police for operations in Rhodesia, wearing South African Police markings, and later being supplemented by similarly marked Cessna 185s.

Bush wars

If the war in Rhodesia, on South Africa's north-eastern border, remained peripheral, problems in the north-west were to prove more important.

The political circumstances by which South Africa slid into isolation are well documented, but resulted from the desire of the minority white population to retain political power, and from the maintenance of a system of separate development – Apartheid – for the different races. This became increasingly unacceptable to the international community, especially after America put its own house in order by abolishing segregation and discouraging discrimination.

Above: The two-seat Cheetah Ds of No. 89 CFS have joined No. 2 Squadron to form that unit's training flight. Some continue to wear the old No. 89 CFS lion rampant badge.

Above: The Cheetah Ds were mostly converted from Mirage IIIDZ and IIID2Z airframes, but some were produced using airframes (perhaps Kfirs) imported from abroad.

Above and below: The Cheetah C is South Africa's newest warplane, and has been surrounded by secrecy. Thirty-eight have been delivered, and most of these equip No. 2 Squadron. The aircraft differs from earlier variants in having a multi-mode pulse-Doppler radar (understood to be an Elta EL/M-2032 developed from the Lavi's EL/M-2035). This gives an entirely new nose shape. The aircraft also has a new frameless wraparound windshield and other improvements. Reports suggest that the Cheetah Cs were produced by the conversion of Israeli Kfirs.

Above: The Cheetah E has been withdrawn from use, and most, if not all, are understood to be in storage. They served with No. 5 Squadron, which has now disbanded.

Above: Accompanying the two-tone grey camouflage adopted for the Cheetah C, this Cheetah E was painted in an unusual two-tone grey colour scheme, using different shades and a different pattern.

Above: Wearing the Atlas Flight Test logo on its tail, this aircraft is the sole Cheetah R, bailed back to Atlas as the testbed for Cheetah improvements and upgrades, including the advanced combat wing.

A culture in which politicians advocated a 'total onslaught' against minority white regimes soon began to prevail in those nearby countries which had black majority governments. Initially, however, the presence of white-ruled Rhodesia and Portuguese Angola insulated South Africa itself, and provided alternative targets for potential enemies. Over a period of time, South Africa found itself becoming increasingly involved in a counter-insurgency war in the territory then known as South West Africa. This started in the early 1960s, when the South West Africa People's Organisation (SWAPO), began its infiltration of what it called Namibia.

South African forces had conquered the territory from the Germans during World War I, and South Africa had been awarded the League of Nations mandate to administer the area. The United Nations did not recognise the mandate, and this consequently put South Africa at odds with the international community. Many countries actively supported independence for the territory, some recognising SWAPO as the sole and authentic representative of the Namibian people. South Africa initially refrained from direct military involvement, leaving the maintenance of law and order to the police. A small number of SAAF Alouette IIIs had been seconded to the South African Police, and these operated with SAP insignia.

Incursion by SWAPO

The first SWAPO incursion into Ovamboland in northern South West Africa took place in September 1965. Police retaliated by attacking a SWAPO camp at Ongulumbashe, arriving there by Alouette III helicopter. For most of the 1960s and early 1970s, the conflict in Namibia remained at a low intensity, with the Alouettes active in the counter-insurgency role. Things were more difficult in Rhodesia.

In 1973 the SAAF transferred its surviving Alouette IIs to Rhodesia, and these augmented large numbers of Alouette IIIs previously loaned to the Salisbury regime. SAAF Pumas also saw service in Rhodesia, but these aircraft were never formally transferred, and may have been flown by SAAF crews. Dakotas were also loaned to Rhodesia. At the end of hostilities, surviving Alouette IIs, Vampires and Dakotas were transferred back to South Africa, culminating in a batch of ex-Rhodesian Air Force Alouettes which served as attrition replacements for the SAAF Alouettes lost in Rhodesian service!

Less noticeable, but equally important, were the forward air control aircraft – at that stage a motley collection of various Austers, flown by No. 42 AOP flight, under army control. The Dornier Do 27 was evaluated as a replacement, and two were procured for further evaluation. The choice eventually fell upon the Cessna 185A, and the first of an initial batch of 24 was delivered in March 1962. Modernisation of the transport component was long overdue, as the Dakotas were becoming progressively more outdated, and as the air force was beginning to feel the lack of a true long-range transport capability. Seven Lockheed C-130B Hercules aircraft were ordered for No. 28 Squadron, the first being taken on charge in January 1963.

The dramatic expansion of the SAAF's combat capability was the most visible and the most vital part of the 1960s modernisation programme.

During this period Britain supplied six new Canberra B(I).Mk 12s (the last new Canberras to be built) to No. 12 Squadron at Waterkloof, as interdictors and light bombers. The first B(I).Mk 12 arrived in October 1963, and was followed six months later by the first of three refurbished ex-RAF Canberra T.Mk 4. trainers. At that stage, Britain was still regarded as one of South Africa's traditional suppliers of armaments but South African politicians were becoming more and more aware of the growing international condemnation of their apartheid policies. The threat of an arms boycott was growing stronger by the day. The USA had already implemented arms sanctions following the delivery of the last C-130B, while Britain itself could no longer be regarded as a reliable supplier for the future, despite the provisions of the Anglo-South African Simons Town Agreement. This was a naval treaty which aimed at ensuring the continued co-operation between the countries' navies following the Royal Navy hand-over of the Simons Town naval base, near Cape Town. Britain undertook to supply South Africa with certain military equipment in return for commitments to continue to ensure the security of Western shipping passing through the vital strategic sea lanes around the Cape.

First French fighters

South Africa looked to France to supply its first true supersonic interceptor. It selected the Mirage IIICZs to re-equip No. 2 Squadron at Waterkloof. The first of 16 Mirage IIICZs arrived during 1963, followed early the following year by three Mirage IIIBZ conversion trainers. The 'Z' suffix denoted Mirages produced for South Africa (using the Dutch spelling of the country name then still in common use – Zuidafrika). The improved multi-role Mirage IIIEZ entered service late in 1965, initially with No. 2 Squadron. By the time the last of the batch of 16 ordered had arrived, No. 3 Squadron had reformed at Waterkloof as a separate unit for the Mirage IIIEZs. That unit also received three Mirage IIIDZs in 1970, while four Mirage IIIRZ tactical reconnaissance aircraft joined No. 2 Squadron during 1967.

The South African Navy was likewise modernised and expanded. Three new Type 12 'Whitby'-class frigates (the SAS *President Kruger*, SAS *President Pretorius* and SAS *President Steyn*) were ordered from British shipbuilders. Two World War II-vintage destroyers (SAS *Simon van der Stel* and SAS *Jan van Riebeeck*) were extensively modernised with the addition of a helicopter flight deck. Six Westland Wasp HAS.Mk 1 ASW helicopters were ordered for these converted destroyers and the first of these arrived in early 1964. In the main they were to be shore-based with No. 22 (Naval) Flight under SAAF control, at AFB Ysterplaat. An additional four Wasps, mainly attrition replacements, were delivered in 1966, and South Africa eventually received a single Scout for use as a ground instructional airframe.

To facilitate co-operation in naval exercises between Britain and South Africa, the Hawker Siddeley Buccaneer, then in widespread service with the Royal Navy's aircraft-carriers, was selected as the SAAF's new maritime strike aircraft. Sixteen Buccaneer S.Mk 50s were ordered. This unique version was a derivative of the Royal Navy S.Mk 2, and was optimised for operations from the hot-and-high base at Waterkloof by fitting two retractable BS 605 rocket boosters on either

side of the arrester hook bay. Their position restricted the full operation of the arrester hook, but, because the aircraft were shore-based, this was not a major drawback. The powered wing-folding mechanism was also deleted from the SAAF Buccaneers. The full AAR capability was retained, enabling a 'Bucc' to be positioned anywhere along South Africa's coastline. Tanker support was not available, so Buccaneers 'buddy tanked', taking fuel from another Buccaneer fitted with the Flight Refuelling Mk 20 podded refuelling system. Prior to the delivery of the first Buccaneer S.Mk 50 to the newly reformed No. 24 Squadron, a hostile Labour government in the UK attempted to cancel the order. Pressure from South Africa, and reference to the terms of the Simons Town Agreement, eventually forced the supply of all 16 airframes then under construction, but the writing was clearly on the wall for future weapons deliveries from Britain, and few can have been surprised when a formal arms embargo was imposed. The blockade was so severe that not even a 'Bucc' lost on the delivery flight was replaced.

Import substitution

From then on, arms procurement became one of the most sensitive issues facing South Africa, and contingency plans had to be made, one being the establishment, from almost scratch, of a world-class aviation industry.

By now, it was becoming increasingly obvious that self-sufficiency had to be considered as an option for the future, since difficulties in obtaining modern aircraft and weapons would only increase while Apartheid existed, and an end to that system then seemed inconceivable. Self sufficiency would obviously include the establishment of an indigenous aircraft industry, something which did not exist at that stage. Atlas Aircraft was consequently registered as a state-owned corporation in 1964. The new corporation, a commercial enterprise, was formed specifically to manufacture jet trainers for the SAAF, and to provide the SAAF with first-line maintenance facilities for its aircraft and engines, and to provide skilled technical personnel to support the SAAF at its bases. Soon after the formation of Atlas, an agreement was reached with Italy's Aermacchi, under which Atlas would licence-produce the MB.326M jet trainer in South Africa.

A production plant was established adjacent to the Jan Smuts International Airport near Johannesburg, but the first MB.326Ms were Italian manufactured and were imported in knocked-down form. Sanctions resulted in the policy of allocating local names to armaments procured from abroad, indigenous antelopes being preferred by the SAAF; thus, the MB.326 became known locally as the Impala. Assembly of the first aircraft took place at AFB Ysterplaat while production facilities were being established at Atlas. The first Impala made its South African maiden flight on 8 November 1966. As production got under way at Atlas, local content was increased so that, by the time the 151st and last example was delivered, virtually the entire airframe and Viper 22-1 powerplant were being locally manufactured.

Although originally intended as an *ab initio* trainer, the SAAF also specified that underwing hardpoints should be fitted, enabling the Impala to be used as an operational trainer. It was in this role that the Impala was introduced into SAAF service, joining the Vampires of the AOS at

Above: Despite the introduction of the Cheetah, a handful of unmodified Mirages remain on the SAAF's books for training, trials and display work. This one flies from Waterkloof.

Above: Before its retirement from No. 2 Squadron this Mirage IIIBZ was repainted in its original colour scheme. It has now been retired for ground display duties.

Above: No. 2 Squadron retain a pair of Mirage IIICZs for display duties. This one (800) was painted up for the unit's 50th anniversary, then for the 25th anniversary of Mirage operations, and has since been repainted to reflect the ongoing celebrations for the SAAF's 75th birthday.

Above: The Waterkloof gate guard is one of the last five SAAF Buccaneers, retired from active duty in 1990. All five survivors were dispersed to museums or for display at SAAF bases. This aircraft was actually the second of the SAAF's 16 Buccaneer S.Mk 50s to be delivered.

Above: This Vampire FB.Mk 52 serves as the gate guard at the SAAF College at Voortrekkerhoogte, Pretoria. Despite its short period of frontline service, the Vampire FB.Mk 52 was of crucial importance, the SAAF's first jet fighter and a long-serving advanced trainer.

Above: The SAAF has now retired its Aérospatiale Super Frelons. Their high-capacity/heavy-lift capability has not been replaced, and will be missed.

Above: The SAAF Museum's Sabre is reportedly under restoration to flying condition, but other Sabres are on static display, including this aircraft at Swartkop. Ten were sold to Flight Systems for drone conversion.

Above: After being sold to a civilian operator, this ex-RN Sikorsky S-55 eventually found its way onto SAAF charge for operation by the SAAF Museum. The aircraft is seen here towing the original SAAF ensign, which can be compared to the new ensign printed on p. 139. The SAAF Museum operates a growing number of airworthy aircraft.

Langebaanweg. As more Impalas became available they replaced the Harvards then being used by the Citizen Force squadrons across South Africa, and later also joined the Flying Training School at Langebaanweg. Early in their career, one or two *ab initio* courses were conducted on Impalas with limited success, and so the Harvard was retained for primary flying training. The venerable Harvards of the Central Flying School at Dunnottar continued as *ab initio* trainers for another two decades.

Transport modernisation

On the transport side, the SAAF acquired five DC-4s from South African Airways during 1966 and 1967, together with five Dakotas also retired by the airline, both types joining No. 44 Squadron at Swartkop. Further modernisation of the transport force was clearly essential, however, and the hunt for new aircraft types continued. Despite their age, the Dakotas proved irreplaceable in some roles and proved so successful in the Bush war that, during the mid-1970s, 17 second-hand examples were acquired from civil sources as far afield as New Zealand, Yugoslavia, Sudan, Zambia and Botswana.

Because the USA and Britain were no longer prepared to supply the SAAF with any overtly military equipment, it had to turn to France, which was never quite so scrupulous. The result was the supply of nine Transall C.160Zs to augment the C-130Bs of No. 28 Squadron. The first of these arrived in January 1970. At the same time, Britain provided four Hawker Siddeley HS 125-400B Mercurius VIP transports for No. 21 Squadron. These joined the unit's sole Viscount and three Dakotas. Three replacement aircraft were delivered late in 1971 following a horrific formation crash by three-quarters of the HS 125 fleet. As pure VIP carriers, these aircraft were not deemed to be true military hardware, and procurement went ahead without problems. The same argument probably prevailed when the US supplied seven Swearingen Merlin IVAs (one of which was fitted out as a ambulance aircraft) to 21 Squadron in 1975.

An additional batch of Cessna 185s (D and E models) were acquired during the same period for No. 42 Squadron at Potchefstroom, ensuring that what amounted to 'army aviation' remained strong and healthy.

It was by then becoming apparent that a heavy-lift helicopter would be required to augment the general-purpose Alouette III. Given the impossibility of acquiring British or American helicopters, and given the excellent relations existing with Sud Aviation, that company's Super Frelon was a natural choice. The first of 16 SA 321L Super Frelons was delivered to No. 15 Squadron at Swartkop during the first half of 1967.

While the Shackleton was continuing to give good service in the maritime role, the Dakota was then considered to be inadequate as a front-line maritime patrol aircraft. The close-inshore maritime fleet of the SAAF was therefore modernised by the acquisition of the Piaggio P-166S Albatross, which replaced the Dakotas in No. 27 Squadron from October 1969. Twenty unarmed Albatrosses were delivered between 1969 and 1973.

During the early 1970s, the three 'President'-class frigates underwent a major refit, including the provision of a helicopter deck. To this end additional Wasps were required and a sympathetic

Conservative government in Britain allowed the Wasp production line to be re-opened to satisfy an SAAF order for seven additional aircraft. However, before their delivery a Labour government was elected and the final Wasp was embargoed. The first six were delivered during the first half of 1974 and were the last aircraft supplied under the Simons Town agreement before its abrogation.

Valuable Puma force

While the SAAF operated a heavy-lift helicopter in the form of the Frelon, and light helicopters in the shape of the Alouette III, the service lacked a modern medium-lift helicopter. The delivery of the first of 20 SA 330C Pumas early in 1970 thus marked a significant milestone. This versatile helicopter would soon prove indispensable, both at home and in the operational area, as the backbone of the SAAF's helicopter component. The Pumas initially equipped No. 19 Squadron at Swartkop and, as more were delivered, that squadron's 'B' flight moved to the coast at Durban for SAR duties. The delivery of a further 47 improved SA 330Hs and SA 330Ls went almost unnoticed at the time. All of the H models were eventually modified to L configuration. The Puma's impact was perhaps most significant in the assault transport role, throughout what was euphemistically termed the 'operational area'. The aircraft were also used for a number of high-profile rescue missions, and also supported South Africa's SANAE research base in Antarctica. The massive fleet of Pumas allowed the reformation of No. 30 Squadron at Ysterplaat in January 1981. During operations in Namibia and Angola, at least three Puma aircrew won the Honoris Crux, South Africa's highest gallantry award.

The next-generation Mirage

The fighter force continued to be upgraded and modernised throughout the 1970s. A single attrition replacement Mirage IIIEZ (delivered in 1972) and four Mirage IIIR2Z tactical reconnaissance aircraft delivered to No. 2 Squadron during 1974 were the last new Mirage IIIs acquired from France. Perhaps the most significant element in the modernisation process was the delivery of the first of 16 radar-equipped air defence-configured Mirage F1CZs for No. 3 Squadron early in 1975. These were followed by the first of 32 attack-optimised Mirage F1AZs for No. 1 Squadron, both units then still based at Waterkloof.

Despite sanctions, South Africa now had a formidable force of the most modern front-line fighters. These were soon to see action in the Angolan conflict where they acquitted themselves well. The re-equipment of No. 3 Squadron with the Mirage F1CZ allowed the transfer of its Mirage IIIEZs and the DZs to the Advanced Flying School at Pietersburg, to join the surviving Sabres and the 11 Atar 09K-50-powered Mirage IIID2Zs delivered from late 1973. This allowed the last surviving Vampire T.Mk 55s and FB.Mk 52s to finally bow out of regular SAAF service.

Meanwhile, as the production run of 151 Impala Mk 1s came to an end late in 1974, production of the MB.326KC (known as the Impala Mk II) was phased in at Atlas. Production of the single-seat MB326KC, which was fitted with a pair of internal 30-mm DEFA cannon, was undertaken in order to satisfy the requirement for a light counter-insurgency aircraft. Like the

Impala Mk 1, the first few aircraft were pattern aircraft delivered from Italy in fully knocked-down state, and local content was progressively phased in during the 100-aircraft production run. Initially, the Impala Mk II entered service with No. 8 Squadron in November 1975 and, in later years, several of the units operating the Impala Mk I (such as Nos 4 and 8 Squadrons) also received the Mk II to enable citizen force pilots to perform operational missions.

Kudu and Bosbok

In tandem with the Impala Mk II production programme, Atlas also produced 40 C-4M Kudu light communication aircraft. The AL-60C-4M Kudu, to give it its full designation, was an indigenous development of the Aermacchi AM-4, specifically tailored to meet SAAF requirements, with a sliding paratroop door and a floor hatch for cargo dropping. The aircraft thus represented an effort to improve a 1960s design that had already been passed on from Lockheed, via Mexico, to Italy. The Kudus, together with 40 Aermacchi AM-3CM Bosbok AOP aircraft (rejected by other military operators and procured as complete aircraft from the parent company), entered service in July 1976 and February 1974, respectively, as replacements for the Cessna 185s. Initially, the Kudu saw service with both Nos 41 and 42 squadrons, but served longest with the former. The Bosbok ('Bushbuck') served most of its SAAF tenure with 42 Squadron based at Potchefstroom, although the first Bosboks were delivered to No. 41 Squadron in February 1974. Ironically the Cessna 185 remains in service to this day, in more recent times with No. 84 Light Aircraft Flying School and No. 11 Squadron, and, after their closure and the phasing out of the Bosbok, with No. 42 Squadron — after the withdrawal of the Kudu and Bosbok. Seventeen Dakotas were acquired secondhand during this period, increasing to 50 the number of aircraft in the fleet and making the SAAF the world's largest military operator of Dakotas at that time. Three further C-54s also joined the SAAF inventory late in 1980.

Many of the aircraft acquired during the far-reaching modernisation period were soon to see active duty. A direct result of the 1974 Portuguese revolution had been chaos in Angola, previously a Portuguese colony. The change of regime posed an immediate threat to the sovereignty of South West Africa, and ultimately to that of South Africa itself. The Portuguese withdrawal from Angola gave SWAPO the freedom to establish bases, with backing from the *de facto* rulers, the MPLA. The situation was deemed serious enough for direct military involvement by South Africa.

War in Angola

The resulting Bush war saw South African Defence Force units, supported by the SAAF, involved in numerous operations in Southern Angola between 1974 and 1987. The protracted conflict began on the 23 August 1976 when C-130Bs flew troops into South West Africa to occupy the strategic waterworks at Calueque, a few kilometres into Angola. Eight SAAF Alouette IIIs assisted with the actual occupation. The water plant had been built with South African funding during the Portuguese administration of Angola, and provided much needed irrigation

Above: **This camouflaged Atlas Impala Mk I wears the red fighting cock badge and 'Usque ad Mortem' motto of No. 8 Squadron, an operator of the single-seat Impala Mk II.**

Above: **This Impala Mk II wears the bat insignia of No. 4 Squadron, a Citizen Force unit which disbanded at Lanseria in 1991. The long strakes on the forward fuselage are the fairings for the type's internal cannon.**

Above: **Impala Mk IIs serve in the COIN, light strike and advanced training roles, with No. 8 Squadron and with No. 85 Combat Flying School. This aircraft is from No. 8 Squadron.**

Above: **The blast panel adjacent to the gun muzzle of this No. 85 CFS Impala Mk II is entirely stripped of paint. The type is an excellent gunnery platform, ideal for training.**

Above: **Most Impala Mk Is used in the advanced flying training role are painted silver overall. This one served with the recently disbanded No. 86 AFS at Langebaanweg. Most of the type's roles will be taken over by the PC-7 Mk II.**

Above: **An Impala Mk I wears the old-style 'Silver Falcons' team markings. The five-aircraft team, flown by instructors from 85 CFS, has performed over 300 displays.**

Above: **This Impala Mk II was specially painted to celebrate an anniversary for No. 85 CFS. The striking colour scheme includes a huge representation of the unit's gannet badge. The aircraft is seen here in flight near its base at Langebaanweg during March 1995.**

water to the farmlands in the north of South West Africa. This was the beginning of Operation Savannah, which saw South African forces, supported by SAAF helicopter, transport and reconnaissance missions, penetrate Angola right up to the outskirts of Luanda. The aim of Operation Savannah was to help the pro-Western FNLA and UNITA liberation movements against the Cuban-backed Marxist MPLA. The MPLA aimed to take over the country before the elections which would accompany Angolan independence on 11 November 1975. The South Africans were forced to withdraw when US support for the initiative failed to materialise.

With the end of Operation Savannah, the MPLA formed the new government, actively supporting SWAPO and giving it sanctuary in Southern Angola. South Africa's quarrel was essentially with SWAPO, but because of the active Angolan support for SWAPO's Peoples Liberation Army/PLAN, South African forces found themselves involved in clashes with Angolan government (FAPLA) forces during their incursions into Southern Angola.

Operation Reindeer began on 4 May 1978 and saw the SAAF attack SWAPO training bases at Cassinga and Chetequera in response to a dramatic SWAPO incursion into South West Africa. The air attack was initiated by Mirages, which were followed by Buccaneers. On completion of the raid, ground forces were evacuated using Pumas and Super Frelons. By now there were permanent detachments of Pumas and Alouette IIIs to Ondangwa, Mpacha and Rundu, with a Super Frelon detachment at Mpacha. During Operations Rekstok and Safraan, mounted during March 1979, Impala Mk IIs, Mirage IIIEZs, Bosboks and Kudus made their operational debut in the combat area, with Impala and Mirage detachments at Ondangua, and an Impala detachment at Mpacha in the Caprivi Strip. Operation Safraan was mounted against SWAPO training camps near the Caprivi strip, while Operation Rekstok consisted of air strikes and heliborne raids on SWAPO camps in southern Angola. While performing a low-level air attack on 14 March 1979, in Southern Angola, the SAAF suffered its only Canberra loss, when the pilot was wounded by small arms fire and was unable to maintain control of his aircraft.

Operation Sceptic and MiG-kills

Operation Sceptic saw the largest SADF mechanised infantry assault since World War II. It was launched on 20 May 1980 against SWAPO bases, and its southern headquarters. The operation commenced on 7 June with attacks by 12 Mirages and four Buccaneers on the southern HQ, and by 16 Mirages on the main SWAPO HQ at Lubango. Two of these Mirages were damaged by SA-3s but returned safely, landing at Ruacana and Rundu. Three days later two further air strikes followed. Eighteen Mirages attacked the southern HQ with eight 250-kg bombs each, while four Buccaneers attacked a SWAPO camp at Mulola with eight 450-kg bombs each. Operation Sceptic lasted for three weeks and saw the extensive use of Pumas and Alouette IIIs in support of ground forces. During this operation the SAAF suffered its first loss by an surface-to-air missile when an Alouette III was shot down. During this period, three Impala Mk II pilots were killed after being shot down in

separate incidents. A month later, Alouette III gunships, armed with side-firing 20-mm cannon, were first reported in Operation Klipklop performing an attack on the SWAPO transit point at Chitado. During Operation Protea, which was initiated in August 1981, a major SAAF attack was made on 23 August against Angolan air defence installations, and these were seriously damaged – although the main objective of Protea was to attack the SWAPO North Western and Northern Front headquarters at Xangongo and Ongiva. An Alouette III was shot down on 25 August. In November 1981, Operation Daisy was launched against SWAPO bases at Bambi and Cheraqurera, which were captured by ground troops following an SAAF attack. On 6 November 1981 an SAAF Mirage F1CZ flown by Major Johann Rankin, shot down an Angolan Air Force MiG-21 using its 30-mm cannon, the first SAAF dogfight kill since World War II.

A second victory

Early in 1982 a SAAF Puma was shot down, and later in May 1982 an Impala Mk II was downed near Cuvelai. During an attack on Cassinga (Operation Mebos) a SAAF Puma was shot down, killing all 15 on board. A Bosbok was also lost in July, killing both crew. Whilst escorting a recce mission in Southern Angola during December 1982, two Mirage F1CZs were jumped by four Angolan MiG-21s. In the ensuing engagement, one of the MiGs was shot down by Major Rankin (the same pilot responsible for the first kill, again using the Mirage's 30-mm cannon). This added to six air-to-air victories scored by SAAF Impalas during the Bush war.

During Operation Askari the SAAF mounted a major attack on Angolan air defences. During this, on 22 December 1983 an Impala Mk II was hit by a SAM which failed to explode. The warhead of a new SAM-9 was identified stuck in the rudder of the Impala. It was now clear that Angola had acquired the very latest air defence systems, and this was a source of grave concern. Attempted peace negotiations in 1985 produced a Joint Angolan South African Monitoring Commission which aimed to oversee the withdrawal of South African forces from Angola, but SWAPO could not be persuaded to take part and the conflict continued. An SAAF Dakota was hit in the tail by an SA-7 on 1 May 1986 but the pilot made an exceptionally skillful landing at Ondangua without further damage to the aircraft. During Operation Egret in September 1985, aimed at preventing a major SWAPO infiltration into SWA, the Angolan Air Force took an increasingly offensive stand, and in addition to MiG-21s the SAAF encountered MiG-23s, although engagements were inconclusive.

High-threat area

During Operation Moduler, which took place in the latter half of 1987, the SAAF was faced with what was arguably the most sophisticated air defence system of Soviet origin outside the WarPac countries, but fortunately there were no losses. Moduler was followed by Operation Hooper, the last major SADF offensive in Southern Angola. This opened on 13 January 1988 with an attack north-east of Cuito Cuanavale. By now the South African forces were not only operating against SWAPO, but were actively supporting the pro-Western Angolan UNITA forces

against the government's own armed forces. The SAAF played a major part in this and follow up attacks, but was restricted by a loss of air supremacy. The Mirage F1AZs of No. 1 Squadron flew 683 sorties, supporting ground forces, and delivering 3,068 bombs. Most of these sorties had to be flown low, under Angolan MiG-23 CAPs and avoiding FAPLA radar defences. One F1AZ was shot down and another was lost in an landing accident at Rundu following a missile hit. The small Buccaneer contingent from No. 24 Squadron, by now reduced to five operational aircraft, delivered 701 bombs during 99 sorties, without loss. By this time, the politicians had succeeded in negotiating a withdrawal of Cuban forces from Angolan soil, in exchange for South African withdrawal from Angola, the granting of independence to Namibia, and the ultimate withdrawal of South African forces from Namibia itself. During August 1988, the last South African forces left Southern Angola. Peace had finally arrived.

Chain of command

At the height of the long war, the SAAF had been transformed into a major tactical air arm, with several geographic commands reporting to Air Force Headquarters. Main Threat Area was responsible for all of the bases in the Transvaal and for AFB Bloemspruit, in Bloemfontein. Western Air Command was of similar importance and was responsible for operations in the 'operational area' (Angola/Namibia). Southern Air Command was responsible for the coastal air bases, and was additionally responsible for SAR and SAR co-ordination. These three geographical commands were augmented by Air Force Training Command, Air Logistics Command, Airspace Control Command and Tactical Support Command.

The modern SAAF reached its peak during the early 1980s, but thereafter decline started to set in. Sanctions began to bite, and almost nothing new was added to the inventory during the early part of the decade. A small number of Aztecs were acquired as spoils of the South West Africa/Angola war, two Beech Queen Airs were bought secondhand from civil owners, and five Beech King Air 200Cs (four for the SAAF and one for the South African Police, replacing the Merlins which were sold to civil operators) were acquired new with US government approval. (One of the 200Cs was later sold and replaced with a Model 300C.) No. 21 Squadron was expanded when a single Dassault Falcon 50 was added to the Mercurius fleet in 1982. This was followed by a Citation 550 in 1983, an additional Falcon 50 in 1985 and a Falcon 900 in 1992, the latter for use as Presidential aircraft on long-range flights.

South Africa's ultimate weapons

The front-line aircraft fleets, however, had not been expanded, and heavy operational use and war attrition had made a major impact on unit establishments, and on the fatigue life remaining on surviving aircraft. Among the worst hit were the Buccaneers, whose numbers had dwindled to about six by 1985. Ordinarily, a fleet this small would not have made viable sense, but the aircraft's secondary nuclear role had made it essential to keep them in service.

Of all South Africa's weapons projects, its (strangely) short-lived nuclear programme was potentially the most far-reaching. If Israeli help

Above and left: The new 'Silver Falcons' colour scheme is similar to the old, but replaces orange and blue stripes with light and dark blue. The overall effect is extremely smart, and helps the team to reflect the professionalism of the SAAF.

The PC-7 Mk II (left) has been selected as the SAAF's replacement for the T-6 Harvard (below). The indigenous Ace (above) remained a technology demonstrator until the prototype was lost in a flying accident.

Above: The Harvard remains in use with the Central Flying School, although numbers are dwindling as the PC-7 Mk II enters service. As they are retired, they are being sold off gradually, to avoid a glut of T-6s on the warbird market.

Above: The dramatically painted Harvard 7001 was built up from spares and is named 'Inkwazi'. It is used primarily as a display aircraft when not operating in the training role, and is accompanied to air displays by a similarly painted four-wheel drive vehicle. Harvards are now being sold off in significant numbers.

has been 'suspected' in such areas as the development of EW equipment or aircraft, the close ties between the two nations' nuclear research programmes are virtually undeniable. In the early days of Israel's quest for the bomb much technical assistance came from France, but raw materials came from South Africa. In 1963 South Africa began substantial shipments of uranium ore, or 'Yellowcake', to Israel by sea, guarded by Israeli special forces. After the Six-Day War, when Israel's international isolation became increasingly profound (as was that of South Africa), co-operation between the two became even closer. By the mid-1970s South Africa (like Israel) felt threatened by an array of hostile neighbours, and the seeds of more serious weapons development were sown. In return for South Africa's resources and, more importantly, a test-site far from the Middle East, Israel agreed to fast-track South Africa's nascent and highly secret nuclear industry.

The first concrete evidence of this came in 1977. A Soviet Cosmos satellite detected signs that pointed clearly towards preparations for a nuclear test at an underground site in the Kalahari. American satellites confirmed the Soviet suspicions and an orchestrated campaign by the USA and USSR forced the test's abandonment. Two years later, on 22 September 1979, Israel did test in South Africa. On that day a US VELA satellite observed the characteristic double flash of a nuclear detonation in the Indian Ocean near the Prince Edward Islands. Israeli technicians had exploded a 3-kT enhanced radiation device (neutron bomb). It is believed that this was the third in a series of tests, which had hitherto been concealed by thick cloud and bad weather. Two days later Prime Minister Pieter W. Botha, while addressing the Cape National Party congress, announced, "If there are people thinking of doing anything else, I suggest they think twice about it. They might find we have weapons they do not know about."

With Israeli help, South Africa assembled several such weapons, for use as artillery shells. Furthermore, Israel passed on the technology behind its Jericho 1 and 2 short- and intermediate-range missiles. Since 1989 South Africa has made numerous test firings of its own 'Arniston' missile (so named – by the CIA - after the Overberg missile range at Arniston, where it was first detected) from the Cape Agulhas range. Tests of Arniston and Jericho missiles progressed under the guise of commercial space research and Arniston remains in South Africa's inventory.

It could be argued that South Africa's much hinted nuclear capability was a significant factor in the end of the 'Bush war'. In 1987, with the fighting going badly in Angola, the Vastrap site in the Kalahari was again the scene of hurried preparations for a 'test'. These obvious (to a satellite) signs may well have been the spur for the superpower intervention that brought a political end to the fighting in southern Africa. What is certain is that by 1992 Pretoria felt that the devices in its possession had served their purpose. Thus, on 23 March 1992 President F. W. de Klerk admitted that South Africa did indeed possess six such devices, but that they were being simultaneously dismantled and deactivated in their purpose-built vaults at Adena Laboratories, Pretoria. He also stated that South Africa had received no help with the project. In March 1991 the five-strong Buccaneer force had finally been stood down. The similarity in numbers of weapons and aircraft may well have been more than mere co-incidence.

Unlike the Buccaneer fleet, No. 12 Squadron's Canberras had not been greatly reduced by attrition, and, although the type was still performing a useful role, its performance was such that it could no longer operate in the highest threat areas. While the performance of the Mirage III remained competitive, the aircraft were beginning to feel the effects of their long service, and needed to be refurbished. Furthermore, the aircraft's primitive avionics suite and lack of agility meant that it was losing the advantage it had enjoyed over the newest Soviet fighters then being delivered to neighbours like Angola. A major modernisation programme would clearly be necessary, unless a replacement aircraft could be found. International sanctions had since the late 1970s even been observed by the French (who seldom let political considerations stand in the way of arms sales) and this ruled out any hopes of obtaining a new fighter. Some reports even suggest that an SAAF order for Mirage F1s, including F1BZ two-seat trainers was a casualty of the embargo.

The Cheetah programme

The ambitious Mirage upgrade project captured the imagination of aviation observers worldwide, but many details remain secret to this day, not least because of the disparity between the number of SAAF airframes available for conversion (taking into account attrition and known unconverted Mirages) and the number of Cheetahs actually produced. It seems likely that a number of extra Mirage airframes were obtained from elsewhere, although this has never been officially confirmed.

It was soon apparent that the Mirage IIIBZs, IIICZs and IIIRZs could not be viably upgraded, and these aircraft were earmarked for withdrawal. This left the Mirage IIIDZs, IIID2Zs and IIIEZs in use with No. 85 Combat Flying School and the four IIIR2Zs in use with No. 2 Squadron.

The first priority was to upgrade the two-seat Mirage IIIDZs and D2Zs – replacing their outdated systems and avionics, and bringing all to a common standard with Atar 09K50s. Two surviving DZs and eight surviving D2Zs were brought up to Cheetah D standard together with at least four extra aircraft reportedly based on Kfir parts obtained from Israel. The first Cheetah D was unveiled on 16 July 1986. The programme involved aerodynamic refinements (including a new wing leading edge, and canard foreplanes), installation of a more capable nav/attack system and of a new electronic warfare system, and the addition of an inflight-refuelling system with a non-retractable boom mounted to starboard. The similarity of the Cheetah D to the IAI Kfir TC-7 (apart from the powerplant) led to speculation that the project had been undertaken with Israeli co-operation, but official sources will not comment on this, nor on the suggestion that five additional airframes were acquired from abroad to be utilised for Cheetah D conversions. The first unit to fly the new Cheetah D was No. 89 Combat Flying School, initially at Pietersburg, and later at Louis Trichardt.

Following the successful upgrade of the two-seat Mirages to Cheetah D configuration, Atlas began the conversion of the SAAF's remaining Mirage IIIEZs to Cheetah E standards. Israeli support was suspected again as the Cheetah E displays similarities to the Kfir, and to known IAI-assisted conversions of the Mirage, such as the Chilean Pantera and the Colombian Mirage 5/50 COA upgrade. When converted, the Cheetah Es were delivered to the newly reformed No. 5 Squadron at Louis Trichardt and entered service in 1988. The Cheetah Es retained their original Atar 09C engine, and this, it has been suggested, rendered them lacking in performance. It has been suggested that this shortfall was the reason for the type's withdrawal, while other sources suggest that the high hours clocked up by the aircraft as Mirage IIIEZs was the deciding factor. Officially, the explanation is that the SAAF had an embarrassment of Cheetah airframes, and that since the Cheetah E in its original configuration had only been intended as an interim aircraft it was the natural choice for retirement.

Current developments

Further modifications had been planned for all Cheetah variants. The single so-called Cheetah R, also known as 'Project 855', was a private venture testbed using a Mirage IIIR2Z airframe as a technology demonstrator for a new 'combat wing' and other improvements, including wingtip missile launch rails and further refined avionics. Since the Cheetah Es were grounded and stored in late 1994, these modifications may not now find an SAAF application. They were originally intended for incorporation on service Cheetah Es and Cheetah Ds, but the programme reportedly fell victim to the large-scale SAAF cuts during the early 1990s. Some of the improvements tested may yet be applied to Cheetah Ds and to the new Cheetah Cs, but this remains uncertain. Another possible modification to the Cheetah Cs and Cheetah Ds (and one which would transform the Cheetah Es if they are withdrawn from storage) is an ambitious re-engining plan. The tiny Aerosud company has proposed re-engining both the Cheetah and the Mirage F1 with a derivative of the Klimov RD-33 engine which powers the MiG-29, and single examples of each type have been bailed to the company as testbeds for prototype conversion.

Cheetah C

Atlas is currently producing the last examples of a third Cheetah variant, the Cheetah C. Some 38 of these aircraft are being delivered, all with new serials not previously allocated to SAAF Mirages. Since virtually all the service's Mirages can be accounted for, it was soon obvious that the aircraft were converted from airframes acquired abroad. For this reason, the project was surrounded by secrecy, and until a Cheetah C crashed the aircraft was the subject of much censorship. A Cheetah C photograph slipped through the net and appeared in a South African newspaper before photographs were finally cleared for publication. The origin of the airframes involved remains officially undisclosed, although the popular aviation press seems to suggest they hail from ex-IDF/AF Kfir C-2, -7 stocks, a theory which seems to tally with reported sightings of Kfir-type wings at Atlas. Interestingly, the Cheetah Cs retain Martin-Baker Mk 6 ejection seats, like those of the Kfir, whereas the Mirage-based Cheetahs have newer Martin-Baker Mk 10s. The Cheetah programme, including the various modifications, will be covered in greater depth in a forthcoming volume.

During the mid-1980s South Africa's Mirage F1 fleet was still relatively new, and modernisation

Above: Four of the Boeing 707s delivered to No. 60 Squadron are capable of being configured as three-point inflight-refuelling tankers. The fifth will remain unmodified.

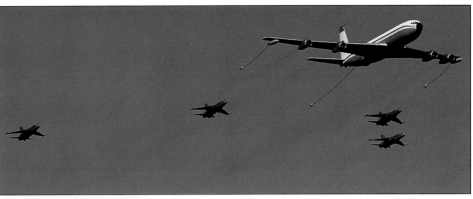

Above: A No. 60 Squadron Boeing 707 streams all three of its hoses, as four Mirage F1AZs close in to refuel. The 707 is the only tanker available for the SAAF's Cheetahs and Mirage F1s.

Above: Fittings on the forward fuselage and internally allow the tanker Boeing 707s to be rapidly reconfigured as Elint aircraft, with cheek fairings similar to those carried by some Israeli Boeings, or by the USAF's Boeing RC-135.

Above: A specially painted Hercules commemorates 50 years of No. 28 Squadron, and 30 years of SAAF Hercules operations. Acquisition of further 'Hercs' is an urgent priority.

Above and below: Withdrawn from use and placed in outdoor storage in January 1993, pending sale, the C.160Z Transalls have been reprieved and were placed back into service with No. 28 Squadron, their original unit. They will probably transfer to No. 44 Squadron, whose Turbodaks will strengthen No. 35 Squadron.

Above: Carrying a dark blue, white and light blue cheatline reminiscent of that applied to the Impalas of the 'Silver Falcons', this C-130 celebrates 75 years of the SAAF itself.

Left and above: The Douglas DC-4 was finally retired in 1995. The type had been used in two slightly different configurations in the Elint (left) and transport (above) roles. The Elint aircraft had a handful of extra antennas, but were otherwise identical to the standard transport aircraft.

programmes for the type were not felt to be quite so urgent as they were for the Mirage IIIs. Nevertheless, plans were put in place for a re-engining programme which eventually resulted in the delivery of a Mirage F1AZ to Aerosud for prototype conversion. In the meantime, the transition to democracy and the accompanying rundown in SAAF strength led to the early retirement of the F1CZs of No. 3 Squadron in September 1992. Four aircraft were allocated to museums, two remain flying with No. 1 Squadron, and the other nine survivors are in storage. They could be resurrected if the re-engining goes ahead.

The Mirage F1AZ attack aircraft had formed the backbone of the SAAF's fighter-bomber force during the Bush war, and its importance was such that it remains in service to this day. While the F1AZ was not itself modified or modernised, many of the weapons which it carried were the result of new development or upgrade programmes.

Airborne weapons

The development of indigenous aircraft ordnance was stimulated by the Bush war and the sanctions problem, which forced Armscor, through its subsidiaries, to develop specific bombs and missiles to suit local conditions. Mirage IIIs and F1s originally carried the traditional armament specified for the type, but support, resupply and replacement of foreign weapons became progressively more difficult. In SAAF service, the Sidewinder, MATRA R530 and R550 were used. The development of a locally designed air-to-air missile started in 1969, initially using the Sidewinder's infra-red sensor. The result was the Voorslag (whip-lash). This was followed by the V2 and the V3A, the latter entering production in 1975. The V3A entered service on Mirage F1AZs in 1978. Although superficially a Magic look-alike, it is in fact an all-new and much-improved missile. It remains in service today, but has been partially replaced by the improved V3B Kukri, and more recently by the V3C Darter. The V3B missile has been cleared for use by all Mirage III/Cheetah and F1 variants. It may also be used on the Impala Mk 2, and the Rooivalk and Puma gunships.

Because they tend to have a longer shelf-life, and because they can readily be manufactured by more nations, conventional bombs and rockets posed less of a problem. Standard 500-lb bombs and MATRA 155 pod with 68-mm SNEB rockets were used by the Canberra, Buccaneer, Impala and Mirage. Mirage IIIs were often seen with the JL 100 combined fuel tank/SNEB rocket pod. The Buccaneers could also carry the AS30 missile, but this soon disappeared from service.

Indigenous ground attack ordnance includes the CB-470 cluster bomb, and a 120-kg fragmentation bomb. A locally developed 'smart' bomb, delivered by a Buccaneer, was reported to have been used successfully during the final stages of the Angolan war, but details are still awaited.

While some aircraft were kept in service through ambitious upgrade programmes, other aircraft were withdrawn without replacement, and whole capabilities were lost. The withdrawal of the last three Shackletons in November 1984, for example, and their replacement by Dakotas – fondly referred to as 'Dackletons' by their 35 Squadron crews – was a typical example.

The Bush war brought about its own requirements, one of which was a dedicated helicopter gunship. (Like the Rhodesians, the SAAF also fit-ted a 20-mm cannon to some Alouette IIIs, and this modification was moderately successful.) Atlas had by that time developed the capability to manufacture many spares and components for the large French helicopter fleet of the SAAF, and by 1984 had the capacity to produce entire airframes. To meet the gunship requirement, the SAAF entered into a contract with Atlas in March 1981 to develop a light attack helicopter using the Alouette III dynamic system.

The result was a technology demonstrator, the Alpha XH-1, first flown on 3 February 1985 and unveiled in 1986. The XH-1 was never intended to be developed beyond prototype stage, but demonstrated systems such as the 700-rpm 20-mm GA-1 cannon – its sole offensive weapon. It was followed by a more sophisticated and powerful technology demonstrator, based on the SA 330J Puma, fitted with stub wings each with three hardpoints, and, in its final form, with a nose-mounted semi-turreted sensor package. This aircraft was designated the XTP-1. There have been suggestions that the XTP-1 was originally intended as the prototype for a proposed gunship conversion of the Puma. First unveiled in 1987, the first of two XTP-1 prototypes was actually used to prove and evaluate many of the systems for the proposed new production helicopter, the Rooivalk (Red Kestrel). This was shown in prototype form for the first time in 1990, under the designation XH-2 (later the CSH-2). The Rooivalk continues its development, despite the SAAF declining to order the type as a result of defence cuts. That decision was since reversed when an initial order for four (for evaluation) was announced. This was later reported to have been increased to 16 to enable a full squadron to form.

Elint and Sigint and tanker force

A major gap in the SAAF inventory during the 1960s and 1970s was a dedicated inflight-refuelling tanker aircraft, while the lack of a dedicated modern Elint/Sigint aircraft had also become increasingly obvious. This shortfall in the inventory was remedied by the procurement of four Boeing 707s from Israel, with a fifth being acquired locally. As with the Cheetah programme, Israeli involvement is also suspected (but not officially admitted) in the ensuing modification of the Boeings from Israel, which were delivered to No. 60 Squadron from 1986. These have subsequently been converted as AAR tankers and EW/Elint platforms, and bear an astonishing resemblance to some IDF/AF Boeing 707s.

The acquisition of the Boeing 707s enhanced the SAAF's Elint capability considerably. Previously two DC-4s from No. 44 Squadron had been modified to serve as limited Elint platforms, but these were withdrawn from service and sold by tender early in 1995. Little has been disclosed by official sources about the equipment carried by the EW/Elint 707s, but a local contractor displayed equipment it supplied to the SAAF at the 1994 DEXA military exhibition.

The Boeing 707s now also provide the SAAF's only air-to-air refuelling capability, the buddy-pod equipped Buccaneers having been retired. Four of the five Boeings have been fitted with a three-point drogue system for refuelling Cheetah C/Ds and Mirage F1AZs. The latter are equipped with a retractable refuelling probe in the nose. The fifth 707, acquired later, is a pure freighter and is, as yet, without Elint or AAR capability.

Although the SAAF had taken delivery of a large number of Pumas, by the end of the 1980s they were starting to show their age. An upgrade or replacement would clearly be necessary. The Oryx helicopter was an Atlas-designed Puma upgrade, with an astonishing performance improvement similar to that offered by the Super Puma. Technical details are still officially unavailable, but the main feature is a more powerful turboshaft motor said to be a local derivative of the Turboméca Makila 1A1, manufactured by Atlas as the Topaz. Other improvements are similar to those applied to the AS 532 Cougar, yet a standard Puma/Super Puma fuselage is retained. New serial numbers are worn by the Oryx, perhaps indicating that the aircraft were converted from newly acquired secondhand Pumas or Super Pumas, or even from new 'green' Puma or Super Puma airframes from Indonesia or Romania. The South African magazine *Air Report* suggested that some SAAF Pumas were converted to Oryx standards, but this seems unlikely except in the case of the XTP-1 demonstrators, which had already been brought up to virtual Super Puma standards. The first delivery to the SAAF was made in 1988, although the type only became operational with No. 19 Squadron at Louis Trichardt early in 1994.

The eternal Dakota

The SAAF itself also initiated an aircraft upgrade programme, which involved the conversion of the greater part of the Dakota fleet to turbine power (Pratt & Whitney PT6A-65), similar to the conversion offered by Aero Modifications International Inc. (AMI). The first phase of the programme involved the conversion of two of the SAAF's Dakotas by a civilian company, Wonder Air, at Wonderboom Airport, Pretoria. Thereafter, production lines for all the remaining SAAF turbine conversions were established at Ysterplaat, Cape Town and Snake Valley (adjacent to AFB Swartkop), although Wonder Air, which was later acquired by Professional Aviation, continued to offer a similar turbine DC-3 conversion to civilian operators both locally and abroad. The first C-47TP 'Turbodak' was unveiled on 26 August 1991 at Snake Valley, followed by the first Ysterplaat conversion in October that year. Soon afterwards, 'Turbodaks' entered service with 44 Squadron, now at AFB Waterkloof, as well as 35 Squadron at Cape Town's D. F. Malan Airport, and 86 Multi-Engine Flying School at AFB Bloemspruit. To date some 30 Dakotas have been converted to turbine power, five of these fitted out as plush VIP aircraft. The final few C-47TPs presently being converted at Swartkop are dedicated maritime patrol and EW/Elint versions for 35 Squadron, but the SAAF is reluctant to comment on the equipment to be carried on board.

Amid some secrecy, the SAAF acquired 12 Cessna 208 Caravan Is for No. 41 Squadron from 1988 to replace its Kudus.

The moves by South Africa towards a form of democracy paved the way to the normalisation of aircraft procurement. A pressing need was the replacement of the ageing Harvard *ab initio* trainers, some 88 of which remained in service. A play-off between the Brazilian Tucano, the Swiss Pilatus PC-7 or PC-9 and the locally developed Denel Ovid took place. The Ovid was never a serious contender due to its early development

Above: No. 35 Squadron has now traded in its piston-engined Dakotas for C-47TPs.

Below: The old and the new. A new Turbodak and an old, unconverted SAAF Dakota.

Above: This C-47TP wears the special codes applied to SAAF Dakotas monitoring elections in Mozambique.

Below: Several of the newly converted C-47TPs wear a VIP colour scheme. They have been stretched as well as re-engined.

Below: No. 35 Squadron's piston-engined C-47s replaced Shackletons in the maritime patrol role, and were inevitably known as 'Dackletons'. They wore a similar colour scheme.

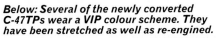

Above: The first two Turbodak conversions were undertaken by Wonder Air at Wonderboom Airport (later taken over by Professional Aviation). Further conversions were undertaken by the SAAF at Ysterplaat and Snake Valley (adjacent to Swartkop).

Above: This Oryx of No. 22 Squadron carries flotation gear similar to that carried by the Puma opposite. It lacks the distinctive undercarriage sponsons fitted to most Oryxes.

Above: The SAAF's SA 330Cs have now all been retired. A handful of SA 330H/L Pumas remain in service, but these will be retired as new Oryx conversions enter service. No. 15 Squadron at Durban retain some Pumas, many of these being equipped with rescue winches, nose radomes for search/weather radar and flotation gear.

Above: Seen while monitoring the elections in Mozambique is an Oryx of No. 19 Squadron, one of three units converting to this new Puma/Super Puma derivative. About 60 are due to be delivered to the SAAF.

status (it was regarded more as a technology demonstrator for advanced composite construction techniques in many quarters). The Swiss offered the SAAF a tailormade PC-7/PC-9 hybrid, which eventually won over the reportedly preferred Tucano. The PC-7 Mk II Astra featured a PC-9 fuselage with a derated PT6A-25C turboprop, and lacked underwing hardpoints.

The first PC-7s began arriving in knocked-down form in Cape Town in September 1994, and aircraft are now being assembled at AFB Ysterplaat. The schedule involved the delivery of 12 aircraft in 1994, 28 in 1995 and the final batch of 20 in 1996, with full service introduction in 1996. The first Astra was delivered to the Central Flying School at AFB Langebaanweg on 17 October 1994.

Defence cuts

The SAAF was a major casualty of the belt-tightening exercises which accompanied the withdrawal from Namibia and the approaching political settlement. The structure of the SAAF has been dramatically altered, with the disband-ment of the geographical commands leaving only a Training Command, an Air Logistics Command and an Air Force Command Post. The latter organisation oversees all front-line squadrons, and two air space control sectors. These are the Bushveld Air Space Control Sector at SAAF Headquarters and the Lowveld Airspace Control Sector at Hoedspruit. A separate Southern Air Force Command Post at Silvermine still looks after maritime SAR co-ordination. Funding was diverted from defence to the ambitious RDP (Reconstruction and Development Programme) which aimed to improve the standard of living of the majority black population. During 1990 severe curtailments in SAAF strength were announced, these being summarised below:

Bases closed down:

AFB Port Elizabeth	– 1990
SAAF facility at Lanseria Airport	– September 1991
AFS Snake Valley	– March 1991; absorbed into AFB Swartkop
AFB Pietersburg	– December 1992
AFB Potchefstroom	– December 1992
Dunnottar	– December 1992

Units disbanded:

No. 16 Squadron at AFB Port Elizabeth
(Alouette III and Puma – October 1990)
No. 6 Squadron at Port Elizabeth
(Impala Mk 1 – October 1990)
No. 12 Squadron at AFB Waterkloof
(Canberra B(I).Mk 12/T.Mk 4 – November 1990)
No. 25 Squadron at AFB Ysterplaat
(Dakota and King Air 200 – October 1990)
No. 27 Squadron at D. F. Malan Airport (Cape Town International)
(P-166S Albatross – October 1990)
No. 11 Squadron at AFB Potchefstroom
(Cessna 185 – early in 1991)
No. 10 Squadron at AFB Potchefstroom
(Seeker RPV and PA-23 Aztec – March 1991)
No. 24 Squadron at AFB Waterkloof
(Buccaneer S.Mk 50 and Impala Mk 1 – March 1991)
No. 4 Squadron at Lanseria
(Impala Mk 1/II – September 1991)
No. 30 Squadron at AFB Ysterplaat
(Puma – November 1991)
No. 84 Light Aircraft Flying School at AFB Potchefstroom
(Cessna 185 – December 1991)
No. 81 Light Aircraft Flying School at AFS Lanseria
(mainly civil Cessna 172s – 1991)

No. 3 Squadron at AFB Waterkloof
(Mirage F1CZ – September 1992)
No. 5 Squadron at AFB Louis Trichardt
(Cheetah E – October 1992)
No. 7 Squadron at Langebaanweg
(Impala Mk 1 – December 1992)
No. 31 Squadron at AFB Hoedspruit
(Puma and Alouette III – December 1992)
No. 83 Jet Flying School at AFB Langebaanweg
(Impala Mk 1 – December 1992)
No. 89 Combat Flying School at AFB Pietersburg
(Cheetah D – absorbed into No. 2 Squadron as its training flight and moved to AFB Louis Trichardt
No. 107 and **114 Air Commando Squadrons**
No. 250 Air Defence Unit

Units moved but still operational:

No. 85 Combat Flying School from AFB Pietersburg to Hoedspruit
(Impala – 1992)
No. 44 Squadron from AFB Swartkop to AFB Waterkloof
(C-47/C-47TP/DC-4 – July 1992)
No. 42 Squadron from AFB Potchefstroom to AFB Swartkop
(Cessna 185 – December 1992)
Central Flying School from AFB Dunnottar to AFB Langebaanweg
(Harvard – December 1992)
No. 2 Squadron from AFB Hoedspruit to AFB Louis Trichardt
(Cheetah C/D – January 1993)
No. 2 Squadron was never officially disbanded when the Mirage IIIs it operated were withdrawn from service
No. 19 Squadron from AFB Swartkop to AFB Louis Trichardt
(Oryx/Alouette III)
No. 41 Squadron from AFB Swartkop to AFB Waterkloof
(Cessna Caravan I)

Aircraft withdrawn from use, without replacement:

English Electric Canberra B(I).Mk 12
(all survivors sold to Peru – November 1990)
English Electric Canberra T.Mk 4
(two preserved and one sold to Peru – November 1990)
Piaggio P-166S Albatross
(two preserved, remainder sold – October 1990)
Atlas C-4M Kudu
(two preserved, remainder sold – late 1991)
Aermacchi AM-3CM Bosbok
(two preserved, remainder sold – September 1992)
Westland Wasp HAS.Mk 1
(five preserved, two sold to Malaysia, two scrapped – in stages from 1988)
Aérospatiale SA 321L Super Frelon
(three preserved, remainder scrapped – December 1990)
Buccaneer S.Mk 50
(all remaining five airframes preserved – March 1991)
Vickers Viscount 781D
(sold to a civilian operator in Zaïre – August 1991)
IAI Seeker RPV
(in storage, but available for *ad hoc* use)
Piper PA-23 Aztec 250
(two aircraft sold on the civil market)
Beechcraft Queen Air
(two aircraft sold on civil market)
Dassault Mirage IIIBZ/IIICZ/IIIRZ/IIIR2Z
(all survivors preserved or in storage – 1990)
Dassault Mirage IIICZ
(two, and one IIIBZ – still flying, 1995)
Dassault Mirage F1CZ
(four allocated to museums, two still flying and remainder in storage – September 1992)
Douglas DC-4 and C-54
(one preserved, one donated to SAA, two sold and three for sale in 1995, one of which went to SAA)
Atlas Cheetah E
(all in storage)
Aérospatiale SA 330C Puma
(two preserved, remainder sold to Atlas)

Aircraft fleets reduced in strength:

Douglas C-47/DC-3 Dakota
(unconverted variants retired, three preserved, one to UK, one to SAA, one earmarked for Dakota Assn of SA; remainder sold or to be sold by public tender)

Sud-Est Alouette III
(many in storage and some sold to Atlas)
Aérospatiale SA 330H/L Puma
(many in storage and some sold to Atlas)
Atlas Impala Mk 1
(surplus examples sold in USA or scrapped/displayed)
Atlas Impala Mk II
(surplus examples in storage)

The SAAF today is a much leaner force. First-line air defence will have to be by the Cheetah C interceptors, based at the northernmost base, Louis Trichardt. The delivery of the 38 ordered is almost complete. With the withdrawal of the Cheetah E the Cheetah C will remain the sole interceptor, as funding for a replacement for the E is unlikely. The government's Reconstruction and Development Programme will probably also curtail a Cheetah C replacement for some years.

With the Cheetah Cs providing the SAAF's air interception capability, the control is exercised by an Airspace Defence Command, comprising ATC, radar and air defence artillery components, with it headquarters at Hoedspruit. Air Defence artillery was until recently provided by No. 250 Air Defence Unit (now closed down), equipped with Thomson-CSF/MATRA Crotale systems, locally known as the Cactus. South Africa con-tributed a major share of the research and devel-opment funding for the Crotale, first delivered in 1969. The Short Tigercat SAM system (locally known as the Hilda) had reached the SAAF via Jordan during mid-1984 and was used for point defence, but has now been withdrawn from use, the Cactus system remaining the sole air defence artillery equipment.

Ground-attack and training force

The SAAF's ground attack capability centres around the 25 surviving Mirage F1AZs based at Hoedspruit, supported by some 20 Impala Mk IIs employed as operational trainers with No. 85 Combat Flying School. The Impala Mk II has served the SAAF well, especially during the Bush war, although attrition was high – more Impala Mk IIs were lost than any other SAAF aircraft type during that conflict. Today some 50 Impala Mk IIs remain, half in storage at Pietersburg, the remainder being shared between No. 85 CFS at Hoedspruit and No. 8 Squadron at Bloemspruit.

The Impala, in its Mk I form, continues to form the backbone of the SAAF's training organisa-tion, and is the mount of the national aerobatic team. The 'Silver Falcons' were formed in 1968, and today operate from Hoedspruit with five specially painted aircraft. All members of the team are full-time instructors at No. 85 CFS.

Ab initio training is at present being carried out at the Central Flying School at Langebaanweg, where the first course with the new Pilatus PC-7 Mk II will commence in 1996. The remaining Harvards are continuing in use until then, but are being progressively sold off in small batches to avoid a glut in the warbird market. In 1986 a Harvard aerobatic team was reformed at the Central Flying School. As with the 'Silver Falcons', this team has seen international exposure, achieving a first for the SAAF when it performed at the FIDAE air show in Chile in 1994. It left its aircraft behind for sale, and picked up new mounts on its return to South Africa.

After gaining their SAAF wings, SAAF pilots are allocated into categories for advanced training, with jet and combat training taking place on Impala Mk Is and IIs at No. 85 Combat Flying

Left: This SA 330J is operated by No. 22 Squadron from Ysterplaat on behalf of the Department of Environmental Affairs, and regularly deploys aboard SAS Agulhas.

Above: Four AM-3C Bosboks formed the 'Spikes' aerobatic team, now disbanded.

Below: The prototype Atlas C-4M Kudu served with the TFDC before its retirement.

Left: The Alouette IIIs of No. 15 Squadron are now being retired, effectively replaced by the nine BK 117s inherited from the Homeland air forces.

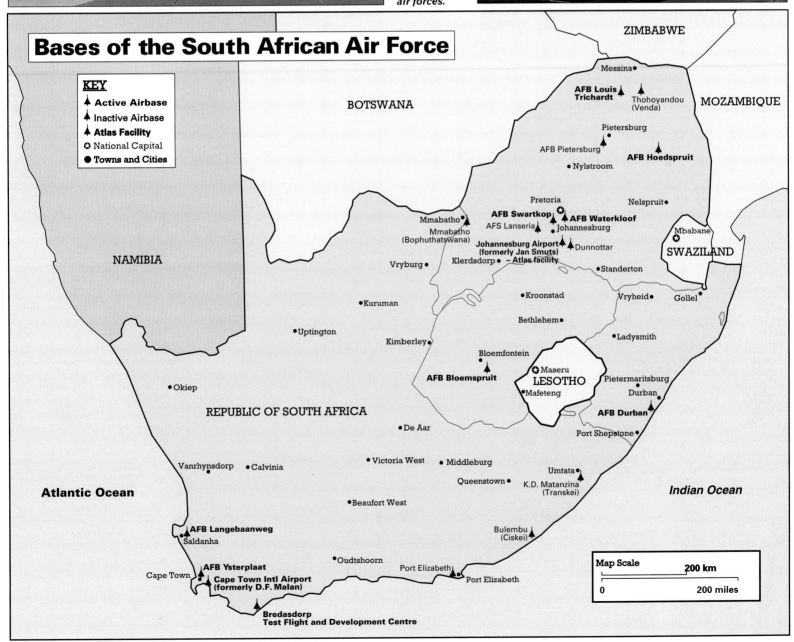

Bases of the South African Air Force

KEY
- ▲ Active Airbase
- ▲ Inactive Airbase
- ▲ Atlas Facility
- ✪ National Capital
- ● Towns and Cities

ZIMBABWE

BOTSWANA

MOZAMBIQUE

NAMIBIA

Messina●

AFB Louis Trichardt ▲ ▲Thohoyandou (Venda)

Pietersburg
AFB Pietersburg ▲ ▲ **AFB Hoedspruit**
● Nylstroom

Nelspruit●

Pretoria
Mmabatho● ▲ **AFB Swartkop**✪ ▲ **AFB Waterkloof**
Mmabatho AFS Lanseria▲ ●Johannesburg
(Bophuthatswana)
Johannesburg Airport ▲ ▲Dunnottar
(formerly Jan Smuts)
Vryburg● Klerdsdorp● – Atlas facility ●Standerton

Mbabane
✪
SWAZILAND

●Kuruman
●Kroonstad Vryheid● ●Gollel

●Uptington Bethlehem●

Kimberley● ●Ladysmith

Bloemfontein●
●Okiep ✪ Maseru Pietermaritzburg
AFB Bloemspruit **LESOTHO**
●Mafeteng Durban●

REPUBLIC OF SOUTH AFRICA **AFB Durban**▲

●De Aar Port Shepstone●

Vanrhynsdorp● ●Calvinia ●Victoria West ●Middleburg
Umtata●
Queenstown● K.D. Matanzina▲

Atlantic Ocean (Transkei) **Indian Ocean**

●Beaufort West

Bulembu▲
(Ciskei)
AFB Langebaanweg▲
Saldanha●

●Oudtshoorn
AFB Ysterplaat▲ Port Elizabeth●
Cape Town● ▲**Cape Town Intl Airport** ●Port Elizabeth
(formerly D.F. Malan)

▲**Bredasdorp**
Test Flight and Development Centre

Map Scale 200 km
0 200 miles

School at Hoedspruit, from where progression is made to the Cheetah Ds of the training flight of No. 2 Squadron at Louis Trichardt (this flight being the former No. 89 Combat Flying School) or directly to No. 1 Squadron for Mirage F1AZ conversion. Those advancing to transport types will do their multi-engine training on C-47TPs at No. 86 Multi-Engine Flying School at Bloemspruit, which base also provides the Alouette IIIs of No. 87 Helicopter Flying School.

It is envisaged that the Impala will be withdrawn by 2002, and its replacement is viewed as such a high priority that funding will be provided even at the expense of the RDP. The SAAF's reported preferred replacement is the BAe Hawk, but this choice may be ruled out by the type's relatively high price tag, despite its formidable capability. The prospects for the Hawk might well be influenced by any British decision on the purchase of Rooivalk. The Impala Mk I will reportedly soon be phased out, as its function will be adequately fulfiled by the newly delivered PC-7 Mk II.

The helicopter force plays an important part, with no fewer than five helicopter units dispersed across South Africa at strategic locations. The Oryx, a much upgraded and powerful derivative of the Puma, will, as the last of the standard SA 330L Pumas are withdrawn, become the prime helicopter in SAAF service, with the ubiquitous Alouette III performing secondary roles. No. 15 Squadron in Durban is now the last SAAF unit operating Pumas, but they will be retired and replaced during 1995 by the Oryx. By then the Oryx production line would have ended and all Pumas withdrawn from SAAF service.

The role of the helicopter units varies according to the location. Often No. 22 Sqn hits the headlines with its fire-fighting or mountain rescue missions. The fire-fighting is done using the specially developed 370-US gal (1400-litre) Monsoon bucket slung underneath an Oryx and fitted with valves controlled from within the helicopter. The bucket can be refilled in seconds and the technique is seen as quite successful in the absence of a dedicated water bomber.

Naval commitment

Another function of No. 22 Squadron is to provide helicopters for SA Navy ships, two of whose supply ships are equipped to carry helicopters. The locally built SAS *Drakensberg* may carry two Oryxes, but the recently acquired former Russian Ro-Ro ice breaker, SAS *Outeniqua* (ex-*Juvent*), can only store two Kamov Ka-32s in its hangars, and may have to be refitted to accommodate the larger Oryx. An Alouette III may be carried by the SAN 'Hecla'-class survey ship, SAS *Protea*. Two SA 330J Pumas are operated by No. 22 Squadron for the Department of Environmental affairs for operation from the Antarctic supply vessel SA *Agulhas*.

The coastal helicopter units are a vital SAR component of the SAAF, and are often called upon to lift injured seamen off passing vessels. The biggest feat to date was the safe rescue by Pumas of Nos 19 and 30 squadrons of all 571 passengers and crew from the stricken 7,554-ton ocean liner *Oceanos*, off the Transkei Wild Coast on 3 August 1991. The Alouette III fleet is now rapidly reaching obsolescence, and a replacement might well be one of the types built by Eurocopter France, possibly licence-manufactured by Denel's Atlas Aviation facility.

The transport component of the SAAF recently has been much involved in humanitarian work, particularly in Africa. Several aid missions to Rwanda and Somalia have been flown by C-130Bs of No. 28 Squadron, assisted by 60 Squadron's Boeing 707s. Recently these aircraft, together with a component of Oryx helicopters, a single C-47TP 'Turbodak' and Caravan Is, played a vital part in the monitoring of the Mozambique elections. Similar assistance was rendered during the Angolan elections some 18 months earlier.

Transport realignment

The sudden pressure to provide transport facilities undoubtedly led to the decision to reintroduce the C.160Z Transall into service as from early 1995. Originally withdrawn in January 1993, eight Transalls remained in open storage at Waterkloof (with one going to the SAAF Museum) and survived several disposal attempts to sell them to a civilian operator in Zaïre or to local scrap metal merchants. Early in 1995 preparations were being made to train the necessary ground crew for the Transalls and, since a certain degree of expertise remains with No. 28 Squadron, the aircraft will initially be placed there, but it is planned to move the Transalls to No. 44 Squadron once training is complete.

This will release some 'Turbodaks' – sorely needed by the other units. The C-47TP 'Turbodak', which equips two squadrons (Nos 35 and 44) as well a training school, No. 86 Multi-Engine Flying School, will soldier on for some time. At least 30 have been converted to date, and the programme will end in 1995 when the last batch (believed to number six aircraft) is delivered from the Swartkop line (formerly the Snake Valley facility) to No. 35 Squadron. On the transport side, the SAAF would like to augment its ageing C-130B fleet (which is presently receiving an avionics upgrade) with four additional Hercules, but in the interim has reintroduced the nine Transalls withdrawn in January 1993. The SAAF's original plan was to trade in the Transalls for three secondhand C-130s, but this did not happen. In the longer term there is a requirement for some 10 extra Hercules, in order to support the Army's Rapid Deployment Force. On the light transport side, the Cessna 185 will, like the 'Hercs', receive an avionics upgrade and remain in service for some time. The SAAF is reportedly happy that these still provide cost-effective communications flying between bases.

The last Turbodaks will be dedicated maritime patrol versions, equipped for reconnaissance and EW duties, but details have not yet been released. Patrol capability will be limited and restricted to close inshore work. They will have no offensive anti-ship or anti-submarine capability, although this is not a major problem since none of the country's neighbours has an offensive submarine capability, and since South Africa is no longer in a position to plan to meet a global threat. The procurement of a long-range patrol aircraft seems unlikely in the near future, cost being the prime reason. Long-range maritime searches are flown by No. 28 Squadron's Hercules aircraft and co-ordinated by the Maritime Rescue Control Centre at Silvermine near Cape Town.

Available to the SAAF are several part-time air commando squadrons (Nos 101 to 112, with 107 and 114 recently disbanded) utilising private aircraft flown by their owners on mainly communi-

cations duties. Although no longer operational as a unit, the former No. 10 Squadron IAI Scout and Armscor (Kentron) Seeker RPVs remain in storage, and are available for use. During the general elections of April 1994, Seeker RPVs were put to good use as monitoring platforms.

The Test Flight and Development Centre is situated between Bredasdorp and Ariston 100 km (62 miles) east of Cape Town. Originally based at Waterkloof, it moved to a new facility near Bredasdorp during the late 1980s. The work carried out by this unit remains classified, but various aircraft are based there to test new equipment and ordnance. Presently the unit has examples of the Mirage F1AZ, Cheetah C, SA 330L Puma, Impala Mk I/Mk II on strength. A PC-7 Mk II shortly will join this group of aircraft.

The SAAF cherishes its past, and has undertaken to preserve its heritage. The SAAF Museum (which has the status of a fully fledged SAAF unit) is headquartered at Swartkop, but has branches throughout South Africa. The collection has 114 aircraft, and aims to include one example of every type operated by the SAAF. The recent cut-backs provided the museum with a formidable collection of aircraft types, and each of the recently withdrawn types is represented in its collection, several in flying condition. The museum acquired the XH-1 after its participation in the Rooivalk development programme. At present, airworthy types include a Shackleton MR.Mk 3, two P-166S, an Alouette II, a Sikorsky S-55, two Vampire T.Mk 55s, a Fieseler Storch, a Hornet Moth, a Patchen Explorer, a Fairchild Argus, a Dakota, a Chipmunk, a Wasp, a Kudu and a Percival Provost. Soon a Spitfire Mk IX and a F-51D Mustang will join the historical flight, and a Canadair CL-13B Sabre Mk 6 and Aérospatiale Super Frelon are under restoration.

The way ahead

The new constitution states that South Africa should have a 'modern, balanced, sophisticated and technologically advanced' air force to safeguard the 'sovereignty of the state'. Operational emphasis has been shifted more towards support and humanitarian roles, with the offensive capability drastically reduced to a 'core-capability' retaining the necessary expertise to enable rapid expansion should the need arise. The government has accorded great priority to the Reconstruction and Development Programme, which places heavy emphasis on socio-economic improvement. This has already affected defence spending, and as such the SAAF will in the short term have to do without costly hi-tech re-equipment programmes such as the procurement of a Cheetah C replacement or the re-establishment of a long-range maritime patrol capacity.

Some senior SAAF officers do acknowledge some gaps in the core force, the lack of an attack helicopter being frequently stated. Even a single squadron of Rooivalks would make many in the SAAF extremely happy. In an interview in *Air Report*, Chief of the Air Force Lieutenant General James Kriel was quoted as believing that the SAAF "can fulfil its current obligations, but has reached its bottom line. If we have to close down another squadron we may not be able to fulfil our obligations." Kriel is upbeat in the interview, and details some of the new considerations facing the air force. The need to show the new generation of politicians that the SAAF is frugal and apolitical

Above: The Cessna 185 continues in service with No. 42 Squadron at Swartkop.

Below: Cessna 185s have outlived the AM-3C Bosboks also used for observation.

Above: The SAAF's Cessna Caravans were acquired clandestinely, and as a result wear a quasi-civilian colour scheme. They serve with No. 41 Squadron.

Below: Known as the Mercurius in SAAF service, the BAe 125 still serves with No. 21 Squadron at Waterkloof.

Above: One of five King Air 200s used by No. 35 Squadron at D. F. Malan airport. A number of King Air 300s are used by No. 41 Squadron at Waterkloof. The aircraft bear little trace of their military ownership.

Above: The Dassault Falcon 900s of No. 21 Squadron wear South African civil registrations and a pseudo-civilian colour scheme, using the dark and light blues now used as the air force's colours.

Above: An example of the CASA C.212-200 in full Bophutatswana Defence Force markings. CASA C.212s also served with the air arms of Transkei, Ciskei and Venda.

Above: One of the Bophutatswana CASA C.212s, actually a CASA C.212-300 (T-310), is seen here wearing a newly allocated SAAF serial, in service with No. 86 Multi-Engine Flying School at Bloemspruit.

Above: The prototype Airtech CN.235 found its way to Bophutatswana in 1991, and was the largest aircraft operated by any of the homeland air forces. Like the smaller 'Bop' air force CASA C.212s, the CN.235 has been transferred to the strength of No. 86 Multi-Engine Flying School, at Bloemspruit.

is discussed, as are the possibilities of training pilots from newly-friendly African states like Malawi and the need to live down the SAAF's old reputation among nations that had once been enemies.

The SAAF has not so far had too many problems in integrating former members of the ANC's armed wing, but is instituting an equal opportunities programme to make such integration easier, without diluting standards by applying affirmative action. In the event of disputes, if a Soviet Bloc trained pilot is felt to need extra training, for example, the SAAF hopes to call on independent arbiters "such as the RAF, because our doctrines are very similar." The integration of equipment from the air arms of the former independent homelands has proved more difficult, however, and is detailed later in this article.

Great stress is being placed on maintaining the proficiency and skills of pilots and other members of the SAAF. Flying hours totals are carefully set, and enforced, and relevant role training is maintained, despite cost considerations. Fighter pilots must undertake at least three weapons practice camps a year, for example, while every transport

pilot must fly a specified number of live parachute drops.

The widespread SAAF rationalisation programme known as Force Design 2000 will be complete by December 1995, when No. 8 Squadron, now based at AFB Bloemspruit, closes down and its Impalas are incorporated into No. 1 Squadron. Although it was envisaged to disband No. 1 Squadron at the same time, and retire its Mirage F1AZs, this was carefully reconsidered, since this would have left the SAAF with only a single advanced fighter squadron (2 Squadron). Should the No. 2 Squadron Cheetahs have been grounded for any reason, South Africa would suddenly have found itself without a frontline fast jet. Present funding projections, according to official SAAF sources, will enable No. 1 Squadron to remain active for another 10 years. The 1995/96 defence budget has not been cut back as much as was feared and stands at US$2.9 billion. This represents 2.1 per cent of South Africa's GDP and is only slightly down on the 1994/95 budget, which was the last in a line of progressively pared-back allocations since 1989.

SAAF Order of Battle
(as at 1 February 1995)

UNIT	TYPE	BASE
No. 1 Sqn	Dassault Mirage F1AZ	Hoedspruit
No. 2 Sqn	Atlas Cheetah C/D	Louis Trichardt
No. 8 Sqn	Atlas Impala Mk I/ II	Bloemspruit
No. 15 Sqn	Puma, BK 117	Durban
No. 17 Sqn	Oryx, Alouette III, SA 365N	Swartkop
No. 19 Sqn	Oryx, Alouette III	Louis Trichardt
No. 21 Sqn	HS 125-400B, Cessna 550, Falcon 50 and Falcon 900	Waterkloof
No. 22 Sqn	Oryx, Alouette III, SA 330J Puma	Ysterplaat
No. 28 Sqn	Lockheed C-130B	Waterkloof
No. 35 Sqn	C-47TP, King Air 200C	D. F. Malan Airport
No. 41 Sqn	Cessna Caravan I, King Air 300	Waterkloof
No. 42 Sqn	Cessna 185, Pilatus PC-6	Swartkop
No. 44 Sqn	C-47TP	Waterkloof
No. 60 Sqn	Boeing 707	Waterkloof
TFDC	Various types	Bredasdorp

Training Command

CFS	Harvard, PC-7, PC-7 Mk II Astra	Langebaanweg
No. 86 MEFISC	-47TP, CASA C.212, CN.235	Bloemspruit
No. 87 HFS	Alouette III	Bloemspruit
No. 85 CFS	Impala Mk I/II	Hoedspruit

Homeland air forces

Self-governing homelands (or *bantustans*) for the black population of South Africa were established by the old regime. Four of these homelands – Transkei, Bophutatswana, Venda and Ciskei – obtained 'full' independence, a status only recognised by South Africa and the individual states themselves, although none of these had any offensive capability. Upon the reunification of South Africa on 10 May 1994, these air forces technically became part of the South African National Defence Force, and the last of these (Ciskei) was reintegrated with the SANDF in December 1994. All aircraft technically became SAAF property.

Transkei

Transkei was the first homeland to opt for 'independence', in 1975. It only created an air component, the Transkei Defence Force Air Wing, in 1986 when it purchased two MBB BK 117A-3 helicopters, flown in full camouflage but with South African civil registrations (ZS-HRJ and ZS-HRR). Two CASA C.212-200s (TDF-01 and TDF-02) were acquired during the same year, but one was lost on 6 July 1993. The main base of operations was the K. D. Matanzima airport, near Umtata. On the dissolution of the TDF Air Wing in November 1994, the remaining CASA C.212 was transferred to the SAAF's No. 86 Multi-Engine Flying School.

Bophutatswana

Bophutatswana became 'independent' in December 1977. The air component of the Bophutatswana Defence Force, which in the late 1980s became the Air Wing, was formed in March 1981 and was the largest of the homeland air forces. Main base was the airport at Mmabatho, outside Mafikeng (formerly Mafeking).

Initial equipment consisted of two Alouette IIIs (T200 and T240) acquired on the civil market, and a single AS 335F Ecureuil (ZS-HMF). In 1982, two Helio H295 Couriers (T100 and T110) were acquired but these were replaced by a Partenavia P-68CTC and a P-68 Observer (T180 and T190). Two CASA C.212s (T300 and T310) were added to the fleet in 1985 and 1988, followed by the Airtech CN.235 prototype (T330) in 1991. In May 1987, two MBB BK 117A-3s (T250 and T260) were procured. The 'Bop Air Force' acquired a training component in early 1990 in the shape of three Pilatus PC-7s (T400, T410 and T420). A single PC-6 (T320) was obtained in March 1990, whereupon the two P68s were sold. The AS 355 was disposed of in July 1992, with a single SA 365N1 Dauphin (ZS-HVI) joining the fleet in September 1992. One of the Alouette IIIs (T200) was damaged beyond repair on 21 August 1985.

The CASA C.212s and the CN.235 have been transferred to No. 86 Multi-Engine Flying School at Bloemspruit, the three PC-7s are now with the Central Flying School, the single PC-6 is with No. 42 Squadron, and the Dauphin is with No. 17 Squadron. All the homeland air forces BK 117s are with No. 15 Squadron. The BDF Alouette IIIs are stored, pending sale.

Venda

Venda is situated in the northern Transvaal and gained its 'independence' in 1979. An air wing was formed as part of the Venda Defence Force in 1983, mainly tasked with police support in operations against *dagga* (marijuana) plantations. Main operating base of the Venda Defence Force Air Wing was the P. R. Mphephu airport west of the capital, Thoyoyandou.

The first aircraft was an Alouette III (VDF-001). The restrictions posed by the Alouette III prompted the acquisition in 1985/86 of an MBB

BK 117A-1 (VDF-010) and a further BK 117A-3 (VDF-020). First fixed-wing type was the CASA C.212-300 (VDF-040) acquired in 1988. A Cessna Citation 551 (VDF-030) joined the fleet in June 1992 as a VIP transport. To date, the VDF Air Wing's Citation has now joined the SAAF's No. 21 Squadron and the CASA C.212 has joined No. 86 Multi-Engine Flying School at Bloemspruit as a VIP aircraft.

Ciskei

Ciskei is situated in the south-east of South Africa, and the Air Wing of the Ciskei Defence Force was formed in 1980. Main base was the Bulembu airport near King William's Town/ Bisho. The first aircraft was a BN-2A Islander (ZS-KLK) acquired in June 1980, followed by a Short SC-7 Skyvan (ZS-KMX) in February 1981. The first helicopter was an MBB BO 105CBS procured in July 1981, followed by three MBB BK 117A-1s (ZS-HMP, ZS-HNC and ZS-HND) in 1983/84.

The only aircraft to ever wear a military serial number was the presidential IAI 1123 Westwind, CA-01, acquired in May 1983 but disposed of soon afterwards. An additional Skyvan (ZS-LFG) and another Islander (ZS-LKE) were acquired in 1982 and 1983, with a further Islander (ZS-LSE) joining the fleet in September 1985. Two Rockwell S-2R (ZS-LRY and ZS-LRZ) crop-sprayers, together with a PA-18 Super Cub (ZS-LSA), were bought in Israel in June 1985. For training, two Cessna 152Ls (ZS-LSN and ZS-LSP) were acquired in 1986. Disposal of the Ciskei Defence Force aircraft has not been finalised. The BO 105 crashed in 1992. Two of the Islanders have joined the SAAF so far, a third (ZS-LKE)) having been sold some time ago. The two Cessna 152s were sold by public tender in January 1995. The Skyvans' fate is still to be determined.

Louis Vosloo – with additional material by the Editors.

Above: A single Pilatus PC-6 Turbo-Porter was delivered to Bophutatswana, in whose colourful markings it is seen here. The aircraft's ruggedness and STOL capability were highly prized.

Above: Now operating with No. 42 Squadron at Swartkop, the former BDF Pilatus PC-6 has been assigned a SAAF serial number and has proved a useful complement for the unit's Cessna 185s.

Above: The two Alouette IIIs operated by Bophutatswana were placed in storage when the homelands were reintegrated. They are to be sold or scrapped.

Above: Wearing Bophutatswana's former markings is one of two BK 117A-3s operated by the air arm.

Below: Despite the lack of commonality with the SAAF's own Pilatus PC-7 Mk II fleet, Bophutatswana's PC-7s have been transferred to the CFS.

Above: The fate of Ciskei's two Short Skyvans has yet to be decided. They seem unlikely to be taken onto SAAF charge, except perhaps in the very short term.

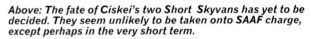

Above: A bizarre false 'window' makes this former Venda Defence Force Cessna Citation 550 resemble a Citation 560. In any case, it now flies with the SAAF's No. 21 Squadron.

Above: Ciskei had three MBB BK 117A-1s, and these will almost certainly join the SAAF's No. 17 Squadron at Swartkop – along with other BK 117s from Venda, Transkei and Bophutatswana. Apart from a short-lived presidential IAI Westwind, Ciskei Defence Force aircraft all wore civil registrations.

Above: The straightforward CASA Aviocar was a popular aircraft with the air forces of the independent homelands. Venda's wingletted CASA C.212-300 has joined the SAAF's No. 86 Multi-Engined Flying School.

INDEX

Page numbers in **bold** refer to an illustration

Picture acknowledgments

Front cover: Geoff Lee/British Aerospace. **4:** Paul Jackson. **5:** Vito Cecchetto (two), E.A. Sloot. **6:** Saab, W. Turner, Flt Lt Stuart Andrews. **7:** Peter R. Foster. **8:** Tim Senior, R.L. Ward (two). **9:** J.B.E. Hale, Derek Bower. **10:** J.B.E. Hale, RAF Strike Command, Thomas Girke, Yaso Niwa. **11:** Yaso Niwa (two). **12:** Lockheed, Sikorsky. **13:** Alan Bayliss, Ted Carlson/Fotodynamics. **14:** Robert Hewson (two). **15:** Ted Carlson/Fotodynamics, Tom Kaminski. **16:** Paul Bennett, Lockheed. **17:** Robert Hewson, British Aerospace, T. Gibbons. **18:** Joe Papay. **19:** Major Jeff White/USMC, USAF via Tim Ripley. **20:** Ugo Gabbana (two), Tim Ripley. **21:** A. Buonomo (two), Joe Papay. **22:** Yves Debay, A.B. Ward. **23:** Tim Ripley, Yves Debay, A.B. Ward. **24:** A. Buonomo, Jeremy Flack/API. **25:** Flt Lt Tom Barrett, A.B. Ward. **26:** USAF via Tim Ripley, Ugo Gabbana. **27:** Joe Papay. **28:** Chris Pocock, Lockheed via Chris Pocock. **29:** Lockheed via Chris Pocock, Joe Cupido. **30:** Robert Hewson, Anders Nylen. **31:** Robert Hewson, Peter Liander. **32:** Yefim Gordon (two), Tieme Festner. **33:** Yefim Gordon (two), Jon Lake, Robert Hewson. **38:** Ulrich de Bruyn via D. Lamarque, D. Lamarque. **39:** D. Lamarque, Ulrich de Bruyn via D. Lamarque. **40:** Dirk Lamarque (two), Jon Lake. **41:** Ulrich de Bruyn via D. Lamarque (two), Dirk Lamarque. **42:** Ulrich de Bruyn via D. Lamarque. **43:** Antoine Roels, Ulrich de Bruyn via D. Lamarque. **44:** Antoine Roels, Dirk Lamarque. **45:** Antoine Roels, Dirk Lamarque. **46-47:** British Aerospace. **48-51:** British Aerospace via Michael Stroud. **52:** British Aerospace via Michael Stroud, MoD. **53-55:** British Aerospace via Michael Stroud. **56:** British Aerospace, British Aerospace via Michael Stroud. **57:** British Aerospace. **58-59:** British Aerospace via Michael Stroud. **60:** Joe Cupido (two). **69:** British Aerospace via Michael Stroud. **70:** British Aerospace via Michael Stroud. **71:** Geoff Lee, British Aerospace via Michael Stroud. **72:** British Aerospace via Michael Stroud, Geoff Lee. **73:** British Aerospace. **74-75:** British Aerospace via Michael Stroud. **76:** British Aerospace, British Aerospace via Michael Stroud. **78-79:** British Aerospace, British Aerospace via Michael Stroud. **80-83:** British Aerospace. **84:** British Aerospace via Michael Stroud. **85-86:** British Aerospace. **87:** British Aerospace, A&AEE. **88:** British Aerospace via Michael Stroud (two). **89:** McDonnell Douglas (two). **90:** Joe Cupido (three). **91:** Henry B. Ham, McDonnell Douglas. **92:** British Aerospace, J.Kyte via R.L. Ward, R.L. Ward (two). **93:** British Aerospace (two), Terry Senior, M.J. Gault, David Donald, M.P. Attrill. **94:** David Donald, British Aerospace (two), M.P. Attrill. **95:** Tim Laming via Ted Carlson, M.P. Attrill (two), David Donald. **96:** British Aerospace, Gerry Turner, Dylan Eklund, British Aerospace via Michael Stroud. **97:** R.L. Ward (two), British Aerospace (three), R.J. Wilson. **98:** British Aerospace (four), Stephen Kill, MAP. **99:** David Donald, Terry Senior, British Aerospace (two). **100:** Tim Senior, British Aerospace, Terry Senior (three). **101:** Patrick Allen, British Aerospace, RAE, Terry Senior. **102:** British Aerospace (two), David Donald, Terry Senior (three). **103:** British Aerospace via Michael Stroud, Terry Senior (two), British Aerospace. **104:** British Aerospace via Michael Stroud (two), British Aerospace. **105:** Terry Senior, British Aerospace, British Aerospace via Michael Stroud. **106:** British Aerospace via Michael Stroud, Andy Thomson via Terry Senior. **108:** Terry Senior (two), British Aerospace via Michael Stroud. **109:** British Aerospace via Michael Stroud, M.J. Gault, Swiss air force via Michael Stroud. **110:** McDonnell Douglas, Greg L. Davis, Chris A. Neill. **111:** Chris A. Neill, British Aerospace (two). **112:** Lockheed Fort Worth (two). **113:** NASA (two), NASA via Bob Burns. **114:** Lockheed Fort Worth, Bryan Ward, Henry B. Ham (two). **116:** Tom Ross, Jeremy Flack/API. **117:** Randy Jolly, McDonnell Douglas via Robert L. Lawson, Robert L. Lawson, Doug Youngblood, MAP. **118:** Rick Morgan via Robert L. Lawson, Lockheed Fort Worth (three), Henry B. Ham. **119:** Lockheed Fort Worth, W. Turner, Henry B. Ham. **120:** Henry B. Ham, David Donald. **121:** Lockheed Fort Worth, Henry B. Ham, Randy Jolly. **122:** Lockheed Fort Worth, Jeremy Flack/API, Henry B. Ham, Randy Jolly. **123:** Gilles Auliard, Gary Chambers, Randy Jolly. **124:** Lockheed Fort Worth. **125:** Ted Carlson/Fotodynamics. **126:** Randy Jolly, Chris Ryan. **127:** Lockheed Fort Worth, Henry B. Ham, Randy Jolly. **128:** Henry B. Ham (two). **129:** Mitsubishi (two). **130:** José Terol (two), Hans Nijhuis. **131:** José Terol. **132:** José Terol (two), Hans Nijhuis. **133:** José Terol. **134:** Hans Nijhuis, Tim Ripley. **135:** Hans Nijhuis (three). **136:** José Terol (three). **137:** Hans Nijhuis, José Terol (two). **139:** Louis J. Vosloo (five), Ian Malcolm, Neville A. Beaven. **140:** Louis J. Vosloo (four), Ian Malcolm (three). **141:** Louis J. Vosloo (three), Ian Malcolm, Herman Potgieter, Chris Lofting. **145:** Ian Malcolm (three), Ben J. Ullings, Achille Vigna, Louis J. Vosloo. **147:** Ian Malcolm, Louis J. Vosloo (three), Austin J. Brown, Chris Lofting, Ben J. Ullings. **149:** Louis J. Vosloo, Chris Lofting (four), Ian Malcolm, Richard Gennis, Ben J. Ullings. **151:** Louis J. Vosloo (five), Ian Malcolm (three), Chris Lofting. **153:** Louis J. Vosloo (two), Ian Malcolm, Ben J. Ullings. **155:** Louis J. Vosloo (seven), Chris Lofting (two). **157:** Chris Lofting (three), Louis J. Vosloo (six).